Study Guide
to Accompany
General Chemistry SECOND EDITION
and
General Chemistry with
Qualitative Analysis SECOND EDITION

Study Guide
to Accompany
General Chemistry SECOND EDITION
and
General Chemistry with
Qualitative Analysis SECOND EDITION

Raymond E. Davis
Professor of Chemistry
University of Texas at Austin

SAUNDERS GOLDEN SUNBURST SERIES

SAUNDERS COLLEGE PUBLISHING

Philadelphia   New York   Chicago
San Francisco   Montreal   Toronto
London   Sydney   Tokyo   Mexico City
Rio de Janeiro   Madrid

Address orders to:
383 Madison Avenue
New York, NY 10017

Address editorial correspondence to:
West Washington Square
Philadelphia, PA 19105

Text Typeface: Times Roman
Compositor: Progressive Typographers
Acquisitions Editor: John Vondeling
Developmental Editor: Jay Freedman
Project Editor: Maureen Iannuzzi
Managing Editor & Art Director: Richard L. Moore
Art/Design Assistant: Virginia A. Bollard
Text Design: William Boehm
Cover Design: Carol Field
Text Artwork: Phila Tek
Production Manager: Tim Frelick
Assistant Production Manager: Maureen Iannuzzi

Study Guide to Accompany General Chemistry, Second Edition and
General Chemistry with Qualitative Analysis, Second Edition   ISBN 0-03-0635691

3456   018   987654321

CBS COLLEGE PUBLISHING
Saunders College Publishing
Holt, Rinehart and Winston
The Dryden Press

To Sharon, Angela, Laura, and Brian,
with love and appreciation

Preface

The science of chemistry is an extremely broad subject of study, with implications ranging from applications in the research laboratory, industry, medicine, and agriculture, through innumerable uses in our daily lives, to the thrilling intellectual exercise of making sense of such a vast subject. The only thing that makes all of this a manageable study is getting it organized. Thus, we systematize our observations, trying to see common features to many different experimental results; we use the resulting summaries of observed behavior, called scientific laws, to help us predict chemical and physical behavior in unknown or untested cases; and we try to understand what is going on in terms of broad concepts such as the atomic theory. The merging of literally millions of chemical and physical observations, both qualitative and quantitative, into the ever-growing science of chemistry is one of the proudest intellectual achievements of the human mind.

The biggest challenge for many students undertaking their first (or even their first college-level) study of chemistry is usually determining what, in the wealth of detailed information in a chapter, comprises the key central themes of that chapter, and what other material merely supports, explains, or exemplifies these main ideas. This Study Guide was written to assist students in their study of chemistry from the text *General Chemistry, Second Edition* by Whitten and Gailey. It is intended to serve as a supplement to lectures and text readings. In preparing this Study Guide, I have been guided by the belief that the primary functions of such a guide are similar to those of an effective teacher — to summarize, to focus study toward particular goals, to stimulate practice at applying concepts and sharpening skills, and to provide an assessment of how the study is progressing. Each chapter contains five parts:

(1) a *Chapter Summary,* which summarizes the main themes of the chapter, tying together the various main ideas of the chapter, and relating it to previous study and to topics to be encountered later;
(2) a list of explicit *Study Goals,* each with references to appropriate sections in the text and to text exercises related to that goal;
(3) a list of some *Important Terms* from the chapter; many of these are in the Key Terms list in the text, while others are important terms that first appeared in earlier chapters;
(4) a *Preliminary Test,* consisting of many questions (averaging more than 80 per chapter) of easy to moderate difficulty; these supply extensive practice at applying the terminology, basic concepts, and fundamental

calculations of the chapter, laying necessary groundwork for practice with more difficult exercises from the textbook;

(5) the *Answers to the Preliminary Test,* containing answers to *all* Preliminary Test questions, many with additional comments, reasoning, or stepwise solutions presented.

The next few pages, *TO THE STUDENT,* will make suggestions to guide you in developing systematic, productive study habits, coordinating material from classroom, text readings, Study Guide, and homework.

My gratitude and my great respect are due to John Vondeling of Saunders College Publishing, who suggested to me the writing of the first edition of Study Guide, and who has encouraged and guided me in every aspect of my involvement in the project. I am especially appreciative to my friends, Professor Ken Whitten and Professor Ken Gailey, for their cooperation, their enthusiasm, and their many helpful suggestions at all stages. I also thank the students in my many introductory chemistry classes; our study of chemistry together, their difficulties and successes, and their many questions, have helped to provide the point of view from which the guide was written; their welcome comments have aided in whatever improvement this second edition represents, and I would appreciate further comments and suggestions from other readers of this guide. Most of all, I thank again my children, Angela, Laura, and Brian, and especially my wife, Sharon, for extending their patience, understanding and support through yet another writing project.

To the Student

The true understanding of chemistry is not just memorizing material, and you certainly will not perform adequately in your chemistry course if you try just to *remember* everything that you hear or read. The keys to your successful study of chemistry are (1) *organizing* the material and (2) practicing *applying* the concepts and skills of the course to particular problems or experiments — this should be your central goal in any study session. You will find that your performance on examinations will be directly related to the amount of real practice that *you* have devoted to thinking about and applying the concepts, and to solving problems and answering questions. You will find that almost everything in your study of chemistry will depend on a firm working knowledge of material that you have already covered, so do not fall behind in your study and do not neglect a topic just because you have already taken the exam covering it!

The most helpful way to study is to take the most active role you can. Just reading (your class notes, the text, examples) rarely does as much good as getting involved — for instance, working the examples out yourself, or outlining a text chapter. The following study suggestions may be helpful to you:

(1) You should always read a little ahead of the material that will be covered in class. Your instructor will probably not assume that you have completely understood the text material before class, but it is always helpful if you have read ahead at least lightly so that you have some idea what is coming. This Study Guide contains a Chapter Summary of the main ideas and a list of definite Study Goals for each chapter. Even though you may not understand these in much detail before you hear lectures over the chapter, read them so that some of the words begin to be familiar and you can recognize key ideas when they come up in class. For the same reasons, at least looking in advance at the list of "Important Terms" in this guide will help you to pay attention when these come up in class.

(2) Try to take class notes that are sufficient to remind you of the general development being presented in class. You will not be able, nor should you try, to write down everything that is said, or even everything that appears on the board or the screen. It is much more important to pay attention and think about the reasoning being presented.

(3) Very soon after each class (the same day if possible) rewrite your class notes. This should be done not just to improve their legibility, but to expand them by adding material that was mentioned in class but that you did not have time to write down fully. As you rework your class notes, read the

appropriate sections of the text (perhaps your instructor has suggested specific pages, sections, or examples to supplement the class discussion); but do not *just* read—incorporate this material into your improving notes. As you do this, you should think carefully about what you are writing—do not just copy. In this way, you will be organizing the material in your mind, relating the various ways the same topics are explained in the lecture, in the text, and in the Study Guide, and incorporating more examples than class time permitted. At this stage, too, you should reread the Chapter Summary in this guide. The list of Study Goals that this guide contains will serve as a framework for organizing your study of the text and lecture notes, and will aid in determining the direction which your own study should be taking. These goals emphasize both what are the central ideas of the chapter and what you should be able to accomplish with these ideas. So some of the Study Goals will say that you should "Know what is meant by . . . ," "Relate . . . to . . . ," or "Understand . . . ," while others emphasize that you should "Be able to calculate . . . " or "Know how to . . . ." Each goal is accompanied by a list of the text sections that are related. Please note two important points about this reworking of your notes: (a) it should be done as *soon* as possible after each class, while the material is still fresh in your mind, and (b) it involves *writing* about the material, which forces you to concentrate more effectively than if you just read.

(4) You should try, as early as possible, to get a working knowledge of the important new terms as they arise, and to review terms from earlier chapters. Each chapter of this Study Guide contains a short section entitled "Some Important Terms in This Chapter." You should try to write down, in your own words, what these terms mean to you. Then look them up in the textbook—many of them appear in the Key Terms list in the text, while you will have to find others in the chapter (or preceding chapters)—and try to improve your own definitions. Again, *do not* just read the definitions or copy them from the text—trying to put them into your own words, in your own writing, makes you think.

(5) It is very important that you *use* the material as much as possible. The best way to do this is to answer questions and to work problems using the concepts you are learning. It is crucial to do this as soon as possible after each class—do not wait until a day or two before the examination, or you will be missing something that would help you comprehend new material which will come in the next class meeting! This phase of your study should follow roughly this order:

(a) The Preliminary Test questions in this Study Guide. These short questions, averaging more than 70 per chapter, are designed to help you master the fundamental terminology, the basic concepts, and the main types of calculations from the chapter. At the end of the guide chapter, you will find answers to *all* Preliminary Test questions, many with comments, reasoning, stepwise solutions, or text study suggestions included. These questions are usually easier than homework or questions in the main text, and they help you learn to use terms and concepts a little at a time. Do not cut this portion of the study short—it is usually best to "overlearn" these basic terms and operations as you will be using them in many combinations in more difficult questions.

(b) Examples from the textbook. Be sure that you work these out yourself. A good approach is to cover up the solution to the example and then uncover it a line at a time, after you have already tried to figure out the next step of the reasoning or calculations for yourself. Write down as fully as you can the reasoning for each step.

(c) Homework which your instructor may assign or distribute. These may be as simple as the Study Guide questions, or they may involve using several ideas in the same question. In any case, be systematic in your answering of the questions.

(d) Exercises at the end of the chapter in the Whitten & Gailey text. Some of these are quite simple, similar to the Study Guide or homework; others may be moderately or very difficult. Many of these questions require you to combine and use several concepts in your reasoning, to see whether you really understand the material. Again, the Study Goals in this guide will help you to find related exercises from the text, helping you to focus your study. The answers to all even-numbered numerical problems are in the back of the text; work those before the other numerical problems, so that you know when you have gotten the correct answer (but do not just start with the known answer and work backwards!). Then work other problems that are similar to these.

(6) Finally, when you are doing your final preparation for examinations or quizzes, the Study Goals and the Preliminary Test questions in this guide will help you to pinpoint topics you need further work on.

Many students find it helpful to set aside a separate portion of the notebook for working problems and answering questions. At every stage of this problem working and question answering, be as thorough and systematic as possible. Write down *why* you are doing each operation in solving a problem—writing down the reasoning forces you into the discipline of thinking about what you are doing, so it will be easier to do the next time even if the problem appears to be different. In this way, it will also be easier for you to review this material at exam time. As you do this, you will find that a wide variety of problems and questions actually involves only a few *central concepts,* but that these can be combined in many different ways. The more practice you have had at working and applying these concepts to specific situations, the better you will be learning the material.

You may wish to modify this suggested study approach to suit your own tastes, and your instructor may have additional suggestions. Whatever you do, be systematic in your study, and take as active a part as you can in working problems—writing is always better than just reading. In this way, you can share in the excitement and enjoyment of the complex, useful, and fascinating subject of chemistry.

Contents

1

Foundations of Chemistry

Chapter Summary

The main goals of this chapter are (1) to begin to get an idea what chemistry is about and the ways in which the science of chemistry views the material world, and (2) to acquire some skill in some of the manipulations, of both numbers and quantitative ideas, and also of words and concepts, that are useful and necessary in the understanding of chemistry.

Notice that we say "begin," because our progress in understanding chemistry, like any complex subject, does not go in a single straight line. Rather, we begin with a few simple ideas, usually oversimplified or under-stated at this stage. As we develop these ideas and expand them into others, we find that we have to keep coming back to rethink these same ideas, to sharpen our thinking and our perception of what they mean. For example, very early in this chapter we encounter the idea of **energy**. This concept plays a central role in our understanding of chemistry, yet we are barely introduced to it, in a rather formal and not too useful way, at this stage. If the authors told us, here in Chapter 1, everything we will need to know about energy for our study of chemistry, it would be a very long chapter and we would get very confused. Rather, we are told enough to get us started with the notion, and then our ideas of energy, both conceptual and quantitative, are further developed and used at many stages throughout the book: later in Chapter 1, in the first introduction to heat as a form of energy; in Chapter 3, where we learn about light as a form of energy, the study of which leads to important knowledge about the spatial arrangements of the particles in atoms and how these are held to one another; again in Chapters 4, 5, and 6, where the concept of energy helps us to understand why elements combine to make chemical compounds; in Chapters 8 and 9, to help explain the properties of and conversions among gases, liquids, and solids; and in Chapter 13, where the further study of energy changes helps us to predict whether a specified change or reaction can take place. At each stage, we learn a little more about energy, and a little more about chemistry. Thus, we should be willing to have our interest aroused in many of the topics which appear early in this first chapter — matter, energy, physical changes, chemical changes, etc. — while not insisting on a complete definition or understanding of all of these new concepts at one sitting.

In the later sections of the chapter, 1 – 7 through 1 – 13, we will be introduced to some of the very important quantitative skills that we will use almost constantly in our study of chemistry. It is impossible to overemphasize how much our progress in understanding chemistry will depend on our ability (eventually) to perform easily many of the manipulations we learn here. The development of such skills takes work and personal practice. It is easy to watch your instructor or your roommate work some problems and then to nod and say, "Yes, I can work that kind of problem." You probably cannot, until after *you* have worked such problems, and many of them, yourself, with progressively less reliance on text, instructor, or study partner. Only then will you have the skill at quantitative manipulation that you will need in your further study of chemistry. And then you need to keep that skill sharp by frequent review and practice, just as you could keep a hard-earned ability to play a musical instrument or to ride a unicycle only by further practice.

The chapter opens with an introduction (Section 1 – 1) to the two central concepts of chemistry — matter and energy. Since chemistry is a study of matter and its properties, of the changes that matter undergoes, and of the energy changes accompanying these changes, we need to begin to get an idea what some of these words mean. Section 1 – 2 takes us further into this by summarizing our experience in various statements known as **laws.** (It is important to realize at this point that in science a **law** is not an arbitrary pronouncement about how something is to be — rather it is a statement that summarizes what is common among a large number of observations and is thus a generalization of our experience that we can hope to use to predict the outcome of further experiments.) We learn here some important generalizations that we will use often throughout the course — the Law of Conservation of Matter (which will be used, for example, in Chapter 2) and the Law of Conservation of Energy (a basic idea of central importance in Chapter 13). Matter is observed (Section 1 – 3) to occur in one of three **states: gas, liquid, and solid.** A much more detailed coverage of this topic will be encountered in Chapters 8 and 9. We describe any sample of matter in terms of its **properties** (Sections 1 – 4 and 1 – 5), which may be **chemical properties,** involving the change of the substance into a different substance (a **chemical reaction**), or **physical properties,** not involving such a reaction. From studying the properties of substances, we learn (Section 1 – 6) that a particular sample may be either a **pure substance,** any specimen of which has identical properties to those of any other specimen of the same substance, or a **mixture,** with properties that can vary with gradually differing composition. The relation of some of the properties of a particular kind of mixture, a **solution,** to its composition will be one of the subjects we study in Chapter 10. Further, a

pure substance may be either an **element,** one of the approximately 100 substances that cannot be decomposed into simpler stable substances, or a **compound,** made up of two or more different elements in a **fixed ratio.**

Several million different substances are known, each with its characteristic set of properties and each capable of undergoing a number of different chemical reactions. Thus, not only would it be terribly dull and tedious to approach chemistry as simply a catalog of substances and their properties and reactions, but that approach is quite impossible due to the magnitude of the effort. One alternative approach is to group together substances and reactions that are similar and to study them in terms of generalizations that apply to all; this is the approach, for example, of Chapters 7, 12, and 20 through 30, the so-called "descriptive chemistry" approach. A different approach is to try to understand properties in terms of the ways and strength with which the extremely small particles that make up the substances are joined together. Thus, we are concerned with topics such as atomic structure (Chapter 3) and chemical bonding (Chapters 4 through 6). Section 1–6 introduces us to the ideas of atoms and molecules, which will be the focus of most of our study of chemistry from the standpoint of underlying principles. This study will relate the behavior of particles that we cannot individually see, manipulate, or measure to the properties that we can measure or observe for substances.

The remainder of the chapter deals with a number of basic skills that we must master before further study. The first of these, Sections 1–7 and 1–8, deals with the systems of units that we use to express the results of measurements—the **metric system** and the related **SI system** of units. As we can see, each system arbitrarily defines a certain amount of the quantity we wish to describe (distance, mass, volume, time, energy, etc.) to correspond to a particular unit. See, for example, the marginal note in Section 1–7 describing the arbitrariness of the length we call a "meter." Once we accept the meaning of each of these units, we then find it convenient to alter the size of units so as to keep numbers to a manageable size. Just as in our English system of measurements we prefer to describe some lengths or distances in inches while others are more conveniently (or more conventionally) described in feet, yards, miles, or light-years, so in the metric or SI systems we invent related units of different magnitudes. The convenience of the latter two systems is that the related units are described by a set of prefixes applied to any basic unit and that these prefixes all correspond to alteration of the unit by multiplying or dividing it by some power of ten. This makes conversion within the system very easy, just a matter of shifting the decimal point. The conversion process from any one unit to any other related one may be accomplished by the simple and straightforward method introduced, with many examples, in Section 1–10. Be diligent in practicing the application until it is an easily used and reliable tool for you. Subsequent sections of the chapter will introduce you both to the meanings and to some of the calculations related to such quantities as heat, temperature, density, and specific gravity. You should also become familiar with the concept of **significant figures,** a way in which we indicate how well we know a measured quantity or something we have calculated from a measured quantity.

In your study of Sections 1 – 7 through 1 – 13, keep in mind that you are developing and sharpening tools and skills you will need for much of your further understanding of chemistry. In this study, do not be content with the limited goal of just learning how to go through the motions in a prescribed way to work or answer a certain type of question. Rather, always keep in mind *why* you (or the textbook, or your instructor) are approaching a problem in a particular way. Always look at the question first to see what is *given* and what is *asked for.* This approach will often be helpful in getting started on questions even if they are not numerical problems. Writing down a list of these quantities, with units, is often helpful. Then try to remember a relationship you can use to relate the given to the unknown quantities. Sometimes this will require thinking of two or more successive relationships, as in several of the examples of Sections 1 – 7 through 1 – 13. Once the relationship is realized, you may then need to manipulate it, perhaps to rearrange it algebraically, to isolate the one unknown quantity in terms of the known ones, and then to carry out the arithmetic required. Carrying through all the units on all appropriate quantities can also be very helpful here. Finally, it is always a good idea to just *think* about the question of whether the answer obtained is a reasonable one. As an example of this last step, suppose we recall that 1 cm is about the width of a little fingernail; if we had calculated that 1 ft = 4.72 cm, using conversion factors that we had been given, we could see by thinking about the size of the numerical result that it must be wrong—it takes more than 4.72 human-fingernail widths to span 1 ft. (In this example, when we go back over it, we see that we divided when we should have multiplied.) This last step, that of thinking about the answer to see whether it is reasonable, is usually not a guarantee that we have the *correct* answer, but frequently it can tell us that the answer we have reached is certainly an *incorrect* one, and that we should begin to search for our error.

Above all, you should strive to develop in yourself the discipline of thinking and working systematically when dealing with problems. Do not just switch on your calculator when you see that a problem involves numbers. Think your way through the problem, at least in broad terms, and then write down the steps by which you will arrive at your answer before doing the actual computations. In this way, if you arrive at an incorrect answer, you can review the process by which you worked the problem and perhaps find the mistake. If you get the correct answer, it will be easier for you to review and check the result, and then to review in a later study session.

The section entitled "To The Student" at the beginning of this study guide suggests how you might organize your study of chemistry. Begin that systematic approach with this fundamental chapter.

Study Goals

These study goals will help you determine specific directions your study should take. Use them to help organize your class notes and text study. Each study goal is accompanied by an indication of related sections in the textbook *General Chemistry* by Whitten and Gailey. When appropriate, some (but not necessarily all) typical related exercises at the end of the main text chapter are indicated.

1. State (a) the Law of Conservation of Matter, (b) the Law of Conservation of Energy, and (c) the Law of Conservation of Matter and Energy. Be able to express these in words other than those used in the text. Give examples of each. (Section 1 – 1; Exercises 3 through 5)
2. Describe and distinguish among the general properties of gases, liquids, and solids. (Section 1 – 2; Exercise 6)
3. Define, distinguish among, and give examples of (a) a chemical change, (b) a physical change, (c) a chemical property, (d) a physical property, (e) an intensive property, (f) an extensive property, (g) an endothermic change, and (h) an exothermic change. (Sections 1 – 3 and 1 – 4; Exercises 1, 2, 8, through 10, and 50 through 52)
4. Define, distinguish among, and give examples of (a) a pure substance, (b) a mixture, (c) an element, (d) a compound, (e) an atom, and (f) a molecule. (Sections 1 – 5 and 1 – 6; Exercises 11 and 12)
5. Know the names and symbols of the elements in Table 1 – 2. (Section 1 – 5; Exercises 13 through 16)
6. Distinguish between (a) mass and weight; (b) accuracy and precision; (c) density and specific gravity; and (d) heat and temperature. (Sections 1 – 8, 1 – 11, and 1 – 12; Exercises 17 and 53)
7. Be familiar with conventions regarding exponential notation and significant figures and apply them properly when doing mathematical operations. (Section 1 – 9; Exercises 18 through 27)
8. Know the meaning of all the metric prefixes listed in Table 1 – 5. Know at least one conversion factor (Table 1 – 7) relating metric and English units of (a) mass, (b) length, and (c) volume. (Sections 1 – 7 and 1 – 8; Exercises 29 through 31)
9. Be able to construct unit factors from simple equalities. Be able to use

these (dimensional analysis) in calculations involving conversions from one set of units to another. (Section 1 – 10; Exercises 32 through 49)

10. Carry out calculations relating density, specific gravity, mass, and volume to one another. (Section 1 – 11; Exercises 53 through 69)

11. Convert a specified temperature in degrees Celsius, degrees Fahrenheit, or kelvins to the corresponding temperature on the other two scales. (Section 1 – 12; Exercises 70 through 72)

12. Be able to carry out calculations relating heat capacity or specific heat to the heat transfer that accompanies temperature changes. (Section 1 – 13; Exercises 73 through 83)

Some Important Terms in This Chapter

To the student: Each new topic that you encounter in your study of chemistry will include some new terms. A firm grasp of the meanings of these new terms will help you to understand explanations that use them, as well as to communicate clearly both in asking your instructor questions and in giving your answers on examinations. Here are a few of the important new terms from Chapter 1. In the space provided, you should write *in your own words,* and as carefully as possible, your understanding of the meaning of these terms. *Do not just look them up and copy them.* After you have written your definitions, check the Key Terms list at the end of the text chapter for a brief definition. Reread the more detailed explanations and examples in the chapter and then try to write a better definition in your own words. These are only some of the most important terms in the chapter—pay attention to others you encounter in the Key Terms list or in your reading.

matter

mass

energy

Law of Conservation of Energy

Law of Conservation of Matter

Law of Conservation of Matter and Energy

kinetic energy

potential energy

physical change

chemical change

properties

compound

element

atom

molecule

unit factor

density

specific gravity

heat

temperature

specific heat

heat capacity

Preliminary Test

Each chapter of this Study Guide contains a number of questions in the form of a preliminary test. The questions in these tests are fairly simple, usually involving the fundamental terminology and basic concepts; many questions involve only one idea or one skill at a time. You should use the questions of these preliminary tests as an initial check of your understanding of fundamental terms, basic concepts, and main problem types of the chapter. A satisfactory performance on the preliminary test for a chapter means that you are ready to proceed with further detailed study, assigned homework, or problem solving from the text. You will find that working many problems and answering many questions at the end of the chapter will also provide necessary practice in understanding and applying the material of the chapter with increasing confidence and skill.

True-False

Mark each statement as true (T) or false (F). Do not guess. Try to understand why a statement is true or, especially for those that are false, what makes it false.

_____ 1. The Law of Conservation of Matter probably does not apply outside our solar system.

_____ 2. Although a sample of matter can change its kinetic energy, its potential energy is always fixed unless it undergoes a chemical reaction.

_____ 3. If we have two samples of matter, the one that is traveling at the higher speed has the higher kinetic energy.

_____ 4. For most substances, the gaseous state is less dense than is the liquid state.

_____ 5. For most substances, the solid state is denser than the liquid state.

_____ 6. When we do not stir a liquid its molecules are motionless.

_____ 7. Observation of the chemical properties of a substance involves the conversion of at least some of the substance into other substances.

_____ 8. A substance whose melting point is $-7.1°C$ and whose boiling point is $58.8°C$ is a liquid at room temperature.

_____ 9. The substance referred to in Question 8 must be bromine.

___ 10. When a liquid on a surface evaporates it removes some heat from the surface.

___ 11. Most of the known elements actually occur in very small amounts on the earth.

___ 12. Most of the naturally occurring elements occur in combination with other elements, rather than as free elements.

___ 13. One of the elements that occurs in our atmosphere in considerable quantity is present in nature both as a free element and in compounds.

___ 14. Different samples of a compound can have compositions that are different, but only slightly so.

___ 15. A mixture has properties that are similar to those of its component substances.

___ 16. A compound has properties that are similar to those of its constituent elements.

___ 17. The term "atom" can apply only to an element, not to a compound.

___ 18. The term "molecule" can apply only to a compound, not to an element.

___ 19. Molecules always consist of more than one atom.

___ 20. Elements that do not exist in stable form as single atoms are always diatomic.

___ 21. A molecule of a compound must consist of at least two atoms.

___ 22. The weight of a body depends on where it is; its mass does not.

___ 23. In the SI system of units, the meter (m) is more important than the kilogram (kg).

___ 24. One gram is about the same mass as one ounce.

___ 25. It is easy to tell, looking from across the room, the difference between a 1-L bottle and a 1-qt bottle.

___ 26. Since 1 m = 39.37 in, the number of inches in 13.83 m is correctly described as $13.83 \times 39.37 = 544.4871$.

___ 27. Since one dozen is 12 of the objects in question, the number of eggs in 16 dozen is written, to the correct number of significant figures, as $16 \times 12 = 192$ eggs.

___ 28. Density and specific gravity are the same thing.

___ 29. The mass of a 1.25-L sample of saturated brine solution, specific gravity 1.45, is 1.81 kg at 25°C.

___ 30. When we add heat to an object, we always raise its temperature.

___ 31. No matter what temperature scale we use, one degree is always the same increment in temperature.

___ 32. In order to tell the specific heat of an object, it is sufficient to know of what substance the object is composed; in order to tell its heat capacity, it is necessary to also know how much of the substance we have.

___ 33. When a piece of iron is allowed to rust, the resulting rust is observed to weigh more than the original piece of iron. This is an example of an exception to the Law of Conservation of Matter.

Short Answer

Answer with a word, a phrase, a formula, or a number (with units as necessary).

1. An example of an exothermic process is _____.
2. Three examples of mixtures are _____, _____, and _____.
3. Three examples of elements are _____, _____, and _____.
4. Three examples of compounds are _____, _____, and _____.
5. Arrange the following in order from smallest to largest: meter, kilometer, millimeter, centimeter, micrometer.
6. Of the units in Question 5, the one most convenient for measuring the distance from Philadelphia to Paris would be the _____, whereas the distance from home plate to first base on a baseball field would be more conveniently given in terms of the _____.
7. Now that we mention it, the distance from home plate to first base (90 ft), expressed in metric units, is _____. (Refer to Table 1–6 for needed conversion factors.)
8. The mass of my 2.8-kg dog, expressed in pounds, is _____.
9. The distance 221,463 miles, expressed in kilometers, is _____.
10. The mileage rating of an automobile that is capable of 27.5 miles per gallon could also be expressed as _____ km/L.
11. The number 221,463, expressed in exponential notation, is _____.
12. The number 0.000473, expressed in exponential notation, is _____.
13. Another name for exponential notation is _____.
14. In order to comply with a request to keep a room at 68.0°F, we would have to set a thermostat calibrated on the Celsius scale at _____.
15. The heat capacity of a 250-g block of metal whose specific heat is 0.22 cal/g°C is _____. (Be sure to supply units.)
16. The amount of heat necessary to raise the temperature of N grams of water by M degrees Celsius is _____. (Be sure to supply units.)
17. In trying to identify a sample of a pure substance, we make the following observations:
    (a) Its mass is 142.6 g.
    (b) It is a shiny solid at room temperature.
    (c) It is easily etched by hydrochloric acid.
    (d) It melts when heated to 540°C.
    (e) It is 24.4 cm long.
    (f) It is a good conductor of electricity.

(g) It burns in air

Of these observations, the ones that would be helpful in identifying the substance of which the sample is composed are ——————.

18. Of the properties listed in Question 17, —————— are chemical properties, while —————— are physical properties.

19. Milk of Magnesia contains the substance known as magnesium hydroxide. Analysis of any pure sample of magnesium hydroxide shows that it consists of 41.7% Mg, 54.9% O, and 3.4% H by mass. This information represents an example of the Law of ———————————— ——————————.

20. The information given in Question 19 shows that magnesium hydroxide is a (an) ————————————.

21. The only element listed in Table 1–1 of the text that is a gas at room temperature (about 21°C) is ————————————.

22. Fill in the missing entries in the following table of elements.

Element Name	Element Symbol
hydrogen	——————
——————	C
——————	Ca
fluorine	——————
——————	O
phosphorus	——————
potassium	——————
——————	S
zinc	——————
——————	Hg

Multiple Choice

In these and all multiple choice questions in this guide, each question has only one best answer. Select the best answer.

_____ 1. Based on all of the evidence available, we believe that the Law of Conservation of Matter and Energy is
(a) always true.   (b) usually true.   (c) always false.
(d) usually false.

_____ 2. Which of the following is _not_ an example of a compound?
(a) table salt   (b) baking soda   (c) nitrogen   (d) carbon monoxide

_____ 3. The formula of a molecular substance tells the number of atoms of each type in the molecule. For which of the following compounds does the molecule contain the largest number of atoms?
(a) nitrogen, N_2 (b) methane, CH_4 (c) formaldehyde, CH_2O (d) ammonia, NH_3 (e) water, H_2O

_____ 4. Which of the following units of volume is largest?
(a) milliliter   (b) liter   (c) centiliter   (d) deciliter
(e) quart

_____ 5. Refer to Table 1–6 of the text. The conversion factor by which we would multiply a volume in quarts to convert it into milliliters is
(a) $\dfrac{1.057\ qt}{1\ L} \times \dfrac{1\ L}{1000\ mL}$.   (b) $\dfrac{1.057\ qt}{1\ L} \times \dfrac{1000\ mL}{1\ L}$.
(c) $\dfrac{1\ L}{1.057\ qt} \times \dfrac{1\ L}{1000\ mL}$.   (d) $\dfrac{1\ L}{1.057\ qt} \times \dfrac{1000\ mL}{1\ L}$.

_____ 6. Refer to Table 1–6 of the text. The conversion factor by which we would multiply an area in square miles (mi^2) to convert it into square kilometers (km^2) is
(a) $\dfrac{2.588881\ km^2}{1\ mi^2}$.   (b) $\dfrac{2.589\ km^2}{1\ mi^2}$.
(c) $\dfrac{1\ mi^2}{2.588881\ km^2}$.   (d) $\dfrac{1\ mi^2}{2.589\ km^2}$.

_____ 7. The prefix "centi-" means
(a) the same as the unit to which it is attached.
(b) 1/1000 of the unit to which it is attached.
(c) 1/100 of the unit to which it is attached.
(d) 100 of the unit to which it is attached.
(e) 1000 of the unit to which it is attached.

_____ 8. Two samples, each of them a pure substance, are found to have different melting points. Which one of the following statements about the substances is true?
(a) The two samples are certainly different pure substances.

(b) The two samples are probably different pure substances, but we need more information to tell for sure.

(c) The two substances are certain to have identical chemical formulas.

(d) Both substances are certain to be compounds and not elements.

(e) The two substances are certain to have different densities.

_____ 9. Which of the following processes is an example of a chemical change?

(a) Fermentation of wine

(b) Formation of salt by evaporation of sea water

(c) Separation of a solid from a liquid by filtration

(d) Condensation of moisture on a cold surface in a humid room

(e) Writing on a piece of paper with a pencil

_____ 10. Which of the following is greatest?

(a) 100 cm   (b) 0.001 km   (c) 1.00 m   (d) 1000 mm

(e) All of the preceding quantities are equivalent.

_____ 11. The melting point (freezing point) of mercury is $-35°C$. What is the temperature, in degrees Fahrenheit, below which a mercury thermometer would not be usable because the mercury in it would be frozen?

(a) $-35°F$ (b) $-63°F$ (c) $-31°F$ (d) $-5.4°F$

_____ 12. We know that air is a mixture and not a compound because

(a) it can be heated.

(b) it can be compressed.

(c) it is colorless.

(d) its composition can vary.

_____ 13. A sample of matter that contains three kinds of atoms could be

(a) a solution.   (b) a heterogeneous mixture.   (c) a compound.   (d) a homogeneous mixture.   (e) Any of the preceding four answers could be correct.

Answers to Preliminary Test

Do not just look up the answers. Think about why the answers that appear here are correct. Reread sections of the text, if necessary. Practice many of the suggested exercises in the textbook.

True-False

1. False. We have never observed any exceptions to this law, and our understanding of the atomic structure of matter makes us believe that exceptions cannot occur.

2. False. Its gravitational potential energy, for instance, depends on its vertical position.

3. False. Kinetic energy depends on both mass and speed. Remember that energy is the capacity for doing work. It might be easier to break a window with a very heavy rock thrown at low speed than with a very lightweight rock thrown at a higher speed.

4. True. (True, in fact, for all substances.)

5. True. Water is one of the very few exceptions to this generalization.

6. False. Think about the diffusion of a drop of red dye throughout an unstirred glass of water. Try to relate what you study to your own experience.

7. True

8. True. Room temperature is usually about 21°C (70°F). Think about starting with a sample of the substance at such a low temperature that it is a solid, and then warming it. When it reaches -7.1°C, it melts—i.e., the solid changes to liquid. It would then need to be heated to 58.8°C for the liquid to boil. Thus, it is a liquid over the temperature range -7.1 to 58.8°C.

9. False. It may be (see Table 1–1), but we cannot be sure just from these two data. Perhaps there is another substance with, coincidentally, the same melting and boiling points as bromine but with other very different properties.

10. True. For example, recall the cooling effect of the evaporation of perspiration.

11. True. See Table 1–2 and the accompanying discussion in Section 1–5.

12. True. Recall (Section 1–5) that only about one fourth of the elements occur as free elements.

13. True. Oxygen occurs both as a free element and in compounds such as carbon dioxide.

14. False. A given compound always has the same composition of elements (see Section 1–5).

15. True

16. False

17. True. See Section 1–6.

18. False. See Section 1–6.

19. False. See the description of the noble gases in Section 1–6 and in Figure 1–9.

20. False. P_4 and S_8 are exceptions discussed in Section 1–6.

21. True. A compound is, by definition, composed of two or more elements, and the atoms of each element are different from the atoms of any other element. See Section 1–6.

22. True. See the discussion in Section 1–8. Keep in mind, however, that weight relationships are just as useful as mass relationships in most

chemical situations, since a chemical reaction usually takes place at constant gravity.

23. False. One, the meter, is the fundamental unit for the measurement of length, while the other, the kilogram, is the basic unit for the measurement of mass.

24. False. Perhaps you have read in the grocery store that a 1-lb (16-oz) can of coffee contains 454 grams.

25. False. Some soft drinks are now being packaged in 1-liter bottles, which contain only about 6% more than 1 quart.

26. False. Significant figures! The answer would be correctly written as 544.5 inches. See Section 1–9 in the text and pay attention to Exercises, such as 24 through 27 at the end of the chapter.

27. True. These are all exact numbers, not obtained from measurement. See Section 1–9.

28. False. Density is the ratio of the mass of a sample of a substance to its volume and thus has units expressed as mass/volume. It will have a different numerical value for the same object, depending on the units used to describe mass and volume. Specific gravity is the ratio of the density of a substance to that of water at the same temperature and is thus dimensionless. See Section 1–12.

29. True. Remember that the density of water is 1.00 g/mL at 25°C, so that at that temperature density and specific gravity are numerically equal. Thus, the density of the brine solution is 1.45 g/mL. Constructing the necessary unit factors,

$$? \text{ g solution} = 1.25 \text{ L} \times \frac{1000 \text{ mL}}{1 \text{ L}} \times 1.45 \frac{\text{g solution}}{\text{mL solution}} \times \frac{1 \text{ kg}}{1000 \text{ g}}$$
$$= 1.81 \text{ kg}$$

Notice that the result of carrying out the computation on a calculator is 1.8125. Rounding to the correct number of significant figures gives the answer 1.81.

30. False. Consider, for example, that when we add some heat to ice at 0°C, we melt some of it to form water, but the temperature does not change. Reread Section 1–4 and then study Section 1–12 carefully.

31. False. For instance, on the Celsius scale the difference between the freezing and boiling points of water is $100 - 0 = 100$ degrees, while measured on the Fahrenheit scale, this *same difference* in temperature is described as $212 - 32 = 180$ degrees.

32. True. Specific heat is an intensive property; whereas heat capacity is an extensive property. Refer to Section 1–11 for a reminder of the terms "intensive" and "extensive," and then study Section 1–13 carefully.

33. False. The iron reacts with the moist air, and the increase in weight is due to something (oxygen) being added to the iron. There are no known

violations of the Law of Conservation of Matter in ordinary chemical reactions. See Section 1–1.

Short Answer

1. Many valid examples come to mind. Any process in which energy (usually heat) is given off to the surroundings could be cited. Burning a piece of metallic magnesium in air (Section 1–1), combustion of a fuel, conversion of matter into energy as in a nuclear reaction (Section 1–1), and freezing of a liquid (Section 1–4) are among the many adequate answers.
2. Again, ·many answers would suffice. Among the ones mentioned in Chapter 1 are a solution of salt in water, a solution of salt in water (Figure 1–3), air, a mixture of sand and salt, and a mixture of very fine iron powder and powdered sulfur.
3. There are presently more than 100 known answers to this question. Some of the elements mentioned in this chapter are hydrogen, oxygen, fluorine, krypton, silicon, aluminum, iron, sulfur, and chlorine. How many others can you find mentioned in the chapter? Of how many have you seen a sample? You should memorize the list in Table 1–2.
4. Now there are several million correct answers! Among those mentioned in the chapter are iron(II) sulfide, sodium chloride, water, carbon dioxide, methane, and ethyl alcohol.
5. Micrometer, millimeter, centimeter, meter, kilometer. Refer to the prefixes given in Table 1–4 and be sure that you know them.
6. Kilometer, meter
7. 27.43 m. The conversion factors needed are

$$? \, m = 90 \, ft \times \frac{12 \, in}{1 \, ft} \times \frac{1 \, m}{39.37 \, in} = 27.43 \, m.$$

Notice that the limitation on the number of significant figures is in the relationship 1 m = 39.37 in, since 1 ft is *exactly* 12 in, and the distance required is, by definition, exactly 90 ft.

8. 6.2 lb. $? \, lb = 2.8 \, kg \times \dfrac{1000 \, g}{1 \, kg} \times \dfrac{1 \, lb}{453.6 \, g} = 6.2 \, lb$. Watch the significant figures—the number on the calculator was 6.1728395, but I certainly do not know the weight of my dog that precisely.

9. 3.563×10^5 km. $? \, km = 221,463 \, mi \times \dfrac{1.609 \, km}{1 \, mi} = 3.563 \times 10^5 \, km$

10. 11.5 km/L. $? \, km/l = 27.5 \, \dfrac{mi}{gal} \times \dfrac{1.609 \, km}{1 \, mi} \times \dfrac{1 \, gal}{4 \, qt} \times \dfrac{1.057 \, qt}{1 \, L} =$

$11.5 \, \dfrac{km}{L}$

11. 2.21463×10^5
12. 4.73×10^{-4}
13. scientific notation
14. 20.0°C. See how the rules for significant figures are applied in this case. See Section 1–12 and especially Example 1–17 for conversion of this type. Be sure to pay attention to problems like Example 1–18, where two stages of conversion are necessary. Exercises 70 through 72 will provide useful practice.
15. 55 cal/°C. See the definition of heat capacity of a body, Section 1–13.

$$? \, cal°C = 0.22 \, \frac{cal}{g°C} \times 250 \, g = 55 \, cal/°C$$

16. $N \times M$ degrees Celsius. Exercises 73 to 83 in the text give useful practice in calculations involving heat transfer, specific heat, and heat capacity.
17. (b), (c), (d), (f), and (g). These are properties that are characteristic of the *substance* under study. The other properties listed describe *how much* of the substance is present, but not the substance itself.
18. (c) and (g) are chemical properties; the others are physical properties.
19. Definite Proportions. See the marginal note in Section 1–5.
20. Compound. A compound is a pure substance consisting of two or more different elements in a fixed ratio. See Section 1–5 for an introduction to compounds.
21. Oxygen. From looking at the boiling points, we can see that only methane and oxygen are above their boiling points (and hence are gases) at 21°C. However, methane is a compound composed of carbon and hydrogen (Figure 1–13). Oxygen is the only gaseous element in the list.
22.

Element Name	Element Symbol
hydrogen	H
carbon	C
calcium	Ca
fluorine	F
oxygen	O
phosphorus	P
potassium	K
sulfur	S
zinc	Zn
mercury	Hg

You should know all of the element names and symbols in Table 1–2. Remember that if an element symbol is a single letter, it is always capitalized; if the symbol consists of two (or occasionally three) letters, the first is capitalized and the subsequent letters are always lower case.

Multiple Choice

1. (a)
2. (c)
3. (b). Remember that the numerical subscripts apply to the preceding element, and that the subscript is omitted if it is 1. Thus, there are two atoms per molecule in N_2, five atoms per molecule in CH_4, four atoms per molecule in CH_2O, four atoms per molecule in NH_3, and three atoms per molecule in H_2O.
4. (b)
5. (d)
6. (b). Be careful of significant figures.
7. (c)
8. (a)
9. (a)
10. (e)
11. (c)
12. (d)
13. (e)

2

Stoichiometry, Chemical Formulas, and Equations

Chapter Summary

What do chemical symbols and formulas tell us about the kinds and numbers of atoms combined in compounds? As we saw in Chapter 1, a chemical formula indicates the relative numbers of atoms of the elements involved. But we cannot handle or count individual atoms, so how can we interpret chemical formulas in terms of some quantity we *can* measure, such as the masses of the elements present in the compound? How are chemical formulas determined from measurements of the amounts of the elements present in compounds? How do we represent a chemical reaction with symbols? How can we interpret the chemical equations we write so they tell us about the amounts of substances that can react with one another or that can be formed? What is the relationship between the mass of an element or compound and the number of atoms or molecules it contains? Since many important reactions are carried out in solutions, how can we conveniently express the amount of a substance present in a solution? How can we tell how much of a solution should be added for a particular reaction to occur to completion?

These are some of the questions that we address in this chapter. Many of the ideas mentioned here are probably new to you and sound somewhat complicated. You should not worry about that—it is important in your study of this chapter to progress steadily through the material, mastering the ideas and methods associated with one concept or one type of problem before trying to proceed, because later material will probably use the skills you should have mastered earlier. Calculations and principles of the types you will learn in this chapter are used throughout science—in agriculture, home economics, engineering, geology, physics, the biological sciences, medicine, and dentistry. Nearly every chapter in the entire textbook, or any course in chemistry, will use many of the ideas and skills you will develop in your study of this chapter.

You should not be alarmed by the obviously quantitative or mathematical nature of the material in this chapter. No mathematics beyond addition, subtraction, multiplication, division, and simple ratios is used in this chapter—indeed, not much more than that is used throughout the book. As you study, keep in mind the approaches in Chapter 1 and the study suggestions in "To the Student" at the beginning of this guide. Strive to keep aware of the reasons for approaching the problems as we do. Do not just try to learn to work "that kind of problem" by rote. And *think* about your answers.

Early in this chapter, in Section 2–1, we review and expand upon the ideas presented in Chapter 1 about **symbols** and **formulas.** You will find it quite useful to know the names and symbols for the common elements given in Table 1–2, and you will probably learn others as they arise throughout the course. Since there are so many compounds to deal with, you cannot learn all the ones you will need; you will gradually remember many of these, such as water (H_2O), carbon dioxide (CO_2), and ammonia (NH_3) without any particular effort since they will keep coming up in your study. At this stage, you will usually be given the formulas of compounds you need to work the problems. Some of the compounds you encounter exist as **discrete molecules,** while others are collections of **ions** (atoms or small groups of atoms carrying an electrical charge). You will probably need to wait until further study (Chapters 4 and 5) before you can predict which substances are which kind. Likewise, you will gradually acquire some knowledge as to whether a particular substance is likely to be a solid, a liquid, or a gas. Again, this should not worry you at this stage, as the main goal of the chapter is to learn how to extract quantitative information from chemical formulas and chemical equations.

Section 2–2 introduces an idea that we shall use throughout the chapter: Experiments can measure relative atomic masses (usually called **atomic weights**), and these are put on a convenient scale by convention. Thus, the numbers that we look up (e.g., in the table inside the front cover of the textbook) give us the relative masses (weights) of atoms of the various elements. One of the most useful ideas in chemistry, the **mole** concept, is introduced in Section 2–3. Just as we describe 12 of anything as a dozen, we use the word "mole" to describe 6.022×10^{23} of anything. This large number, called **Avogadro's number,** is the number of atoms in a mole of atoms, the number of molecules in a mole of molecules, or even the number of eggs in a mole of eggs. The utility of this idea is that a mole of atoms or molecules is a convenient amount of a substance to work with in the laboratory. Section 2–3 establishes the relationship between the atomic weight and the number of atoms in a given mass of an element. Section 2–4 then extends this relationship to apply it to the masses of molecules (or more generally the masses of **formula units**) and the number of molecules or formula units in a given mass of a substance. The **formula weight** of any substance is a number determined by adding up the atomic weights of the atoms indicated by the formula. For substances consisting of molecules, the formula weight is also appropriately called the **molecular weight.** One mole of a substance is then an amount of that substance whose mass, measured in grams, is numerically equal to its formula weight.

Putting the mole idea together with the concept of relative atomic weights lets us arrive at a way of measuring out equal (or the desired relative) numbers of different atoms or molecules. As an example, suppose that we know that all apples are identical, and that an apple weighs one and one-half (3/2) times as much as an orange, all of which are also identical. If we wanted to have a very large number of oranges and the same very large number of apples, we could avoid counting them out individually by just weighing out apples and oranges in a 3/2-to-1 ratio by weight—e.g., 300 pounds of apples would contain the same number of individual fruits as would 200 pounds of oranges, or 90 tons of apples the same number as 60 tons of oranges. Thus, we have replaced the tedious (or in the atomic and molecular case, impossible) task of counting individual things by the much more convenient approach of weighing out the amounts needed. The rest of this chapter is based on this application of the mole concept, so be sure you understand the ideas of Sections 2–3 and 2–4 and can apply them with ease before you proceed. The time you spend learning this concept, understanding and using the ideas of the mole, the formula unit, the formula weight, and the molecular weight, and practicing the associated calculations will be well repaid later. Exercises 5 through 13 at the end of the text chapter will provide you with much practice in applying the ideas of these two important sections.

Since compounds are composed of more than one element, we sometimes need to know what *fraction of the total mass of a sample is due to each type of atom present*—questions such as "In 50 g of water, how much of the mass is due to hydrogen and how much is due to oxygen?" In Section 2–5, we learn how to interpret chemical formulas in this way. Notice that what we are actually doing is applying two generalizations that are based on the analysis of thousands of compounds—the Law of Definite Proportions (sometimes called the Law of Constant Composition) and the Law of Multiple Proportions, both of which we encountered in Chapter 1.

Of course, sometimes we do not know the identity of the compound with which we are dealing. We can approach this problem by carrying out some experiments (**qualitative** analysis) to find out which elements are present, and then other experiments (**quantitative** analysis) to find out the amounts of the elements present. Using this information, we can figure out the formula of the compound we have. Note that this approach, which is discussed in Section 2–6, is the reverse of the calculation of percent composition which was dealt with in Section 2–5. Such analysis and deduction of formula is important in characterizing any new or unidentified compound.

Up to this point in the chapter, we have been concerned with calculations dealing with only one compound at a time. The remainder of the chapter is concerned with the important question of the relative amount of **products** and **reactants** involved in chemical reactions. In order to quantitatively describe chemical reactions, we must learn to write the appropriate **chemical equation** to represent any reaction, as introduced in Section 2–6. Based on the Law of Conservation of Matter, we realize that we must write each equation in **balanced** form, that is, with equal numbers of atoms of all kinds on the two sides of the equation. (Later in the text, we will see that for equations involving ions, it is also necessary to be sure that the total charges on the two sides of the equation are also balanced; but for the applications in this chapter all substances are written as neutral elements or compounds.)

The central idea of all calculations about amounts of reactants and products involved in reactions is this: *The coefficients in the balanced chemical equation tell us the relative numbers of moles of those substances that react or are formed in the reaction.* From that starting point, we can "translate" the mole terminology into any other unit desired—number of molecules, mass of substances, or even gas volume (as in Chapter 8). As you study this section, pay particular attention to the useful device of constructing **unit factors** to represent the chemical equivalence of the amounts of two substances. This central idea can then be expanded to deal with still other situations—the use of impure reagents (Section 2–9), the failure of a reaction to go to completion (Section 2–10), the presence of one reagent (even if we do not know in advance which one) in excess (Section 2–11), and the occurrence of two reactions simultaneously, depleting reagents by different relative amounts or forming products in different relative amounts (Section 2–12). As you study these sections, try to keep in mind the central idea stated above, and try to see that all these apparently different kinds of problems are really just various applications of that central idea. In this way, you will avoid the trap of setting the limited goal of learning to work only a certain number of types of problems.

We often find it inconvenient or impossible to add pure substances to one another in a chemical reaction, or the reaction may form products that are mixed with (dissolved in) other substances. Thus, we often encounter **solutions** in our use and study of chemistry.

The most important use of solutions in chemistry is the convenience they provide in measuring the amount of a reactant to add to a reaction mixture. Many substances are dangerous or inconvenient to handle when they are pure, or may not even exist as pure substances, so they are handled in the form of solutions. The use of a solution may let us measure some very small required amount of a reactant more precisely than we could with the pure substance. Most reactions result in mixtures of several substances, often in the form of a solution. For these reasons, we need to be able to describe the amounts of substances present in a solution. A simple method of telling how much **solute** is contained in a given solution is in terms of **percent by mass** (Section 2–13.1). Notice that whenever we describe anything in chemistry in terms of percent, we mean "percent by mass," unless we specify otherwise.

Of course, the relative amounts of substances involved in chemical reactions are most simply expressed in terms of moles, as we saw earlier in this chapter. The measure of **molarity** (Seetion 2 – 13.2) relates the number of moles (which we want) to the volume of solution (which we can easily measure). Thus, we use the molarity method as the most convenient way of expressing the amount of a solution that contains the required amount of a substance for a chemical reaction. Calculations of this type, discussed in Section 2 – 14, are quite useful both in the laboratory and in practical applications. They will also aid in our understanding of the properties of solutions (Chapter 10), the rates of chemical reactions (Chapter 14), and the extent to which reactions proceed before reaching equilibrium (Chapters 15 through 18).

Study Goals

Use these goals to help you organize your study. As in other chapters, some typical textbook exercises related to each study goal are indicated.

1. Know the names and symbols of the elements in Table 1 – 2. (Review Section 1 – 5)
2. Be able to interpret a chemical formula (a) in terms of the type and number of atoms present and (b) in terms of the relative masses of elements present. (Sections 2 – 1 and 2 – 2; Exercises 1 through 4)
3. Use the mole, atomic weight, formula weight and molecular weight concepts to relate masses of substances to numbers of atoms, molecules, or ions present. (Sections 2 – 2 and 2 – 4; Exercises 5 through 13, and 27 through 32)
4. Given the formula of a compound, calculate its percentage composition. (Section 2 – 5; Exercises 14 and 15)
5. Given the elemental composition of a compound, calculate the simplest formula of the compound. (Section 2 – 6; Exercises 16 through 26)
6. Distinguish between the simplest (empirical) formula and the molecular formula. Given the molecular weight (even approximately) of the compound, along with a knowledge of its simplest formula, determine its molecular formula. (Section 2 – 6; Exercises 26, 33, 34, 68, and 69)
7. Summarize and be able to use the laws of chemical combination: (a) the Law of Conservation of Matter, (b) the Law of Constant Composition (Definite Proportions), and (c) the Law of Multiple Proportions. Be sure you understand how each of these is based on observation of chemical reactions. Give examples of each, and be able to use each in calculations. (Sections 2 – 1, 2 – 5, and 2 – 6; Exercises 35 through 44)
8. Balance simple chemical equations and know what information is contained in them. (Section 2 – 7; Exercises 45 through 51)

9. Use the concepts of this chapter to do calculations based on balanced chemical equations. (Section 2-8; Exercises 52 through 56)
10. Given the amount of an impure substance that undergoes a definite reaction, and the amounts of products formed, determine the percentage purity of the substance. (Section 2-9; Exercises 57 and 58)
11. Given the amount of a limiting reagent present in a chemical reaction, and the amount of a product formed, determine the percent yield. Given the percent yield and one of the other two variables, calculate the third. (Section 2-10; Exercises 59 through 62)
12. Given the amounts of two, or more, reactants, determine which is the limiting reagent and which is (are) present in excess. Determine the extent of the reaction. (Section 2-11; Exercises 63 through 65)
13. Perform calculations (as in Study Goal 9, above) involving two simultaneous reactions producing a common product. (Section 2-12; Exercises 67 and 70 through 74)
14. Relate the given amount of solute in a given amount of solvent or solution (a) to molarity and (b) to mass percent of solute. (Section 2-13; Exercises 75 through 91)
15. Relate the concentration of a given volume of solution prepared by dilution to the volume and concentration of the concentrated solution from which it was prepared. (Section 2-14; Exercises 97 through 102)
16. Relate the amount of substance required or produced in a reaction to the concentration of a solution containing that substance. (Section 2-14; Exercises 92 through 96)

Some Important Terms in This Chapter

Remember—try to write the meaning of these terms *in your own words.* Then check the readings and the Key Terms list in the chapter. Try to rewrite meanings, again in your own words if possible, to improve them. Do not overlook the other new terms in the chapter.

formula

atomic mass unit (amu)

atomic weight

formula weight

molecular weight

mole

Avogadro's number

formula unit

percent composition

simplest formula

molecular formula

chemical equation

products

reactants

stoichiometry

limiting reagent

theoretical yield

actual yield

solution

solvent

solute

molarity

Preliminary Test

As in other chapters, this test will check your understanding of basic concepts and types of calculations. Be sure to practice *many* of the additional textbook exercises, including those indicated in the Study Goals.

True-False

Mark each statement as true (T) or false (F).

_____ 1. In writing a chemical symbol, we can use either capital or lower case letters, as we prefer.

_____ 2. The chemical symbol for mercury is Me.

_____ 3. I have seen a mole of water, but I have never seen a molecule of water.

_____ 4. When we say that the atomic weight of helium is 4.0, we mean that one atom of helium has a mass of 4.0 g.

_____ 5. The number of oxygen atoms in 16 g of oxygen is 6.022×10^{23}.

_____ 6. The number of oxygen molecules in 16 g of oxygen is 6.022×10^{23}.

_____ 7. One mole of boron has a mass of $10.8 \times 6.022 \times 10^{23}$ g.

_____ 8. If we know only the simplest formula of a compound and are given the required atomic weights, we can calculate the percentage by mass of any element in the compound.

_____ 9. If we know only the true formula of a molecular compound and are given the required atomic weights, we can calculate the percentage by mass of any element in the compound.

_____ 10. If we know only the percentage composition by mass of a compound and are given the required atomic weights, we can calculate the simplest formula of the compound.

_____ 11. If we know only the percentage composition by mass of a compound and are given the required atomic weights, we can calculate the true, or molecular, formula of the compound.

_____ 12. Before we can use a chemical equation to determine the amounts of different substances involved in the reaction, we must balance the equation.

_____ 13. In a balanced chemical equation, the total number of moles of reactants must equal the total number of moles of products.

_____ 14. The equation $2Na + H_2O \rightarrow 2NaOH + H_2$ is balanced.

_____ 15. The balanced equation $Ca + 2H_2O \rightarrow Ca(OH)_2 + H_2$ tells us that 1 mole of calcium atoms would react to give 1 mole of H_2.

_____ 16. According to the balanced equation in Question 15, 18 g of water would be required to react with 40 g of calcium.

_____ 17. When we are told the amounts of two different reactants that are put into a reaction mixture, we should assume that all of both reactants would be used up.

_____ 18. When two reactions occur simultaneously to give a common product, we can use the mole concept applied to the balanced chemical equations to determine the relative amounts by which the two reactions proceed.

_____ 19. In order to tell how to prepare a 20.0% solution of a compound in water, we would have to know the formula of the compound.

_____ 20. In order to tell how to prepare a 0.25 M solution of a compound in water, we would have to know the formula of the compound.

_____ 21. If we wish to make a 1.00 M solution of sodium chloride, NaCl (formula weight 58.5), we would add 58.4 g of NaCl to 1.00 L of water.

Short Answer

Answer with a word, a phrase, a formula, or a number with units as necessary.

1. The symbol for the reactive metallic element magnesium is ___.
2. The element whose symbol is Na is _____.
3. The number of hydrogen atoms in a molecule of tetraethyl lead, $Pb(C_2H_5)_4$, is ___.
4. One mole of hydrogen peroxide, H_2O_2, contains the same number of hydrogen atoms as ___ mole(s) of water.
5. One mole of hydrogen peroxide contains the same number of oxygen atoms as ___ mole(s) of water.
6. In order to balance the equation $Al + HCl \rightarrow AlCl_3 + H_2$, the numbers which we must put in front of Al, HCl, $AlCl_3$, and H_2 are, respectively, ___, ___, ___, and ___.
7. The number of oxygen atoms in n moles of a substance whose formula is $C_aH_bO_c$ could be expressed as _____.
8. In order to calculate the formula weight of a given compound from its known formula, we _____.

9. According to one theory of the origin of the universe, the age of the universe is about 10 billion years. The number of seconds that have elapsed since the origin of the universe would then be _____ times Avogadro's number.

10. Suppose we calculate the masses of carbon which would combine with 1 g of oxygen in the two compounds carbon monoxide and carbon dioxide. We could then use these two results as an illustration of the Law of _____.

11. The chemical formula we derive from information only about percentage composition of the elements in the compound is referred to as the _____ of the compound.

12. In order to tell whether the simplest formula, as derived from percentage composition data, corresponds to the true molecular formula, we need to make some independent measurement or determination of the _____ of the compound.

13. Using the balanced chemical equation

$$3Ca(OH)_2 + 2H_3PO_4 \rightarrow Ca_3(PO_4)_2 + 6H_2O$$

the unit factor that relates the number of moles of $Ca_3(PO_4)_2$ formed to the number of moles of $Ca(OH)_2$ reacting is _____.

14. Using the balanced chemical equation in Question 13, the unit factor that relates the mass of $Ca_3(PO_4)_2$ formed to the mass of $Ca(OH)_2$ reacting is _____.

15. The maximum percentage yield which a reaction can give is _____.

16. Suppose we know the molarity of an aqueous solution of sulfuric acid (formula weight 98.1), and we wish to express the concentration as mass percent sulfuric acid. The one additional value which would allow us to calculate the conversion is the _____ of the solution.

Multiple Choice

Select the one best answer.

_____ 1. What is the symbol for the element potassium?
(a) K   (b) P   (c) Pb   (d) W   (e) Po

_____ 2. The element whose symbol is Cl is
(a) carbon.   (b) chlorine.   (c) copper.   (d) calcium.
(e) californium.

_____ 3. How many grams of hydrogen would combine with 12.0 g of carbon to form the compound ethylene, C_2H_4?
(a) 1.0 g   (b) 2.0 g   (c) 4.0 g   (d) 8.0 g   (e) 12.0 g

_____ 4. Which of the following is *not* a correct description of 16.0 g of methane, CH_4?

(a) 1 mole of methane

(b) The amount of methane that contains 12.0 g C

(c) $16.0 \times 6.022 \times 10^{23}$ molecules of methane

(d) One gram-molecular weight of methane

_____ 5. Suppose we have 100 g of each of the following substances. Which sample contains the largest number of moles?

(a) H_2O, formula weight 18.0

(b) HCl, formula weight 36.5

(c) $AlCl_3$, formula weight 133.3

(d) $MgCO_3$, formula weight 84.3

(e) Impossible to tell, unless we know what reaction will take place with the substance

_____ 6. An unknown element (call it X) combines with oxygen to form a compound known to have formula XO_2. We observe that 24.0 g of element X combines exactly with 16.0 g of O to form this compound. What is the atomic weight of element X?

(a) 48.0   (b) 32.0   (c) 24.0   (d) 16.0   (e) 12.0

_____ 7. What mass ratio of carbon to oxygen is required to form CO_2 with no excess of either element?

(a) 0.375 g C/g O   (b) 1.33 g C/g O   (c) 2.67 g C/g O

(d) 0.75 g C/g O

_____ 8. For a molecular substance, which of the following statements is true?

(a) The molecular formula must be the same as the simplest formula.

(b) The molecular formula must be proportional to the empirical formula, but with all integer subscripts multiplied by an integer greater than 1.

(c) The molecular formula must be proportional to the empirical formula, with all integer subscripts divided by an integer greater than 1.

(d) The molecular formula may be the same as the simplest formula.

(e) The molecular formula and the empirical formula are not necessarily related.

_____ 9. A compound, whose simplest (empirical) formula is known to be CH_2O, is found by another experiment to have a molecular weight of 180. How many hydrogen atoms are in one molecule of this compound?

(a) 2   (b) 6   (c) 8   (d) 12   (e) 18

_____ 10. Ethylene, C_2H_4, burns in oxygen to produce carbon dioxide and water. The correct form of the chemical equation that describes this reaction is

(a) $C_2H_4 + O \rightarrow CO_2 + H_2O$

(b) $2C_2H_4 + O_2 \rightarrow 2CO_2 + H_2O$
(c) $C_2H_4 + 2O_2 \rightarrow 2CO + 2H_2O$
(d) $C_2H_4 + 3O_2 \rightarrow 2CO_2 + 2H_2O$

_____ 11. In the reaction $CaCO_3 \rightarrow CaO + CO_2$, 100 g of calcium carbonate ($CaCO_3$) is observed to decompose upon heating into 56 g of calcium oxide (CaO) and 44 g of carbon dioxide (CO_2). This is an illustration of
(a) the Law of Conservation of Matter.
(b) the Law of Conservation of Energy.
(c) the Law of Gravity.
(d) the Law of Multiple Proportions.
(e) the conversion of matter into energy.

_____ 12. We place 1.6 g of S in a closed container with 1.6 g of O_2. These elements then react as completely as possible, by the equation $2S + O_2 \rightarrow 2SO$. At the end of the reaction, how many grams of S and O_2, respectively, would be left over, unreacted? (Use atomic weights S = 32, O = 16).
(a) 0.8, 0.8   (b) 0.8, 0.0   (c) 0.0, 0.8   (d) 0.0, 0.0
(e) None of the preceding answers is correct.

_____ 13. Two reactions that occur in the production of iron (Fe) are $2C + O_2 \rightarrow 2CO$, followed by $Fe_2O_3 + 3CO \rightarrow 2Fe + 3CO_2$. Note that the carbon monoxide, CO, formed in the first reaction is then used in the second reaction. According to these reactions, how many moles of oxygen, O_2, are required to produce 8 moles of Fe?
(a) 3   (b) 6   (c) 9   (d) 12   (e) None of the preceding answers is correct.

Answers to Preliminary Test

Do not just look up answers. Think about the reasons for the answers.

True-False

1. False. When a symbol consists of only one letter, it is always a capital letter; when it consists of two letters, the first is always capitalized and the second is always lower case. Even though this convention seems (and is!) arbitrary, like any convention of communication it must be applied in the same way by everyone who hopes to use it to communicate. For example, to a chemist CO cannot mean cobalt — it means a compound consisting of carbon and oxygen atoms in a 1:1 ratio.
2. False. Mercury is Hg. See Table 1–2.
3. True. Individual molecules are too small to see or measure, but 1 mole of

water is 18 g, which is about 1.2 tablespoons of water. (Can you still carry out the conversions to show that 1 mole of water is 1.2 tablespoons? The density of water is 1.0 g/mL, there are 4 cups in a quart, there are 16 tablespoons in a cup, and there are more conversion factors in Table 1-7).

4. False. What we mean is that it has a mass of 4.0 arbitrary units on a scale relative to which a carbon atom has a mass of 12.0 units. This is an example of a situation where thinking about the size of the number helps to avoid a wrong answer. A newly minted U.S. nickel coin has a mass of about 5 g—do you think a single helium atom has a mass of 4 g?

5. True. Sixteen grams of oxygen is 1 mole of oxygen atoms. One mole always contains Avogadro's number of items, so this contains 6.022×10^{23} oxygen atoms.

6. False. Oxygen is a diatomic substance (O_2), so 16 grams of oxygen, which contains 6.022×10^{23} oxygen atoms, would contain only half that many oxygen molecules, or 3.011×10^{23} O_2 molecules.

7. False. One mole of an element is the amount of the element whose mass in grams is numerically equal to the atomic weight. Thus, 1 mole of boron has a mass of 10.8 g. Think about the size of the number. We should remember that a mole of atoms of any substance is a convenient amount of material to handle in the laboratory. The number stated in the question, $10.8 \times 6.022 \times 10^{23}$ g, is larger than the mass of the earth!

8. True. See Section 2-5.

9. True. See Section 2-5.

10. True. See Section 2-6.

11. False. Review the distinction between the molecular formula and the simplest formula, Section 2-6.

12. True

13. False

14. False. Count the number of oxygen atoms on the two sides of this reaction. Count also the number of hydrogen atoms. Can you balance this equation?

15. True

16. False. 36 g of water would be required.

17. False. We must realize that they can react only in the mole ratio indicated by the balanced equation, and therefore, in a weight ratio which we can calculate. Review the limiting-reagent type of problems in Section 2-11.

18. True. See Section 2-12 for examples.

19. False. Remember that 20.0% is taken to mean "by mass." We would just need to add the compound to the solvent in a 1:4 ratio by mass, so that 20.0% of the mass of any amount of solution would be due to the compound.

20. True. This method of expressing solution concentration deals with the

number of moles, which we would need to convert to number of grams (since we cannot directly measure moles) by knowing the formula weight of solute.

21. False. 1.00 M means that the solution contains 1.00 moles of solute (NaCl) per liter of *solution* (not per liter of solvent).

Short Answer

1. Mg
2. sodium
3. 20
4. 1
5. 2
6. 2, 6, 2, and 3
7. $n \times c \times 6.022 \times 10^{23}$ O atoms
8. add the atomic weights for the number and type of elements given in the formula.
9. 6.3×10^{-7}, or 0.00000063. Put another way, when the universe is 1.6 million *times* as old as it is now, Avogadro's number of seconds will have elapsed. This gives some notion of what a large number this is. Recall, however, that Avogadro's number of carbon atoms has a mass of 12 g, and that number of water molecules is about 1.2 teaspoons — this gives a feel for how small atoms and molecules are!
10. Multiple Proportions. See Section 2–5.
11. simplest formula or empirical formula
12. molecular weight or formula weight
13. $\dfrac{1 \text{ mole } Ca_3(PO_4)_2}{3 \text{ mole } Ca(OH)_2}$
14. $\dfrac{310.3 \text{ g } Ca_3(PO_4)_2}{3 \times 74.1 \text{ g } Ca(OH)_2}$
15. 100. This would mean that the reaction went to completion as written, stopping only when one of the reactants was completely gone.
16. density (or specific gravity). See Example 2–33 which is a similar problem stated in a different way.

Multiple Choice

1. (a). Be sure you know the elements that correspond to the symbols in the other answers.
2. (b). Be sure you know the symbols for the elements in the other answers.
3. (b). From the formula, we see that there are $(4 \times 1.0 \text{ g H})/(2 \times 12.0 \text{ g C})$ or 1 g H/6 g C. Thus, 12 g of carbon would require 2 g of hydrogen. Notice that we do not need the reaction by which the ethylene is formed in order

to answer the question. Note that it is immaterial that hydrogen gas is diatomic (H_2), since we are dealing with the mass of hydrogen.

4. (c). Since 16.0 grams is 1 mole of methane, it contains 6.022×10^{23} molecules of CH_4.

5. (a). Notice that we do not need to actually calculate the number of moles — since the number of moles is equal to the number of grams/formula weight, the compound with the lowest formula weight is present in the highest number of moles (for the same weight present).

6. (a). According to the formula, 1 mole of X atoms would be combined with 2 moles of O atoms, or 32.0 g of O. Since 24.0 g of X is seen to combine with 16.0 g of O, it would take 48.0 g of X to combine with 32.0 g of O at the same ratio — hence the atomic weight of X is 48.0.

7. (a). If you got answer (c), you probably calculated the inverse of the requested ratio. If you got (d), you forgot that there are two O atoms for every C atom. If you got (b), you made the mistake in (d), and also calculated the inverse ratio.

8. (d). See Section 2–6.

9. (d). The formula weight of the simplest formula is 30, and that of the true molecular formula is six times that. Thus, the molecular formula must be $C_6H_{12}O_6$.

10. (d). Equation (a) shows oxygen as atoms instead of as diatomic molecules, and is not balanced. Equation (b) is not balanced. Equation (c) is balanced, but shows carbon monoxide rather than carbon dioxide as a product. (Equation (c) could occur if there were a shortage of oxygen in the combustion process — notice that it requires less O_2 per mole of C_2H_4 than does the "complete" combustion reaction to CO_2 given in (d). See Example 2–17 for a brief discussion of burning in the presence of excess O_2.)

11. (a)

12. (c). This is a problem in which you must determine which is the limiting reagent. See Section 2–11 for examples.

13. (b). Using the unit factor approach, you should be able to find out that 12 moles of CO must go into the second reaction to produce 8 moles of Fe. In order for the first reaction to produce those 12 moles of CO, 6 moles of O_2 would be required.

3

Atomic Structure

Chapter Summary

In this chapter, we learn about the constitution of atoms by asking questions such as the following: Of what particles are atoms composed? How are these particles arranged in atoms? Are all atoms of a given element identical? If not, how do they differ and how are they alike? Since we cannot see or measure atoms or the particles of which they are composed, what evidence do we have for the descriptions in this chapter? How do we describe, for a given element, how many electrons the atom has, where these electrons are, and how strongly they are held? (This last question is a particularly important one, since electrons are the particles in atoms that are affected in chemical reactions.)

First, let us make a few observations about how the ideas presented in this chapter were developed. It is not our intent to learn the history of chemistry for its own sake. But if we can see how ideas about atoms and their architecture have been developed, it can help us to develop our own understanding in a gradual and, hopefully, logical way. (If the text or your instructor were to just begin by telling you all information currently known or believed about atoms and subatomic particles, you would soon be overwhelmed, and would learn little.) Such a development along historical lines can also let us appreciate that chemistry is a living, developing science, with new evidence being found and old evidence being continually reassessed or reinterpreted. We can then see that we describe the atom as we do, not because many of these properties of atoms or their particles can be directly observed, but because these descriptions are in best accord with the observations that we can make.

The first important idea about atoms in modern chemistry was the theory proposed by Dalton. Notice, as you study the postulates of Dalton's theory, that what he was trying to do was to "explain" things that could be observed, such as the Law of Conservation of Matter and the Law of Constant Composition, in terms of things he could not directly observe, or even "prove" the existence of, such as atoms and molecules. Some features of the Dalton theory are still useful to us in understanding chemistry; other features have required modification in light of later observations. As you study the chapter, try to notice this pattern in the development of ideas.

Section 3–1 introduces us to the three fundamental particles that we will need to work with in our understanding of chemistry—the basic particle of positive charge **(proton)**, the fundamental particle of negative charge **(electron)**, and the neutral particle **(neutron)**. Much of our study of chemistry will be concerned with understanding the arrangements of these particles in atoms and the relationship of these arrangements to chemical and physical properties. We are first introduced to the properties of the charged subatomic particles, in Sections 3–2 and 3–3, through a discussion of the experiments that led to the realization of the existence and the subsequent characterization of the electron and the proton. Section 3–4 discusses the classic experiment that led to the idea of the nuclear atom, the Rutherford gold foil experiment. In this description of the atom, the protons and neutrons (Section 3–5) are in an extremely small volume in the center of the atom, called the **nucleus.** Thus, the nucleus of the atom contains all of the positive charge and nearly all of the mass of the atom. The electrons, accounting for all of the negative charge, but for only a tiny fraction of the mass of the atom, are distributed throughout the essentially empty space comprising the rest of the atom.

In Sections 3–6 and 3–7, we learn how to characterize different kinds of atoms according to the numbers of protons, neutrons, and electrons they contain. Many important new ideas that will be used frequently in your further study are introduced in these two sections. The **atomic number** tells the number of protons in the nucleus of an atom of the element. It is important to realize that the atomic number characterizes each element uniquely; no two elements have the same atomic number, and two atoms having different numbers of protons in their nuclei must be different elements. All atoms except the common form of hydrogen also contain neutrons in their nuclei. The neutrons, then, contribute to the total mass of the atom, but do not alter its electrical properties, and thus do not affect chemical properties. The existence of different forms of a given element (same atomic number and therefore the same number of protons) having different numbers of neutrons in the nucleus can thus give rise to atoms that are chemically identical but have different masses — **isotopes.** The total number of particles in the nucleus of a particular atom is characterized by the **mass number,** which tells the total number of protons and neutrons in the nucleus. The description of the mass spectrometer, which aided in figuring out this aspect of atomic structure, is helpful in understanding these concepts. Since most elements occur naturally as a mixture of isotopes, which behave the same chemically, any determination on a chemical basis of the "atomic weight" will necessarily lead to a measure of the **average** atomic weight of all isotopes present. This idea, which is discussed in Section 3–7, is the basis for our presently used atomic weight scale, on which the mass of one atom of the most abundant isotope of carbon is assigned a mass of exactly 12 **atomic mass units (amu).** The question of the energy relationships in the nucleus of the atom, the **binding energy** of the nucleus, is addressed in Section 3–8. This topic, related to the release of energy accompanying nuclear reactions such as those that occur in atomic bombs and in nuclear reactors, will be encountered again in Chapter 28.

Since the most important aspect of atomic structure as it relates to chemistry is the arrangement of the electrons around the nucleus, the remainder of Chapter 3 is devoted to this topic. Most of our knowledge about electrons in atoms comes from a study of the ways in which matter (the electrons in matter, actually) interacts with light. Section 3–9 deals with the nature of light, which can sometimes be considered as a **wave** phenomenon (periodically varying electrical and magnetic fields—hence the name **electromagnetic radiation**). We learn that different colors of light correspond to different wavelengths or different frequencies of alternation of these fields. The other, equally important interpretation of light, applicable to other kinds of experiments, is in terms of a **particle** model, in which light consists of streams of particles called **photons,** each of which, for a given color of light, consists of a particular amount of energy, a **quantum** of energy. This dual description in terms of both wave and particle nature can also be applied to very small particles, such as the electron, Section 3–10.

The important observation that when atoms are excited to make them give off light (atomic spectra, Section 3–11), they give off only particular colors of light, i.e., only certain energies, tells us that the atoms must be undergoing only certain specific energy changes but not others. The **Bohr theory** of the atom introduces two ideas that, although we will modify and enlarge them later, are of central importance in our understanding of atoms. These ideas are (1) that an electron in an atom can be only in certain allowed places and (2) that when it is in one of these allowed places, it possesses a certain amount of energy. In the simple Bohr theory of the atom (which actually only works really well for simple atoms like hydrogen) the electrons are assumed to travel in well-defined orbits, each characterized by a positive integer, n, known as a **quantum number.**

The modern **quantum-mechanical picture of the atom,** which we shall use throughout our study of chemistry, is introduced in Section 3–12. This theory really applies the same fundamental ideas as the Bohr theory, but it extends and describes them in a highly mathematical approach, called **quantum theory.** In this mathematical approach, each electron in the atom is treated as though it were a wave and is described by a wave equation called the Schrödinger equation, later made more general by Dirac. Even though we do not need to be concerned with the mathematical details, we must describe the solutions to these wave equations—the wave functions. We will use the solutions to these equations frequently in our study of chemistry.

In your study of the important Sections 3–12 to 3–15, keep in mind that this more refined and elegant theory, even though it looks quite complex, is really just concerned with two features of an electron in the atom: *where the electron is* and *what its energy is.* You will learn that each electron in an atom, corresponding to one of the solutions of the wave equation, is described by a particular set of four numbers, known as the quantum numbers. These four numbers have interpretations that are presented in Section 3-13. We can summarize the quantum numbers and the rules by which they are assigned as follows:

1. The principal quantum number, n, describes the main energy level that the electron occupies. This n can be any positive integer. Increasing values of n describe main energy levels that are at increasingly greater distances from the nucleus.
2. The subsidiary quantum number, l, designates the shape of the region in space that the electron occupies, the **orbital.** The allowed values of l are integers from 0 up to $(n - 1)$. In the commonly used notation, values of l equal to 0, 1, 2, and 3 are designated by the indicators s, p, d, and f, respectively. Different values of l for the same value of n represent different sublevels within the main energy level n.
3. The magnetic quantum number, m_l, designates the orientation of one of the equivalent orbitals having the same set of n, l. The values of m_l range from $-l$ up to $+l$, by integers.
4. The spin quantum number, m_s, is associated with the direction of the spin of the electron and with the orientation of the resulting magnetic field. Allowed values of m_s are $+\frac{1}{2}$ and $-\frac{1}{2}$.

Each valid set of n, l, and m_l defines one **atomic orbital,** which may be interpreted as a region in which there is a high probability of finding the electron. Section 3-14 describes these atomic orbitals with respect to the quantum numbers n (distance from nucleus), l (orbital shape), and m_l (orbital orientation). Orbitals that have the same values of n and l, but differ in their m_l values, are described as **equivalent** or **degenerate** orbitals; in a given atom, the orbitals within an equivalent set have the same energy.

Using rules that are based on the values of the four quantum numbers, you must learn how to tell the arrangement of the electrons in any specified atom, the **electronic configuration.** This topic, which is covered in detail in Section 3-15, is the *most important topic you have yet encountered in chemistry,* in serving as a basis for further understanding. In your study, keep in mind that the application of the rules and procedures that you are learning will enable you to understand chemical bonding, formulas, shapes of molecules, reactivities, and, eventually, properties of compounds. The writing of electronic configurations, in the several different notations that describe the arrangement and energies of electrons in atoms, is worth practicing as much as possible.

We can figure out the electronic configuration of any element by imagining that we add the electrons one by one, letting each occupy the available orbital of lowest energy. This imaginary procedure is called the **aufbau process,** from the German word meaning "to build up." It is very important to remember the order of filling of orbitals: $1s$, $2s$, $2p$, $3s$, $3p$, $4s$, $3d$, $4p$, $5s$, $4d$, $5p$, $6s$, $4f$, $5d$, $6p$, $7s$, $5f$, $6d$, $7p$. A memory aid to help in reconstructing this order is given in Figure 3–25. Two additional rules that govern the order of filling and the number of electrons in the orbitals are the **Pauli Exclusion Principle** (Section 3–13) and **Hund's Rule.**

A final important idea to which we are introduced in this chapter is the grouping of elements with similar outer electronic configurations. We see for the first time a very convenient method of illustrating and categorizing these electronic similarities, the **periodic table.** In subsequent chapters, we will see that the groups of elements with similar outer electronic configurations contain marked similarities in chemical and physical properties, and that the periodic table thus serves as an invaluable aid in classifying elements and their properties.

Study Goals

As in other chapters, some textbook exercises related to the study goals are indicated.

1. Summarize the basic features of Dalton's atomic theory. (Chapter introduction; Exercises 1 through 4)
2. Describe the experiments or ideas of the following scientists and their contributions to our understanding of the structure of atoms: (a) Thomson, (b) Millikan, (c) Rutherford, and (d) Moseley.
3. Describe the three fundamental particles that make up atoms. Describe the experimental evidence that led to the discovery of these three fundamental particles. (Sections 3–1, 3–2, 3–3, and 3–5; Exercises 5 through 9, and 13 through 15)
4. Describe the behavior of charged and uncharged particles and rays in electrical and magnetic fields. (Sections 3–2 and 3–3; Exercises 5 and 7)
5. Describe the nuclear atom. (Section 3–4; Exercise 11)
6. Distinguish between isotopes and atoms. (Sections 3–6 and 3–7)
7. Distinguish among atomic number, mass number, atomic weight, and isotopic weight. (Sections 3–6 and 3–7; Exercises 16 through 36)
8. Describe and illustrate the use of a mass spectrometer. (Section 3–6)
9. From its nuclide symbol, be able to tell the number and type of fundamental particles present in any atom. (Section 3–6; Exercises 16 and 22)
10. Be able to compare the calculated mass of an isotope to its observed mass. Relate the mass defect to the binding energy of the nucleus. (Section 3–8; Exercises 33 through 39)
11. Describe the experiments or ideas of the following scientists and their contributions to our understanding of the structure of atoms: (a) Rydberg, (b) Bohr, (c) Planck, (d) deBroglie, (e) Davisson and Germer, (f) Schrödinger, and (g) Dirac.

12. Understand the wave and particle descriptions of light and why both descriptions are necessary. (Section 3–9; Exercises 40 and 47)

13. Be able to carry out calculations to relate the descriptions of light to its wavelength, frequency, and energy. (Section 3–9; Exercises 40 through 49)

14. Understand the relationship between the observation of atomic line spectra and the idea of distinct energy levels in atoms. Describe how the wavelength of light emitted or absorbed by an atom depends on the separations between its electronic energy levels. (Section 3–11; Exercises 50 through 59)

15. Understand the basis for the description of particles, such as the electron, either as a wave or as a particle. (Section 3–10; Exercises 60 through 62)

16. State and understand the basic postulates of quantum mechanics. (Section 3–12; Exercises 63 and 64)

17. Learn the four quantum numbers, what they represent and what values they can have. (Sections 3–13 and 3–14; Exercises 67 through 70, 76, 78, and 80)

18. Understand the relationship between atomic orbitals and the corresponding values of the quantum numbers. Be familiar with the notations for identifying orbitals. (Section 3–14; Exercises 70 through 72)

19. Describe atomic orbitals. Sketch the shapes of *s, p,* and *d* orbitals. Describe how the same kinds of orbitals in different main energy levels differ. (Section 3–14; Exercises 65, 73, 80, and 81)

20. Learn how the energies of orbitals depend on the quantum numbers. (Section 3–14; Exercises 72 and 77)

21. Learn and apply the rules for the filling of electrons in atomic orbitals. Write out the electronic configurations of specified atoms. Write out the electronic configurations of especially the first 36 elements, both with arrow notation and with condensed notation. (Section 3–15; Exercises 74, 75, 79, 82 through 88, and 95 through 98)

22. Understand how the magnetic properties of an element depend on the number of unpaired electrons in an atom of the element. (Section 3–15; Exercises 89 through 92)

23. Relate the electronic configuration of an atom to its position in the periodic table. (Section 3–15; Exercises 99 through 102)

Some Important Terms in This Chapter

Write the meanings *in your own words* to improve them. Check the Key Terms list and the chapter reading. Then rewrite your definitions, still in your own words, to improve them. Study other new terms and review terms from preceding chapters if necessary.

electron

proton

neutron

atomic number

mass number

atomic mass unit

nucleus

isotope

nuclide symbol

mass defect

binding energy

electromagnetic radiation

frequency

wavelength

photon

quantum

quantum numbers

principal quantum number

subsidiary quantum number

magnetic quantum number

spin quantum number

atomic orbital

s orbital

p orbital

d orbital

f orbital

electron configuration

Aufbau Principle

Pauli Exclusion Principle

Hund's Rule

pairing

group

period

Preliminary Test

As in other chapters, this test will check your understanding of basic concepts and types of calculations. Be sure to practice *many* of the additional textbook exercises, including those indicated in the Study Goals.

True-False

Mark each question as true (T) or false (F).

_____ 1. Most of the mass of an atom is due to the presence of electrons.

_____ 2. The figure "56" in the symbol $^{56}_{26}$Fe represents the total number of electrons and protons in the nucleus of an iron atom.

_____ 3. If we know that the atomic number of an element is 81, then the element must be thallium (Tl).

_____ 4. If we know that an element is thallium, then its atomic number must be 81.

_____ 5. If we know that an atom has mass number 101, then the element must be ruthenium (Ru).

_____ 6. In an atom, the protons and neutrons are in the nucleus, and the electrons are clustered together at some distance from the nucleus.

_____ 7. The characterization of cathode rays showed them to consist of streams of protons.

_____ 8. All cathode ray particles have the same charge/mass (e/m) ratio.

_____ 9. All canal ray particles have the same charge/mass (e/m) ratio.

_____ 10. In the Rutherford experiment, the scattering of streams of alpha particles by the atoms in a metal foil was studied.

_____ 11. The feature that distinguishes the atoms of various elements is their mass number.

_____ 12. All elements naturally exist as mixtures of isotopes.

_____ 13. Atomic numbers are always integers.

_____ 14. Mass numbers are always integers.

_____ 15. Masses of individual atoms are always integers.

_____ 16. Atomic weights are always integers.

_____ 17. The reason that the experimentally observed atomic weight of carbon is listed as 12.011 is due to a slight error in the definition of the atomic weight scale, since it is intended to be exactly 12.

_____ 18. The actual mass of an atom is equal to the sum of the masses of its constituent particles.

_____ 19. The longer the wavelength of light, the higher is its frequency.

_____ 20. The higher the frequency of light, the higher is the energy of one photon of the light.

_____ 21. "A particle is a particle and a wave is a wave, and never the twain shall meet." (Apologies to Rudyard Kipling)

_____ 22. The number of lines in the emission spectrum of an element is equal to the number of electronic energy levels in the atom.

_____ 23. Each combination of n, l, and m_l corresponds to an orbital.

_____ 24. When two electrons occupy the same orbital, they must have opposite spins.

_____ 25. In a given atom, no more than two electrons can occupy a single orbital.

_____ 26. The second main energy level in an atom can have any number of electrons up to 10.

_____ 27. Electrons can exist only in atoms.

_____ 28. All neutral atoms of any given element are identical in all respects.

_____ 29. The higher its value of n, the higher is the energy of an atomic orbital.

Short Answer

Answer with a word, a phrase, a formula, or a number with units as necessary.

1. Fill in the following chart to indicate the effect of positively and negatively charged electrical plates on protons, electrons, and neutrons. Use the notation A for attracted, R for repelled and U for unaffected.

	Proton	Electron	Neutron
Positive plate	(a) ____	(b) ____	(c) ____
Negative plate	(d) ____	(e) ____	(f) ____

2. The charge on the nucleus of a carbon atom is _____.
3. The fundamental particle with positive charge is the _____.
4. The fundamental particle with no charge is the _____.
5. In an atom, the _____ and the _____ are in the nucleus.
6. The two fundamental particles that have nearly the same mass are the _____ and the _____.
7. The two fundamental particles that have equal but opposite charges are the _____ and the _____.
8. Think about the statement, "The nucleus is a combination of protons and neutrons." If we carefully consider the table of atomic numbers and observed atomic weights, we can see that the element _____ must have one isotope that is an exception to this statement.
9. The three kinds of radiation given off by radioactive substances are called _____, _____, and _____.
10. The symbol for an alpha particle is _____; this particle is shown to be identical to the ion that is designated by _____.
11. If a beam containing two kinds of particles having the same mass but different charge is sent through a magnetic field, the particles with the _____ charge would be deflected most.
12. If a beam containing two kinds of particles having the same charge but different mass is sent through a magnetic field, the particles with the _____ mass would be deflected most.
13. Atoms of the same element having different masses are called _____.
14. The symbol $_{11}^{23}Na$ is called a _____ symbol.
15. In the symbol $_{11}^{23}Na$, the number 11 is called the _____ and represents the number of _____ as well as the number of _____ (but only for the neutral atom).

16. In the symbol $^{23}_{11}$Na, the number 23 is called the _____
and represents the _____.

17. The element indium, In, consists of two isotopes. These two isotopes are
designated by the symbols $^{113}_{49}$In and $^{115}_{49}$In. The observed atomic weight of
naturally occurring indium is 114.8. (As a very good approximation, take
the mass of a proton and that of a neutron to be 1 amu and ignore the
mass defect). The natural abundance of the two isotopes is ____ percent
$^{113}_{49}$In and ____ percent $^{115}_{49}$In.

18. The numbers of subatomic particles in a neutral atom of palladium (Pd)
with mass number 106 are ____ protons, ____ neutrons, and ____
electrons.

19. The quantum number that designates the main energy level an electron
occupies is ____, called the _____ quantum number.

20. The quantum number that designates the different possible sublevels
within a main energy level is ____, called the _____
quantum number.

21. The value of ____ designates the shape of the orbital.

22. The value of ____, called the _____ quantum number, designates the spatial orientation of an orbital.

23. The quantum number that designates the spin of an electron is ____.

24. An orbital that is spherically symmetrical has $l =$ ____.

25. An orbital that is spherically symmetrical is designated as a(an) ____
orbital.

26. An orbital with $l = 1$ is designated as a(an) ____ orbital.

27. A p orbital has _____ regions of high electron density.

28. In a single atom, the maximum number of electrons possible in a fourth
main energy level is ____.

29. Two electrons in the same atom that have the same values of n, l, and m_l
must have _____.

30. For any value of the principal quantum number (except $n = 1$) there are
three p orbitals. These three p orbitals correspond to regions of high
electron density in three different directions from the atomic center. The
three p orbitals on the same atom make angles of ____ with each other.

31. In the normal order of occupancy of electronic energy levels, the level
occupied just after $3p$ is ____.

32. In the normal order of occupancy of electronic energy levels, the level
occupied just after $4s$ is ____.

33. The ground-state electronic configuration of bromine (Br) is
_____.

34. The ground-state electronic configuration of arsenic (As) is
_____.

35. The number of unpaired electrons in a neutral atom of sulfur is ____.

36. The number of unpaired electrons in a neutral atom of iron is ____.

37. We describe a particular orbital as a $3d$ orbital. The possible values of the magnetic quantum number for this orbital are _____.

38. Substances that are strongly attracted into magnetic fields are termed _____ substances. The atomic feature responsible for this behavior is the presence of _____ in atoms.

39. In the periodic table, a vertical column of elements is called a _____.

40. In the periodic table, a horizontal row of elements is called a _____.

41. For the elements in Group IIIA, the configuration of the outermost electrons is _____.

42. For the elements in Group VIA, the number of unpaired electrons in each atom is ____.

43. In the periodic table, the nth period begins with the element whose outer electronic configuration is _____ and ends with the one whose outer electronic configuration is _____.

Multiple Choice

Select the best answer.

_____ 1. Two isotopes of the same element must differ in their
   (a) atomic number.
   (b) mass number.
   (c) total charge.
   (d) number of protons.
   (e) number of electrons.

_____ 2. Given the unidentified isotope $^{61}_{27}X$, which one of the following statements is true?
   (a) The atom contains 61 neutrons.
   (b) The neutral atom contains 27 electrons.
   (c) The element must be promethium, Pm.
   (d) The atom contains 34 protons.
   (e) The atom contains a number of protons plus electrons equal to 61.

_____ 3. Which of the following statements about magnesium atoms (Mg) is *not correct?*
   (a) All magnesium atoms have an atomic number of 12.
   (b) All magnesium atoms have the same number of protons.
   (c) All neutral magnesium atoms have 12 protons and 12 electrons.
   (d) All magnesium atoms have the same number of neutrons.
   (e) All atoms with an atomic number of 12 are magnesium atoms.

_____ 4. If an atom has an atomic number of 28 and a mass number of 60, one neutral atom contains
   (a) 28 neutrons.

(b) 32 electrons.

(c) 60 electrons.

(d) 32 protons.

(e) a total number of nuclear particles equal to 60.

_____ 5. Cathode rays are _____ . These particles have the _____ charge/mass ratio of the fundamental particles found in the atom.
(a) neutrons, largest   (b) protons, smallest
(c) electrons, largest   (d) protons, largest   (e) None of the preceding answers is correct.

_____ 6. The discovery and characterization of cathode rays was important in the development of atomic theory because
(a) it indicated that all matter contained protons.
(b) it indicated that all matter contained alpha particles.
(c) it indicated that all matter contained electrons.
(d) it provided a basis for weight calculations in chemical reactions.
(e) it led to the suggestion of the existence of the neutron.

_____ 7. Which of the following provided evidence that most of the mass of the atom, as well as all of the positive charge, is concentrated in a very small core, the nucleus?
(a) The analysis of x-ray wavelengths
(b) The scattering of alpha particles by a metal foil
(c) The deflection of ions in a mass spectrometer
(d) The results of the Millikan oil-drop experiment
(e) The existence of elements with noninteger values for atomic weights

_____ 8. What is the number of electrons in 1 mole of carbon atoms?
(a) 6   (b) 12   (c) $6 \times 6.022 \times 10^{23}$
(d) $12 \times 6.022 \times 10^{23}$
(e) Depends on the isotope of carbon

_____ 9. Suppose that a hypothetical element consists of a mixture of two isotopes. One isotope, having a mass of 44, is present in 70% abundance, while the other isotope, having a mass of 46, accounts for the other 30%. We should expect the experimentally determined atomic weight for this hypothetical element to be
(a) 44.0   (b) 46.0   (c) 45.0   (d) 44.6   (e) 45.4

_____ 10. In an atom
(a) the electrons contain most of the mass of the atom.
(b) the nucleus occupies most of the volume of the atom.
(c) all of the electrons and protons are in the nucleus.
(d) the neutrons are in the nucleus.
(e) the neutrons carry all of the negative charge.

_____ 11. When a beam of charged particles is sent through an electrical or a magnetic field, the path of the particles becomes curved as the particles are deflected by the field. Which of the following statements correctly relates the direction and the amount of this curvature to the properties of the particles?

(a) The direction of curvature depends on the charge; the amount of curvature depends on the e/m ratio.

(b) The direction of the curvature depends on the e/m ratio; the amount of curvature depends on the charge.

(c) The direction of curvature is independent of the charge; the amount of curvature depends on the e/m ratio.

(d) The direction of curvature depends on the e/m ratio; the amount of curvature is independent of the e/m ratio (the charge plays no role in either of these properties).

(e) None of the above statements is correct.

_____ 12. The number of neutrons in one atom of the iron isotope $^{56}_{26}$Fe is

(a) 56.   (b) 26.   (c) $56 - 26$.   (d) $56 + 26$.

(e) not determinable without knowing the observed atomic weight of naturally occurring iron.

_____ 13. The following are all proposals of Dalton's atomic theory. Which part of Dalton's atomic theory was shown to be wrong by the discovery of natural radioactivity?

(a) Atoms of a given element all weigh the same.

(b) Two or more kinds of atoms may combine in different ways to form more than one kind of chemical compound.

(c) Atoms combine in simple numerical ratios to form compounds.

(d) Atoms are permanent, unchanging, indivisible bodies.

(e) Compounds consist of collections of molecules made up of atoms bonded together.

_____ 14. Which of the following must represent an element that is *different* from the others?

(a) Something with 12 protons, 24 neutrons, and 12 electrons

(b) Something with 12 protons, 24 neutrons, and 10 electrons

(c) Something with 12 protons, 26 neutrons, and 12 electrons

(d) Something with 10 protons, 24 neutrons, and 12 electrons

(e) All of the preceding are isotopes of the same element.

_____ 15. The positive rays that are sometimes found in cathode ray tubes are characterized as particles having a smaller charge to mass ratio for heavier elements. The positive ray particles that are formed when the gas in the tube is hydrogen have a larger observed charge to mass ratio than those for any other gas. This can be explained by assuming that

(a) the particles are all alpha particles.

(b) the particles are all identical, regardless of the gas in the tube.

(c) the particles are ions formed by the removal of one or more electrons from neutral atoms of gases in the tube.

(d) each gas consists of a mixture of at least two kinds of atoms.

(e) the positive ray particles are neutrons.

_____ 16. If a beam of each of the following were sent through a mass spectrometer, which would follow the most curved path (that is, be deflected most)?

(a) neutral Ti atoms, mass number 47

(b) neutral Ti atoms, mass number 48

(c) Ti^+ ions, mass number 47

(d) Ti^{2+} ions, mass number 47

(e) Ti^{2+} ions, mass number 48

_____ 17. Which of the following provided evidence that the electrons in atoms are arranged in distinct energy levels?

(a) The observation of line spectra from gas discharge tubes

(b) The scattering of alpha particles by a metal foil

(c) The deflection of ions in a mass spectrometer

(d) The results of the Millikan oil-drop experiment

(e) The existence of elements with noninteger values for atomic weights

_____ 18. Suppose that an atom had available to it *only* the six energy levels indicated below. What would be the total number of lines in the emission spectrum of this element?

_____ $n = 6$

_____ $n = 5$

_____ $n = 4$

_____ $n = 3$

_____ $n = 2$

_____ $n = 1$

(a) 5   (b) 6   (c) 15   (d) 21   (e) 36

_____ 19. Bohr's theory of the hydrogen atom assumed that

(a) electromagnetic radiation is given off when the electron moves in an orbit around the nucleus.

(b) the electron can exist in any one of a set of discrete states (energy levels) without emitting radiation.

(c) since a hydrogen atom has only one electron, the spectrum of hydrogen should consist of only one line.

(d) the electron in a hydrogen atom can jump from one energy level to another without gain or loss of energy.

(e) energy, in the form of radiation, must be continually supplied to keep the electron moving in its orbit.

_____ 20. An electron in a hydrogen atom could undergo any of the transitions listed below by changing its energy. Which transition would give off (emit) light of the longest wavelength? (You will not need to do calculations of the wavelength, but think about the Rydberg equation and the Planck relationship.)

(a) $n = 3$ to $n = 2$　　(b) $n = 3$ to $n = 1$　　(c) $n = 2$ to $n = 1$

(d) $n = 2$ to $n = 3$　　(e) $n = 1$ to $n = 3$

_____ 21. An orbital that has $n = 4$ and $l = 2$ is identified as a _____ orbital.

(a) $2f$　　(b) $3s$　　(c) $4s$　　(d) $4p$　　(e) $4d$

_____ 22. Which of the following is *not* a permitted combination of quantum numbers?

(a) $n = 3, l = 4, m_l = 0, m_s = \frac{1}{2}$

(b) $n = 5, l = 4, m_l = 0, m_s = -\frac{1}{2}$

(c) $n = 3, l = 2, m_l = -2, m_s = \frac{1}{2}$

(d) $n = 2, l = 1, m_l = 1, m_s = \frac{1}{2}$

(e) $n = 4, l = 0, m_l = 0, m_s = \frac{1}{2}$

_____ 23. Can an electron in an atom be described by the set of quantum numbers described below?

$$n = 5, l = 3, m_l = -2, m_s = -\frac{1}{2}$$

(a) No, because l must be equal to $(n - 1)$.

(b) No, because m_l cannot be negative.

(c) No, because n cannot be as large as 5.

(d) No, because m_s must be positive.

(e) Yes

_____ 24. The number of orbitals in a set of equivalent p orbitals is

(a) 1.　　(b) 2.　　(c) 3.　　(d) 5.

(e) The answer depends on the value of n (whether we are talking about $2p$, $3p$, etc.).

_____ 25. Which of the following orbitals has a shape that we describe as "spherically symmetrical"?

(a) An s orbital　　(b) A p orbital　　　　(c) A d orbital

(d) An f orbital　　(e) All of the preceding.

_____ 26. In a given atom, how many electrons can occupy the $3p$ set of orbitals?

(a) 0　　(b) 2　　(c) 3　　(d) 6　　(e) 10

_____ 27. In a given atom, how many electrons can occupy the $4d$ set of orbitals?
        (a) 0   (b) 2   (c) 3   (d) 6   (e) 10
_____ 28. In a given atom, how many electrons can occupy the $2d$ set of orbitals?
        (a) 0   (b) 2   (c) 3   (d) 6   (e) 10
_____ 29. Which of the following atoms would be most strongly paramagnetic?
        (a) S   (b) Co   (c) Cr   (d) Cl   (e) Ne
_____ 30. Which of the following elements has three half-filled $2p$ orbitals in the ground-state electronic configuration of the neutral atom?
        (a) C   (b) N   (c) O   (d) F   (e) Ne
_____ 31. A neutral atom has a ground-state electronic configuration designated $1s^2 \, 2s^2$. Which of the following statements concerning this atom is (or are) correct?
        (a) The element has an atomic number of 4 and is beryllium.
        (b) The atom contains four protons.
        (c) The atom has no unpaired electrons.
        (d) The atom has a total of two orbitals occupied.
        (e) All of the preceding statements are correct.

> *Important:* It is essential to your further understanding of chemistry that you have a firm understanding of electronic configurations. Practice until you can write electronic configurations quickly and comfortably. Use Table 3–4 as a guide to whether you are writing these correctly. You should become comfortable with the various notations for representing electronic configurations.

Answers to Preliminary Test

Do not just look up answers. Think about the reasons for the answers.

True-False

1. False. The electrons are the lightest of the three subatomic particles and contribute little to the total mass.
2. False, for two reasons. First, the electrons are not in the nucleus, and second, 56 is the mass number, which represents the sum of the number of protons and the number of neutrons in the nucleus.
3. True. The atomic number uniquely defines the element.
4. True

5. False. It could be either an isotope of Ru or of another element. Mass number does not uniquely define the element.

6. False. The electrons are distributed throughout a relatively large empty space surrounding the nucleus.

7. False. Cathode ray particles are electrons.

8. True

9. False. The canal ray particles are the positive ions that remain when an atom loses one or more electrons. These have different masses, depending on the identity of the original atom.

10. True

11. False. The atomic number (i.e., number of protons in the nucleus) determines the identity of the element. This is contrary to the earlier Daltonian idea of the atom.

12. False. See Table 3-2 and the accompanying discussion in Section 3-6.

13. True

14. True

15. False. See Sections 3-5 through 3-7.

16. False. The observed atomic weight of an element is the weighted average of the masses of the constituent isotopes. See the sample calculations in Section 3-7.

17. False. The atomic weight scale is defined in terms of the mass of the most common isotope of carbon being exactly 12 amu; naturally occurring carbon also contains other isotopes, so that the average (or experimentally determined) atomic weight is not exactly 12.

18. False. Some of the mass (called the mass defect) is converted into energy. This is the binding energy that holds the nuclear particles (protons and neutrons) together. See the calculations in Section 3-8.

19. False. See Section 3-9. Wavelength and frequency are inversely proportional to one another. This point is illustrated by Example 3-5.

20. True. See Section 3-11. Energy is directly proportional to frequency. Be sure you understand Example 3-6.

21. False. Both light and particles such as the electron can exhibit either wave or particle behavior. See Sections 3-9 through 3-11.

22. False. Each line in the spectrum is the result of a transition between two electronic energy levels in the atom.

23. True. But, remember that orbitals with the same values of n and l but different m_l values have the same energy.

24. True

25. True

26. False. The second main energy level can have a maximum of eight electrons.

27. False. Recall that cathode rays are streams of electrons (Section 3-2) and that atoms can lose electrons to form ions (Section 3-3). Diffraction and

scattering experiments of beams of electrons are mentioned in Section 3–9.

28. False. It is true that all atoms of a given element have the same number of protons; therefore, to be neutral they must also have the same number of electrons. However, it is possible for the atoms to have different numbers of neutrons, and thus, to represent different isotopes of the same element.

29. False. You should know the normal order of electronic energy levels, Figure 3–25. You must remember, however, that the order of energies is sometimes different, depending on the occupancy of the orbitals. See Section 3–15, especially the discussion concerning the configurations of Cr and Cu.

Short Answer

1. (a) R, (b) A, (c) U, (d) A, (e) R, (f) U. Remember that like charges repel, unlike charges attract, and particles having no charge are not affected by an electrical (or a magnetic) field.

2. 6+. Remember that the atomic number gives the number of protons in the nucleus; the only other particles in the nucleus are the neutrons, which are uncharged.

3. proton

4. neutron

5. protons, neutrons

6. proton, neutron

7. proton, electron

8. Hydrogen. Since the experimentally observed atomic weight is only slightly greater than 1, hydrogen must consist at least partially (in fact mostly) of an isotope with mass number 1. This isotope would have only one proton and no neutrons in the nucleus. In fact, this isotope of hydrogen is the only exception to the statement.

9. alpha rays (or particles), beta rays (or particles), gamma rays. Note that gamma rays, which consist of very high energy light, are not called gamma particles.

10. α, He^{2+}

11. larger. The deflection depends on the charge/mass ratio.

12. smaller

13. isotopes

14. nuclide

15. atomic number, protons, electrons

16. mass number, sum of the number of protons and the number of neutrons (or total number of nuclear particles)

17. 10, 90. Let x = fraction of atoms that have a mass number of 113; then

$1 - x$ equals the fraction that have a mass number of 115. So $x(113) + (1 - x)(115) = 114.8$; $113x + 115 - 115x = 114.8$; $2x = 0.2$; $x = 0.1$ and $1 - x = 0.9$.

18. 46, 60, 46

19. n. principal (note — not principle!)

20. l. subsidiary (or azimuthal)

21. l

22. m_l, magnetic

23. m_s

24. 0

25. s

26. p

27. two

28. 32. For $n = 4$, the possible values of l are 0 (one s orbital), 1 (three p orbitals), 2 (five d orbitals), and 3 (seven f orbitals) for a total of 16 orbitals. Each orbital can hold 2 electrons, for a total of 32 electrons possible in this energy level.

29. opposite values of m_s. Study the Pauli Exclusion Principle (Section 3–13).

30. 90°

31. $4s$

32. $3d$

33. $1s^2 \, 2s^2 \, 2p^6 \, 3s^2 \, 3p^6 \, 4s^2 \, 3d^{10} \, 4p^5$. Remember that it would also be correct to write the electronic configuration with all orbitals having the same value of principal quantum number appearing together. Thus, we could have written $1s^2 \, 2s^2 \, 2p^6 \, 3s^2 \, 3p^6 \, 3d^{10} \, 4s^2 \, 4p^5$. This shows $3s$, $3p$, and $3d$ together, even though in the normal order $4s$ fills before $3d$.

34. $1s^2 \, 2s^2 \, 2p^6 \, 3s^2 \, 3p^6 \, 4s^2 \, 3d^{10} \, 4p^3$. See the additional comments in the answer to the preceding question.

35. 2. The electron configuration is $1s^2 \, 2s^2 \, 2p^6 \, 3s^2 \, 3p^4$. In the $3p$ orbitals, the electrons are arranged as ⇅ ↑ ↑. All other electrons are paired.

36. 4. The electron configuration is $1s^2 \, 2s^2 \, 2p^6 \, 3s^2 \, 4s^2 \, 3d^6$. In the arrow notation, the $3d^6$ represents ⇅ ↑ ↑ ↑ ↑. All other electrons are paired.

37. $-2, -1, 0, +1, +2$. Since it is a d orbital, $l = 2$, so m_l can then take any value from $-l$ to $+l$ by integers.

38. paramagnetic, unpaired electrons

39. group

40. period

41. $ns^2 \, np^1$

42. 2. Each of these elements has the electron configuration $ns^2 \, np^4$. The two s electrons are paired in a single orbital. The four p electrons are arranged as ⇅ ↑ ↑.

43. ns^1, $ns^2 \, np^6$

Multiple Choice

1. (b)
2. (b)
3. (d). Since the observed atomic weight of magnesium is greater than 24, there must be an isotope of magnesium that has a mass number greater than 24; this isotope would have a different number of neutrons than the principal isotope, $^{24}_{12}Mg$.
4. (e)
5. (c)
6. (c)
7. (b)
8. (c). The atomic number of carbon is 6, which tells us that *each* atom of C contains 6 electrons (regardless of which isotope we are considering). But 1 mole of carbon contains 6.022×10^{23} carbon atoms, so the total number of electrons is (1 mole C atoms)(6.022×10^{23} C atoms/mole C atoms)(6 electrons/C atom)
9. (d). Calculate as in Examples 3–1 and 3–2 of the text. Atomic weight $= (0.70 \times 44) + (0.30 \times 46) = 44.6$
10. (d)
11. (a)
12. (c)
13. (d)
14. (d). The number of protons in the nucleus (described by the atomic number) determines the element. Answer (d) has a different number of protons, so it must be a different element. Answers (a) and (c) are isotopes of the same element. Answer (b) is an ion formed from answer (a) by loss of two electrons, but it is still the same element.
15. (c)
16. (d). The larger the charge to mass ratio (e/m), the greater the deflection. Neutral atoms would not be deflected, since they have no charge. Answer (d) has twice as great a charge as (c), but the same mass, so (d) would be deflected more. Answer (e) also has a 2+ positive charge, but it has a larger mass, so it has a *smaller* e/m ratio.
17. (a)
18. (c). Each transition from a higher to a lower energy level gives rise to one line in the emission spectrum. An electron could go from level $n = 6$ to any of five lower-energy levels (five possible transitions), from $n = 5$ to any of four lower energy levels (four transitions), and so on. There are 15 such downward transitions.
19. (b)
20. (a). Answers (d) and (e) correspond to absorption of light, not emission. Of the other answers, (a) corresponds to the smallest energy difference

(remember that the energy levels get closer together at higher n), and wavelength is inversely proportional to energy of the light.

21. (e)
22. (a). l can be no larger than $(n-1)$.
23. (e). Review the rules for the allowed values of the quantum numbers, Sections 3–13 and 3–14.
24. (c)
25. (a). See Section 3–14 regarding orbital shapes.
26. (d)
27. (e)
28. (a). There is no such thing as a $2d$ orbital. This would mean that $n=2$ and $l=2$, which would violate the rules for the allowed values of quantum numbers.
29. (c). Cr has the largest number of unpaired electrons of any atom listed.
30. (b)
31. (e)

4

Chemical Periodicity and Ionic Bonding

Chapter Summary

The problem of organizing the properties and reactions of dozens of elements and millions of compounds is made easier by the classification scheme known as the **periodic table.** We were introduced to this table in the latter part of Chapter 3, as a way of representing similarities in electronic configurations of groups of elements. The marvelous utility of the periodic table in chemistry arises from the relationship of properties of the elements to their electronic configurations. Thus, we can use the periodic table (1) to organize our understanding of many properties and (2) to predict properties or reactions of elements with which we may not be familiar or for which the property or reaction in question may not have been studied. The term "periodic" arises because elements with similar electronic configurations, and hence similar properties, recur somewhat regularly as we go through the elements by increasing atomic number. As you study this chapter, you should become increasingly aware of the regularities that many elemental properties exhibit and with the similarities of groups of elements having similar electronic configurations. As a result, you will be increasingly able to interpret the periodic table to remind you of electronic configurations and to predict or correlate properties of substances.

The development of this simple yet powerful correlation, described in Section 4–1, is certainly one of the major intellectual achievements in the history of science. The section also explains the terminology we use to discuss the periodic table—the reference to horizontal rows as **periods** and to vertical columns or groups of elements as **groups,** a terminology encountered in Chapter 3. We are also introduced to the common names of some of the groups of elements—the **alkali metals, alkaline earth metals, halogens,** and **noble gases.** Another way of classifying elements for discussion is in terms of the "last" electron added to the electronic configuration in the *aufbau* process we learned and used in Chapter 3. Thus, elements in which this last electron is in an *s* or *p* orbital (excepting the noble gases) are termed **representative elements,** those in which the last electron is in a *d* orbital are **transition elements** or **transition metals,** and those with it in an *f* orbital are **inner transition elements.** This classification is summarized in Table 4–2, and should be learned. You should be able to tell by a glance at the periodic table into which kind of orbital this last electron went for any element, from the position of the element in the periodic table.

Many chemical and physical properties are related to the positions of the elements in the periodic table. These are the subject of Sections 4–2 through 4–8, which introduce us to some elemental properties that will, in turn, be of use in understanding bonding between elements and the properties of the resulting compounds. You should have two goals in mind as you study these sections. One is to be able to explain how each of these observed trends results from changing electronic configurations across periods and down groups. The second is the reverse—using its position in the periodic table to predict the properties of an element.

Since chemical bonding usually involves only the outermost or incompletely filled shells of electrons, we often concentrate our attention on these so-called **valence electrons.** A formalism for representing and keeping track of the numbers of valence electrons in atoms, the **Lewis dot representation,** is presented and correlated with the element's position in the periodic table in Section 4–2. This formalism is somewhat more cumbersome and accordingly less useful for *d-* or *f*-transition elements and is generally used only for representative elements. Another property that is easily correlated with position in the periodic table is the size of the atom, usually described in terms of the *atomic radii* of the elements (Section 4–4). The correlations that emerge are that the atomic sizes of the (representative) elements within a period decrease regularly as we move from left to right across a period, while within a group the sizes increase as we move from top to bottom. Be sure that you understand how these trends in atomic radii are related to regular changes in electronic configuration.

Chemical reactions result from some kind of interaction of the electrons of the elements involved. Thus, it is important to understand how tightly the electrons of elements are held, and how easily the elements gain or lose electrons. Recall that when an atom loses electrons, a **positive** ion **(cation)** is formed, whereas gain of electrons by an atom results in formation of a **negative ion (anion).** The ease with which these two processes can occur can be measured as, respectively, the **ionization energy** and the **electron affinity** of the element. Sections 4–5 and 4–6 correlate trends in these two properties with position in the table, and hence with electronic configurations of the elements. Careful study of these correlations reveals that the strength with which the electrons are held, or the ease with which additional electrons are taken on, depends both on the size of the atom and on the effectiveness of the positively charged nucleus in attracting electrons in the outermost shell. The ions that are thus formed are characteristically smaller (for cations) or larger (for anions) than the corresponding neutral atoms, comparisons that can also be related to what types of orbitals the outermost electrons occupy and to the effective nuclear attraction for these electrons (Section 4–6).

Section 4–7 introduces a concept that will be useful in subsequent chapters in predicting and understanding chemical bonding. This is the expression of the tendency of an atom to attract electrons on a relative scale known as the **electronegativity scale.** It is helpful to remember the correlations of electronegativity with position in the periodic table—electronegativities generally increase from left to right across a period and decrease from top to bottom within a group. We do not apply this terminology to the noble gases, which, because of their extremely stable configurations, have practically no tendency to gain or lose electrons.

The elements are often broadly classified as **metals, nonmetals,** or **metalloids** (whose properties are intermediate between those of the other two classes). The general physical and chemical properties and the electronic configurations which distinguish among these classes of elements are discussed in Section 4–8.

The second major section of Chapter 4 begins our study of chemical bonding with a discussion of the kinds of chemical bonds that can hold atoms together in compounds, Section 4–9. Here we see that there are two extremes in the possible mode of bonding: (1) **ionic bonding,** in which one atom or group of atoms completely gives up or **transfers** electrons to another, resulting in charged atoms or groups of atoms (ions), and (2) **covalent bonding,** in which electrons are **shared** between two atoms. We can correlate many properties of compounds with the predominant type of bonding which holds them together, while recognizing that these are only extremes in a continuous graduation of bonding, with nearly all bonds being to some degree both ionic and covalent.

The important Section 4–10 contains a detailed description of the first of these extremes, **ionic bonding.** The generalizations that we can see are (1) the elements with low ionization energies readily lose electrons, giving them up to the elements with high electronegativities and high electron affinities, thereby forming ions that then attract one another because of their opposite charge, and (2) the number of electrons an atom gains or loses to form a stable ion depends on its electronic configuration, with the gain or loss resulting in a more stable configuration (usually a noble gas configuration for representative elements). This enables us to understand and predict the formulas of simple **binary** (i.e., two-element) ionic compounds, which are summarized in Table 4–8. Do not try merely to memorize this table, however—understand in terms of the electronic configurations of the elements involved why the formulas of the compounds are as indicated in this table. The electron configuration diagrams and Lewis dot formulas that are used in the discussion of the section are helpful in developing this understanding and will enable you to predict formulas. Some experimental approaches to determining ionic charges are outlined in Section 4–11.

The final section of the chapter, Section 4–12, introduces another convenient way of keeping track of the number of electrons gained or lost in ion formation or of keeping track of the shifts in electron density in covalent bond formation—the **oxidation number** or **oxidation state.** The rules for assignment of oxidation numbers to elements in compounds, presented at the end of this section, will be quite useful in later chapters in assessing bonding strengths, in balancing some types of chemical equations (Chapter 10), in studying the electron-transfer reactions that take place in batteries and in electrolysis cells (Chapter 19), and in systematizing many kinds of reactions of elements (Chapters 7 and 20 through 27). You should practice until you can assign oxidation numbers to all elements in any compound or complex ion whose formula you are given.

Study Goals

Be sure to practice many of the indicated end-of-chapter exercises, in addition to answering the following Preliminary Test.

1. Describe and understand what is meant by periodicity. (Section 4–1, Exercises 1 through 9)
2. Relate the electronic configuration of an atom to the position of the element in the periodic table (also Goal 23 of Chapter 3). Know how to write Lewis dot representations of representative elements, and understand how these are related to group numbers. (Sections 4–1 and 4–2; Exercises 11 through 15)
3. Know which elements are examples of each of the following: (a) alkali metals, (b) alkaline earth metals, (c) halogens, (d) noble gases, (e) representative elements, (f) d-transition elements, (g) inner transition elements or f-transition elements, (h) lanthanides, and (i) actinides. Relate each of these classes to electronic configuration and to position in the periodic table. (Section 4–1; Exercise 10)
4. Summarize horizontal and vertical trends in the periodic table for each of the following properties. Relate each of these properties and their trends to electronic configurations:
   (a) atomic radius (Section 4–3; Exercises 21 through 25)
   (b) ionization energy (Section 4–4; Exercises 26 through 35)
   (c) electron affinity (Section 4–5; Exercises 36 through 38)
   (d) ionic radius (Section 4–6; Exercises 39 through 44)
   (e) electronegativity (Section 4–7; Exercises 45 through 48)
5. Know the contrasting physical and chemical properties of metals and nonmetals. Know where the metals, nonmetals, and metalloids are located in the periodic table. (Section 4–8; Exercises 10 and 16 through 20)
6. Distinguish between the major aspects of ionic and covalent bonding. (Section 4–9; Exercises 49 and 50)
7. Know some of the major differences in physical properties of ionic and covalent compounds. (Section 4–9; Exercises 51 through 53)
8. Predict whether bonding between a given pair of elements or in a given

compound would be covalent or ionic. (Section 4–10; Exercises 54 through 56)

9. Relate the stable ions formed by elements to their electronic configurations and to their positions in the periodic table. (Section 4–10; Exercises 57, 58, and 63 through 69)

10. Predict the formulas of binary ionic compounds from the positions of the constituent representative elements in the periodic table. (Section 4–10; Exercises 59 and 60)

11. Write equations for the reactions of representative elements to form binary ionic compounds. In these equations, be able to represent reactants and products with (a) simple chemical symbols and formulas, (b) electronic configuration diagrams, and (c) Lewis dot formulas. (Section 4–10; Exercises 61, 62, and 70 through 73)

12. Know how the charges on ions may be studied experimentally. (Section 4–11)

13. Know the rules for assigning oxidation numbers and be able to assign oxidation numbers to elements in molecules, ions, and compounds. (Section 4–12; Exercises 75 through 81)

Some Important Terms in This Chapter

Write the meanings *in your own words.* Check the Key Terms list and the chapter reading. Then rewrite your definitions, still in your own words, to improve them. Study other new terms, and review terms from preceding chapters if necessary.

Lewis dot formula

valence electrons

metal

nonmetal

metalloid

periodicity

periodic table

representative elements

d-transition elements

inner transition elements

noble gases

halogens

alkali metals

alkaline earth metals

ionization energy

electron affinity

electronegativity

chemical bonds

covalent bond

ionic bonding

anion

cation

oxidation number

Preliminary Test

As in other chapters, this test will check your understanding of basic concepts. Be sure to practice *many* of the additional textbook exercises, including those indicated in the Study Goals.

Short Answer

Answer with a word, a phrase, a formula, or a number with units as necessary.

1. A statement of the periodic law is _____ ____
_____.
2. The two scientists who are credited with the development of the ideas of periodicity of elemental properties were _____ and _____.
3. The elements in Group IA are referred to as the _____.
4. Calcium and barium are members of Group ___, known as the _____ group.
5. The transition metals are elements that are characterized by electrons being added to the _____.
6. The inner transition elements are characterized by electrons being added to the _____.
7. The members of the halogen group are _____.
8. An element having outer electronic configuration ns^2np^3 would be found in Group ___.
9. The number of valence electrons in an atom of any Group VIA element is ___.

10. The lightest three elements of Group VA, arranged in order of increasing atomic size, are _____.
11. Because of the increasing nuclear charge going left to right across the representative elements of a period, the first ionization energies _____.
12. Because of the increasing nuclear charge going left to right across the representative elements of a period, the atomic radii _____.
13. The Lewis dot representation of an atom of calcium is _____.
14. The Lewis dot representation of an atom of phosphorus is _____.
15. The Lewis dot representation for any halogen atom (represent it as X) is _____.
16. The most stable ion formed by a member of the halogen group would have a charge of _____.
17. The Lewis dot representation of the stable ion formed by bromine is _____.
18. The Lewis dot representation of the stable ion formed by selenium (Se) is _____.
19. The stable ion formed by cesium (Cs) would have the same electronic configuration as a neutral atom of _____.
20. A cation is (larger than, smaller than, the same size as) the neutral atom from which it is formed.
21. Atoms or ions that have the same number of electrons are said to be _____.
22. The neutral atom that is isoelectronic with Sr^{2+} is _____.
23. The formula of the ionic compound of magnesium and oxygen is _____.
24. The formula of the ionic compound of rubidium and sulfur is _____.
25. The formula of the ionic compound of calcium and nitrogen is _____.
26. The sum of the oxidation numbers of all of the atoms in a neutral compound is equal to _____.
27. The sum of the oxidation numbers of all of the atoms in a complex (polyatomic) ion is equal to _____.
28. In most of its compounds, the oxidation number of hydrogen is ___, whereas oxygen almost always exhibits the oxidation number ___.
29. The oxidation numbers of the elements in the compound K_2S are K___ and S___.
30. In the compound NaCl the oxidation numbers of the elements are Na___ and Cl ___.
31. In the compound $NaClO_3$ the oxidation numbers of the elements are Na___, Cl___, and O___.
32. In the sulfate ion, SO_4^{2-}, the oxidation numbers of the elements are S___ and O___.

Multiple Choice

_____   1. Which of the following pairs of elements would be expected to be most similar chemically?

(a) Sn and Sr   (b) S and Se   (c) Ca and Na   (d) Ne and Na
(e) Ga and Ge

_____ 2. For each of the noble gases (except helium) the outermost occupied main energy level contains how many electrons?
(a) 1   (b) 2   (c) 6   (d) 8   (e) 18

_____ 3. Which of the following statements concerning the element iodine is *not correct?*
(a) Iodine would form a covalent compound with any of the alkali metals.
(b) Iodine is in the fifth period of the periodic table.
(c) Iodine has chemical properties similar to those of chlorine.
(d) Iodine is a halogen.
(e) One molecule of iodine contains two atoms.

_____ 4. Zirconium (Zr) is classified as
(a) a representative element.   (b) a transition element.
(c) a lanthanide.   (d) an actinide.   (e) a noble gas.

_____ 5. Which of the following is a transition element?
(a) P   (b) Pd   (c) Ar   (d) U   (e) Na

_____ 6. Which of the following is a representative element?
(a) P   (b) Pd   (c) Ar   (d) U   (e) V

_____ 7. An element with an outer electronic configuration ns^2 (excepting He) is classified as
(a) an alkali metal.
(b) an alkaline earth metal.
(c) a halogen.
(d) a transition element.
(e) an inner transition element.

_____ 8. When the properties of the elements with atomic numbers 114 and 115 are well characterized, they will probably fit into
(a) the actinide series of inner transition elements.
(b) Groups IVA and VA.
(c) a new section of the periodic table, such as Period 8.
(d) the noble gas group.
(e) the halogen group.

_____ 9. Atoms of the elements in the same A group in the periodic table have
(a) the same electronegativity.
(b) the same total number of electrons.
(c) the same size.
(d) the same number of valence electrons.
(e) the same number of protons.

_____ 10. The formulas of the oxides of some second period elements are Li_2O, BeO, B_2O_3, and CO_2. Which of the following is likely to be the correct formula for aluminum sulfide?
(a) Al_2S (b) AlS (c) Al_2S_3 (d) AlS_2

The valence electrons of an atom in its ground state are represented by the configuration $3s^23p^4$. Questions 11, 12, and 13 refer to this atom.

_____ 11. To which group in the periodic table does the element (of which this atom is a part) belong?
   (a) IIA   (b) IIIA   (c) VIA   (d) VIIA   (e) noble gas

_____ 12. If a stable ion of the atom is formed, what is the probable charge on the ion?
   (a) 1−   (b) 2−   (c) 0   (d) 2+   (e) 4+

_____ 13. How many of the valence orbitals of the neutral atom are half filled?
   (a) 1   (b) 2   (c) 3   (d) 4   (e) 0

_____ 14. The number of valence electrons in an isolated carbon atom is
   (a) 0.   (b) 1.   (c) 2.   (d) 4.   (e) 6.

_____ 15. Where in the periodic table are the least electronegative elements found? (Ignore the noble gases.)
   (a) upper left   (b) upper right   (c) lower left
   (d) lower right   (e) middle

_____ 16. Which of the following elements would have the greatest first ionization energy?
   (a) Na   (b) Al   (c) Si   (d) S   (e) Cl

_____ 17. For which of the following elements would the size of the neutral atom (atomic radius) be smallest?
   (a) K   (b) Na   (c) Mg   (d) Ca   (e) Sr

_____ 18. Cesium (Cs) would be expected to have a _____ first ionization energy and a _____ electronegativity.
   (a) large, large   (b) large, small   (c) small, large
   (d) small, small

_____ 19. The alkali metals have low first and high second ionization energies. The alkaline earth metals have relatively low values for both first and second ionization energies. These observations suggest that
   (a) both alkali metals and alkaline earth metals should form very stable ions with charge 1+.
   (b) both alkali metals and alkaline earth metals should form very stable ions with charge 1−.
   (c) alkali metals should form stable 1+ ions, while alkaline earth metals should form stable 2+ ions.
   (d) alkali metals should form stable 1+ ions, while alkaline earth metals should form stable 2− ions.
   (e) alkali metals should form stable 1− ions, while alkaline earth metals should form stable 2− ions.

_____ 20. Which one of the following isoelectronic ions would you expect to have the largest radius?
   (a) S^{2-} (b) Cl^- (c) K^+ (d) Ca^{2+} (e) Sc^{3+}

_____ 21. Which of the following pairs would correctly be described as isoelectronic?
(a) Na and Na^+ (b) Ca and Be   (c) Cu^+ and Zn^{2+}
(d) P^- and P^{2-} (e) H and He

_____ 22. The electron configuration $1s^2 2s^2 2p^6 3s^2 3p^6$ could represent
(a) an atom of Ar.
(b) a Cl^- ion.
(c) a K^+ ion.
(d) any of the ions or atoms mentioned.
(e) none of the atoms or ions mentioned.

_____ 23. What is the ground state electronic configuration of the S^{2-} ion?
(a) $1s^2 2s^2 2p^6 3s^2 3p^4$
(b) $1s^2 2s^2 2p^6 3s^2 3d^6$
(c) $1s^2 2s^2 2p^6 3s^2 3p^2$
(d) The same as the ground state configuration of an Ne atom.
(e) The same as the ground state configuration of an Ar atom.

_____ 24. A barium (Ba) atom would form its most stable ion by the
(a) gain of one electron.
(b) gain of two electrons.
(c) loss of one electron.
(d) loss of two electrons.
(e) loss of 56 electrons.

_____ 25. How many electrons are in the $4s$ orbital of the Ca^{2+} ion?
(a) 3   (b) 2   (c) 1   (d) 0   (e) None of the preceding answers is correct.

_____ 26. All of the following represent stable ions. Four of the five have the noble gas configuration. Which one does *not* have the noble gas configuration?
(a) Fe^{3+} (b) Br^- (c) S^{2-} (d) Ba^{2+} (e) K^+

_____ 27. The ion Br^- can best be described as
(a) a metal ion.   (b) a monatomic anion.
(c) a monatomic cation.   (d) a neutral ion.   (e) a Lewis dot ion.

_____ 28. How many electrons are there in one Cr^{3+} ion?
(a) 24   (b) 52   (c) 27   (d) 21   (e) Cannot be answered without knowing the mass number

_____ 29. How many electrons are present in the valence shell of fluorine in the compound KF?
(a) 6   (b) 7   (c) 8   (d) 9   (e) 10

_____ 30. What should be the formula of an ionic compound containing potassium (K) and selenium (Se)?
(a) KSe   (b) K_2Se (c) KSe_2 (d) K_2Se_2 (e) K_3Se_2

_____ 31. Which of the following is the best Lewis dot representation of Na_2O?
(a) $2Na^+$, $[:\ddot{O}:]^-$ (b) $2Na^+$, $[:\ddot{O}:]^+$ (c) $2Na^-$, $[:\ddot{O}:]^+$

(d) $2Na^+$, $[:\ddot{\underset{..}{O}}:]^{2-}$ (e) None of the preceding answers is correct, because Na and O have similar electronegativities and probably do not form ions.

_____ 32. Which of the following compounds contains an element with an oxidation number of $+6$?

(a) $HClO$ (b) HNO_3 (c) $HClO_3$ (d) $HBrO_4$ (e) H_2SO_4

_____ 33. Each of the following is a known acid containing chlorine. In which one does chlorine have oxidation number $+7$?

(a) HCl (b) $HClO$ (c) $HClO_2$ (d) $HClO_3$ (e) $HClO_4$

_____ 34. Manganese (Mn) exhibits a larger number of oxidation numbers in its compounds than any other of the Period 4 transition metals. The most important oxidation numbers of manganese are illustrated by the following oxides: MnO, MnO_2, and Mn_2O_7. What are the important oxidation numbers of manganese illustrated here?

(a) -2, -4, and -7 (b) $+2$ and $+7$
(c) $+2$, $+3$, and $+9$ (d) $+2$, $+4$, and $+7$
(e) $+2$, $+4$, and $+14$

Answers to Preliminary Test

Short Answer

1. Physical and chemical properties of the elements vary in a periodic fashion with the atomic numbers of the elements.
2. Mendeleev, Meyer
3. alkali metals. Be sure you remember the common group names given in Section 4–1.
4. IIA, alkaline earth metal
5. d orbitals
6. f orbitals
7. F, Cl, Br, I, and At. Of these, only the first four are common. Notice the terminology by which a **group** is sometimes referred to as a **family** of elements.
8. VA. It may be helpful to remember that for the representative elements, the A group number is equal to the number of s and p electrons in the outer shell.
9. 6. Notice that the group number for representative elements also corresponds to the number of valence electrons, and hence, to the number of dots in the Lewis dot representation of the neutral atom.
10. N, P, As. Remember that within a group, atomic radii increase going down the group because of the filling of energy levels with higher n.
11. increase. Keep in mind that higher ionization energy means increasing difficulty in removing an electron.

12. decrease
13. Ca:. But remember that it is arbitrary on which side of the symbol we write the dots, so that C̈a or :Ca or Ca̤ would also be correct representations. We usually do try to indicate paired electrons as pairs of dots.
14. :P̈·
15. :Ẍ:
16. −1. Each halogen has a configuration of ns^2np^5 when neutral, so with a gain of one electron, it would attain the noble gas configuration of ns^2np^6.
17. :B̈r:⁻
18. :S̈e:²⁻. Be sure that you understand the various notations for multiply-charged ions, all of which mean the same thing: This ion (the ordinary chemical formula, not the dot notation) may be represented as Se^{2-}, as Se^{-2}, as Se^{--}, or as $Se^{=}$ in various books.
19. Xe. Cs has 55 electrons with an outer electronic configuration of $6s^1$. After loss of this lone $6s$ electron, it would have 54 electrons, and the same configuration as Xe, a noble gas.
20. smaller than. See the rationale in Section 4−6.
21. isoelectronic. The prefix "iso" means "same." Do you remember *iso*-topes? Watch for further occurrences of this prefix in your study of chemistry.
22. Kr. To form an ion with a charge of +2, Sr must lose two electrons of its original 38, to give 36 electrons in Sr^{2+}.
23. MgO. Each magnesium gives up two electrons ($3s^2$) to form Mg^{2+} ions. Each oxygen accepts two electrons (changing $2s^22p^4$ to $2s^22p^6$) to form O^{2-}. Thus, there are equal numbers of Mg^{2+} and O^{2-} ions formed, so that the ordinary chemical formula is MgO.
24. Rb_2S. Each Rb, an alkali metal, gives up one electron to form Rb^+. Each S, a group VIA element, accepts two electrons to form S^{2-}. Thus, two Rb must form ions for every S that does so. The formula is thus Rb_2S.
25. Ca_3N_2. Same reasoning as for Questions 23 and 24
26. 0. See the oxidation number rules in Section 4−12.
27. the charge on the ion. See Section 4−12 again.
28. +1, −2. The rare exceptions are pointed out in Rule 1 and Rule 5 at the end of Section 4−12.
29. +1, −2. Remember that in an ionic compound, the oxidation numbers are equal to the charges on the ions. It is also handy to recall from the rules in Section 4−12 that the Group IA elements always exhibit oxidation numbers of +1 in compounds, while in binary compounds (only two elements) the Group VIA elements show oxidation number −2.
30. +1, −1
31. +1, +5, −2. First figure out Na (always +1 in compounds) and O (−2 in almost all compounds). Then the sum of all oxidation numbers in a compound must be 0, so Cl must be +5.
32. +6, −2. As in the preceding question, first recall that O has oxidation

number -2. Then the sum of oxidation numbers in a polyatomic ion is equal to the charge on the ion, so S must have oxidation number $+6$.

Multiple Choice

1. (b). Remember that the most pronounced similarities are for elements in the same column (group).
2. (d). All have outer configuration ns^2np^6.
3. (a). Since the electronegativity difference is great from one end of the periodic table to the other, I would be much more electronegative than any alkali metal, and these would combine by ionic bonding, not by covalent bonding.
4. (b). Be clear about these classifications, Section 4 – 1.
5. (b). The term "transition element," without further qualification, refers to the d-transition elements.
6. (a). Remember that the noble gases are not ordinarily considered as representative elements.
7. (b).
8. (b). To see this, you can look at the periodic table and count blocks to see where elements 114 and 115 would fall. Alternatively, you can figure out their configurations — 114 would have outer shell $7s^27p^2$, and will thus fall in Group IVA, with the other ns^2np^2 elements. Reason 115 similarly.
9. (d)
10. (c). Al is in the same column as B, and S is in the same column as O.
11. (c)
12. (b)
13. (b)
14. (d)
15. (c). Electronegativity increases left to right and decreases top to bottom.
16. (e). Higher ionization energy means greater difficulty in removing electrons. First ionization energy increases going left to right across a period. See Figure 4 – 3 and the accompanying discussion in terms of electronic configurations.
17. (c). The trends in atomic radii are that they decrease left to right within a period and increase going down in a group — but the changes going down a group are much more pronounced than those going across a period. Thus, Mg would be smaller than Na since it is further to the right than Na; it would also be smaller than Ca, since it is above Ca. K is larger than Na (further down) and larger than Ca (further to the left). Sr is further down than any other of these, so it is the largest. Study Section 4 – 3.
18. (d). Remember the meaning of these terms. A small ionization energy implies ease of removal of electrons, while a small electronegativity means a poor tendency to attract electrons to it. Both of these descriptions would fit Cs, with outer configuration $6s^1$.

19. (c)
20. (a). All have the same number of electrons (18), arranged in the same energy levels. Sc has the highest nuclear charge ($+21$) to attract these electrons, and S has the lowest nuclear charge ($+16$). Thus, S^{2-} would be poorest at holding its 18 electrons, and S^{2-} would be the largest of these ions.
21. (c)
22. (d)
23. (e)
24. (d)
25. (d)
26. (a)
27. (b). Remember the meanings of the terms. An anion is a negative ion, and a cation is a positive ion. The term "monatomic" means consisting of one atom. No ion can be neutral, by definition.
28. (d). Neutral Cr has 24 electrons; Cr^{3+} has three fewer.
29. (c). In this compound, fluorine exists as the fluoride ion, F^-.
30. (b)
31. (d). One check you can carry out is that the total charges in an ionic compound must be equal to zero, which eliminates answer (a). Answer (b) makes no sense since an Na atom with one valence electron would not be an ion, nor would an oxygen with six valence electrons. Likewise, (c) can be eliminated since Na rarely forms a negative ion, and O would not form a positive ion — and these dot formulas are wrong anyway. Answer (e) is wrong in its statement of properties.
32. (e). Sulfur in this compound has an oxidation number of $+6$.
33. (e)
34. (d)

5

Covalent Bonding and Inorganic Nomenclature

Chapter Summary

This chapter is divided into three major sections. The first of these is a detailed introduction to the topic of **covalent bonding.** Recall that in ionic bonding (Chapter 4) the two atoms involved have such different electronegativities that one completely takes the electron pair away from the other and each attains a more stable configuration. In covalent bonding, the atoms have the same or similar electronegativities, so that they attain more stable configurations only by sharing electron pairs. When *one pair* of electrons is shared, we refer to the bond as a **single bond,** when *two pairs* are shared it is a **double bond,** and when *three pairs* are shared it is a **triple bond.**

The sharing of electron pairs to form covalent bonds may be viewed as a result of both attractive and repulsive forces. The drive to overlap orbitals to share electrons is the attractive force, as described in the discussion of Figure 5-1, while the repulsion is due to the like charges of the two nuclei. For more complicated molecules than H_2, an additional repulsive force is present due to the nonbonding electrons on the two atoms. The energy of the pair of atoms at various distances can always be represented by curves such as those in Figure 5-1. The distance at which the curve becomes a minimum is the most stable distance at which the atoms are bonded, while the depth of the curve below the zero of potential energy represents the strength of the bond—that is, the amount of energy that would need to be supplied to transform the bonded pair of atoms into two separated atoms.

Covalent bonds may be described in terms of two theories. One theory, called the **Valence Bond (VB) theory,** discusses covalent bonding in terms of the overlap of atomic orbitals on the two atoms involved, and the discussion in this chapter is in these terms. The other approach is the **Molecular Orbital (MO) theory,** which, with its advantages and disadvantages, will be the subject of Chapter 6. Two notations are often used as a convenience to aid in counting valence electrons and assessing the stabilities of bond structures: one is the **Lewis dot formula,** in which shared and unshared electrons are each represented by a dot (·); the other is the **dash formula,** in which each shared electron pair is represented by a single line. Other points of terminology to watch out for are these: The terms such as monatomic, diatomic, triatomic, and polyatomic refer to *how many atoms* are in the molecule; for example, N_2 and HF are diatomic molecules, O_3 (ozone) is triatomic, SO_2 is triatomic, and so on. The term **homonuclear** means that the molecule is composed of all one kind of atom (O_2, H_2, O_3 are each homonuclear), while the term **heteronuclear** means that the molecule is composed of more than one kind of atom (HF and SO_2 are heteronuclear). Notice that the same terminology can be applied to ions.

As we see also in Section 5–1, the atoms in a heteronuclear molecule may not attract the shared electrons equally. This leads to an imbalance in the electron distribution in the bond, which we refer to as a **polar** covalent bond, in distinction to **nonpolar** covalent bonds in which the bonding electron pair is equally shared. Such an arrangement is referred to as a **dipole** (or **bond dipole**). Section 5–2 extends this idea to show that some molecules composed of polar bonds are arranged in such a way that the bond dipoles cancel one another out, leaving the entire molecule nonpolar (**dipole moment** equal to zero); in other molecules, the bond dipoles are arranged so as not to cancel, leaving the entire molecule polar (dipole moment not equal to zero). The experimental measurement of this quantity gives us valuable information regarding the three-dimensional arrangement of atoms in molecules, as we shall see in subsequent sections of this chapter.

In Section 5–3, the Lewis dot formula representation is further discussed as a convenience for keeping track of the number and kind of bonds. Section 5–4 introduces a very useful generalization for figuring out dot formulas, the **octet rule.** This rule, which can be expressed in the simple mathematical relationship $S = N - A$, simply reflects the observation that representative elements usually achieve a noble gas configuration in most of their compounds. Since all of the noble gases except helium have eight electrons in their outer shell, this generalization is known as the octet rule. An obvious exception among the representative elements is hydrogen, which attains a noble gas configuration (that of He) by getting only two electrons in its valence shell. You should work through examples in the chapter to understand the application of this rule in the form $S = N - A$. Since drawing Lewis dot representations of molecules and ions is essential to understanding molecular structure and to predicting polarities of bonds and arrangements of atoms, development of the skills presented in these two sections is worth a great deal of practice.

As we work through our understanding of molecules in terms of chemical bonding, we find that sometimes a molecule cannot be properly described by a single Lewis dot formula (that is, by a single valence bond description). In such a case, we introduce the idea of **resonance,** by which we understand the true structure to be the average of several Lewis structures. This is made possible by the **delocalization** of the bonding electrons over several atoms, rather than them being shared explicitly between two atoms. Section 5–5 discusses this extension of the bonding theory.

Of course, we must not take the octet rule ($S = N - A$) too strictly, since there are several types of elements that can form stable compounds by attaining some number of electrons other than eight in their outer shell. Section 5–6 first lists the elements and compounds for which such exceptions are to be expected and then explains several such exceptions. It may help you to notice that all exceptions mentioned either include atoms that are so far from having eight electrons in their valence shell that they cannot easily attain that state by sharing electrons and do not readily form ionic compounds (e.g., elements at the top of Groups IIA and IIIA), or include atoms in which d or f electrons are involved in bonding, or are species containing an odd number of electrons. The chemistry of the transition elements, which obviously must involve the d electrons, is discussed further in Chapters 26 and 27.

The second major portion of this chapter, which is actually introduced in Section 5–7, deals with the understanding of the shapes of molecules and ions in terms of the orbitals used on the two atoms to share electrons. While we need not discuss the details further here, several important ideas should be noted throughout your study of this section of the chapter. Each atom in a polyatomic molecule or ion arranges the electron pairs in its valence shell in such a way as to minimize the repulsion of these electron pairs (**Valence Shell Electron Pair Repulsion,** or **VSEPR,** theory, Section 5–8). In order to attain minimum energy (maximum stability), atoms in molecules may need to modify their orbitals to a different arrangement than would be appropriate in isolated atoms. In the terminology of the **Valence Bond theory,** Section 5–9, this mixing or **hybridization** of atomic orbitals to form **hybrid orbitals** allows us to understand the observed shapes of molecules. We may consider the geometry of molecules and ions to fall into one of several cases, depending on the number of atoms to which a central atom is bonded, and the number of nonbonded electron pairs that this central atom has. For each of these cases, the shape or arrangement in three dimensions of the bonded atoms and the nonbonded pairs around this central atom (the **electronic geometry**) may be predicted by the VSEPR theory, while the number of electrons occupying each type of hybrid orbital and the overlap of these orbitals are discussed in terms of the VB theory. Sections 5–10 through 5–19 discuss the most common bonding arrangements in terms of these two theories. As you study this material, look ahead to the summary in Section 5–20 of molecular and electronic geometries. From this summary, as well as the individual cases discussed in the text, you will find that it is important to distinguish clearly between **electronic geometry** ("Where are the valence-shell electron pairs around the central atom?") and the **molecular geometry** ("Where are the *other atoms* around the central atom?"). As you will see, there are only five common answers to the first question, so that the electronic geometry is usually either (1) linear (sp hybrid orbitals), (2) trigonal planar (sp^2 hybrid orbitals), (3) tetrahedral (sp^3 hybrid orbitals), (4) trigonal bipyramidal (sp^3d hybrid orbitals), or (5) octahedral (sp^3d^2 hybrid orbitals). After you have determined the electronic geometry for a molecule or ion, then you can determine the molecular geometry by considering which of the electronic locations attach the central atom to other atoms, and which ones simply correspond to unshared (nonbonded) electron pairs on that central atom. Thus, for example, molecules that have tetrahedral electronic geometry (electronic group number 4), and thus use sp^3 hybrid orbitals on the central atom, could have a molecular geometry that is tetrahedral (e.g., CH_4), pyramidal (e.g., NH_3), or angular (H_2O). Furthermore, once the overall geometries have been rationalized in terms of these two theories, variations in these shapes can often be understood by consideration of the stronger repulsion of lone pairs for bonded pairs than of bonded pairs for other bonded pairs, and by taking bond polarities into account. Section 5–21 simply emphasizes that the same ideas that have been discussed and developed for molecules can be applied to polyatomic ions.

The final portion of Chapter 5 discusses some of the rules by which we can communicate what substances we are talking about by giving them names that are recognizable. It should be obvious to you that learning this system of naming compounds is part of learning the language of chemistry. Since many of the rules for naming inorganic compounds first require the determination of the oxidation number of one or more of the elements in the compound, you should be sure to review the topic of oxidation numbers in Chapter 4. You will also find it necessary to memorize the names, charges, and formulas for the common ions appearing in Table 5–6. While most of the naming of compounds that you will learn will be according to the systematic nomenclature of the IUPAC convention, many nonsystematic traditional names are still widely used, and it will be necessary to learn to recognize some of these.

Study Goals

Be sure to practice many of the indicated end-of-chapter exercises from the textbook, in addition to answering the following Preliminary Test.

1. Distinguish between the major aspects of ionic and covalent bonding. Know some of the differences in physical properties of ionic and covalent compounds. Predict whether a given compound is covalent or ionic. (Review Sections 4–9 and 4–10, introduction to Chapter 5, Sections 5–1 and 5–2; Exercises 1 through 4)
2. Understand what forces are responsible for the formation of covalent bonds. (Introduction to Chapter 5; Exercises 2 through 4)

3. Distinguish between polar covalent bonds and nonpolar covalent bonds. Distinguish between polar and nonpolar molecules. (Sections 5 – 1 and 5 – 2; Exercise 4)

4. Be able to tell whether a bond is polar or nonpolar. You should be able to do this either with numerical values of electronegativity or on the basis of the positions of the elements in the periodic table. (Section 5 – 1; Exercises 52 through 54 and 57)

5. Draw Lewis dot representations of molecules and polyatomic ions containing only representative elements. Recognize which ones do not follow the octet rule. (Sections 5 – 3, 5 – 4, and 5 – 6; Exercises 6 through 8, 10, and 13 through 24)

6. Distinguish among single, double, and triple bonds. (Section 5 – 3; Exercise 5)

7. Recognize and draw all dot formulas for molecules and ions for which resonance structures are possible. (Section 5 – 5; Exercises 11, 12, and 24)

8. Outline the significance and main ideas of the VSEPR theory. (Sections 5 – 7 and 5 – 8; Exercises 25 through 27)

9. Be able to identify a central atom and count its number of regions of high electron density. (Section 5 – 8; Exercises 28 through 35)

10. Distinguish between electronic geometry and molecular or ionic geometry. (Sections 5 – 8 and 5 – 10 through 5 – 17)

11. Use the VSEPR theory to describe or predict the electronic geometry *and* the molecular or ionic geometry of a molecule or polyatomic ion. (Sections 5 – 10 through 5 – 20; Exercises 28 through 50)

12. Name and describe the types of hybrid orbitals that correspond to each of the possible numbers of regions of high electron density. (Section 5 – 9; Exercises 66 and 67)

13. Be able to use Lewis dot formulas and Valence Bond structures to describe the bonding in molecules and ions having one central atom. (Sections 5 – 10 through 5 – 17; Exercises 64 through 77)

14. Be able to use Lewis dot formulas and Valence Bond structures to describe the bonding in polyatomic molecules and ions. Be sure you understand how double and triple bonding occurs. (Sections 5 – 18 through 5 – 21; Exercises 78 through 85)

15. In the Valence Bond description, distinguish between sigma and pi bonds. (Sections 5 – 18 through 5 – 20; Exercise 85)

16. Given the electronic structure and shape of a molecule, determine whether it is polar or nonpolar. (Sections 5 – 2 and 5 – 20; Exercises 55, 56, and 58 through 63)

17. Given their formulas, name inorganic compounds by the IUPAC system. Write the formulas of inorganic compounds, given their IUPAC names. Name common inorganic compounds by other commonly used traditional methods. (Sections 5 – 23 and 5 – 24; Exercises 86 through 94)

Some Important Terms in This Chapter

Write the meanings *in your own words*. Check the Key Terms list and the chapter reading. Then rewrite your definitions, still in your own words, to improve them. Study other new terms, and review terms from preceding chapters if necessary.

octet rule

covalent bonding

single bond

double bond

triple bond

Lewis dot formula

dash formula

polyatomic ion

central atom

Valence Shell Electron Pair Repulsion Theory

Valence Bond Theory

electronic geometry

molecular geometry

ionic geometry

hybridization

trigonal planar

tetrahedral

trigonal bipyramidal

octahedral

polar bond

nonpolar bond

sigma bond

pi bond

Preliminary Test

Be sure you realize that these preliminary test questions are quite basic and that they are intended to check your understanding of the main ideas and terminology of the chapter. You will need to practice on many additional questions in the text at the end of Chapter 5.

True-False

Mark each statement as true (T) or false (F).

_____ 1. The number of regions of high electron density on the central atom in H_2O is 4.

_____ 2. The number of regions of high electron density on the central atom in CCl_4 is 4.

_____ 3. The number of regions of high electron density on the central atom in NF_3 is 4.

_____ 4. Since all atoms satisfy the octet rule in their bonding, the number of regions of high electron density on the central atom is always 4 or some multiple of 4.

_____ 5. The number of regions of high electron density must be equal to S in the formula $S = N - A$.

_____ 6. All molecules with four regions of high electron density about a central atom have tetrahedral electronic geometry.

_____ 7. All molecules with four regions of high electron density about a central atom have tetrahedral molecular geometry.

_____ 8. A molecule of the type AX_5 (where A is the central atom) could have trigonal bipyramidal molecular geometry.

_____ 9. A molecule of the type AX_5 (where A is the central atom) must have trigonal bipyramidal molecular geometry.

_____ 10. In the molecule BF_3, all F—B—F bond angles are equal.

_____ 11. In the molecule CF_4, all F—C—F bond angles are equal.

_____ 12. In the molecule NF_3, all F—N—F bond angles are equal.

_____ 13. All molecules with tetrahedral electronic geometry must have bond angles equal to 109° 28′.

_____ 14. In the molecule NF_3, all F—N—F bond angles are equal to 109° 28′.

_____ 15. In the molecule PF_5, all F—P—F bond angles are equal.

_____ 16. A molecule containing polar bonds may be polar.

_____ 17. A molecule containing polar bonds must be polar.

_____ 18. A three-atom molecule with linear molecular geometry must be nonpolar.

_____ 19. A three-atom molecule with linear molecular geometry must be polar.

_____ 20. A tetrahedral molecule must be polar.

_____ 21. A tetrahedral molecule must be nonpolar.

Short Answer

1. In the formation of a covalent bond, the principal "attractive force" is _____.

2. In the formation of a covalent bond, the principal "repulsive forces" are due to _____ and to _____.

3. When two atoms combine to form a stable chemical bond, the _____ of the bonded pair of atoms is lower than that of the isolated atoms.

4. When two atoms are joined by a single covalent bond, they share ____ electrons.
5. When two atoms are joined by a double covalent bond, they share ____ electrons.
6. Which of the following molecules would be described as diatomic: He, H_2, Cl_2, HCl, CS_2, NH_3, H_2O, S_8, P_4? _____
7. Which of the molecules in Question 6 would be described as homonuclear? _____. Which as heteronuclear? _____
_____.

8. When the bonding pair of electrons in a covalent bond is equally shared between the two atoms, the bond is called _____; when one atom attracts the shared pair of electrons more strongly than the other, the bond is called _____.
9. A covalent bond will be polar if the two atoms involved differ dignificantly in their _____ values.
10. In which are the covalent bonds more polar, CH_4 or CF_4? _____
11. Two requirements for a molecule being polar are _____ _____ and _____.
12. The theory that accounts for the shape of molecules by considering the repulsion of the outermost electron pairs on the central atom is called the _____ theory.
13. The theory that describes the formation of covalent bonds as being due to the overlap of the atomic orbitals on the two atoms is called the _____ theory.
14. The mixing or rearrangement of individual "pure" atomic orbitals to form new orbitals with different spatial orientations is called _____.
15. The angle between two sp hybrid orbitals on the same atom is ____.
16. The angle between two sp^2 hybrid orbitals on the same atom is ____.
17. The angle between two sp^3 hybrid orbitals on the same atom is ____.
18. Each of the following compounds or ions obeys the Octet Rule. Apply the relationship $S = N - A$ to each of them and draw the Lewis dot formula and the dash formula.

Compound or ion	N	A	S	Dot formula	Dash formula
CH_4					
CCl_4					
NH_3					

Compound or ion	N	A	S	Dot formula	Dash formula
NH_4^+					
CH_3Cl					
CS_2					
PF_3					
ClO_3^-					
SO_4^{2-}					
HCN (C is the central atom)					
C_2H_2					
N_2H_4					
H_2CO (C is the central atom)					

19. The electronic geometry of the central atom in the compound HCN is _____; the hybrid orbitals on the central atom in this compound are ___ orbitals; the molecular shape is described as _____.

20. The electronic geometry of the central atom in PCl_3 is _____; the hybrid orbitals on the central atom in this compound are ___ orbitals; the molecular shape is described as _____.

21. The electronic geometry of the central atom in the compound BCl_3 is _____; the hybrid orbitals on the central atom in this compound are ___ orbitals; the molecular shape is described as _____.

22. The electronic geometry of the central atom in the compound H_2O is _____; the hybrid orbitals on the central atom in this compound are ___ orbitals; the molecular shape is described as _____.

23. The electronic geometry of the central atom in the ion SO_4^{2-} is _____; the hybrid orbitals on the central atom in this ion are ___ orbitals; the ionic shape is described as _____.

24. The electronic geometry of the central atom in the ion AlF_6^{3-} ion is _____; the hybrid orbitals on the central atom in this ion are ____ orbitals; the ionic shape is described as _____.

25. Write the formulas for the compounds or ions that are named below:
    (a) cupric chloride _____   (n) sodium dichromate _____
    (b) copper(II) chloride _____   (o) sodium chromate _____
    (c) sodium acetate _____   (p) sulfurous acid _____
    (d) sulfate ion _____   (q) sulfuric acid _____
    (e) ammonium ion _____   (r) hypobromous acid _____
    (f) permanganate ion _____   (s) bromous acid _____
    (g) sodium hydrogen sulfate ___   (t) bromic acid _____
    _____   (u) perbromic acid _____
    (h) sodium sulfate _____   (v) hydrobromic acid _____
    (i) sodium sulfite _____   (w) phosphoric acid _____
    (j) sodium nitrate _____   (x) carbonic acid _____
    (k) sodium nitrite _____   (y) magnesium carbonate _____
    (l) lithium cyanide _____   (z) potassium hydrogen carbonate
    (m) iron(III) sulfite _____   _____

26. Name the compounds or ions whose formulas are given below:
    (a) $CaSO_4$ _____
    (b) $FeSO_4$ _____
    (c) $Fe_2(SO_4)_3$ _____
    (d) $NaMnO_4$ _____
    (e) $Fe(CN)_3$ _____
    (f) $Ca(NO_2)_2$ _____
    (g) CdS _____
    (h) CrF_3 _____
    (i) AsO_4^{3-} _____
    (j) ClO_4^- _____
    (k) Zn^{2+} _____
    (l) $CoSO_3$ _____
    (m) $Ba(SCN)_2$ _____
    (n) CH_3COO^- _____
    (o) $(NH_4)_2CO_3$ _____
    (p) $NaHCO_3$ _____
    (q) $Fe_3(PO_4)_2$ _____
    (r) NiO _____
    (s) $AgCl$ _____
    (t) $Hg_2(CN)_2$ _____
    (u) H_3PO_3 _____
    (v) $HF(aq)$ _____
    (w) $HI(aq)$ _____
    (x) HIO_3 _____
    (y) HNO_3 _____
    (z) $Hg(NO_2)_2$ _____

Multiple Choice

Select the best answer.

___   1. Which of the following pairs of elements would combine with the most covalent (least polar) bonding?
(a) Ca and N   (b) Fe and Cl   (c) Be and I   (d) C and O   (e) Ca and S

___   2. Which of the following might be expected to be a stable compound?
(a) ArH   (b) NaO   (c) BaSe   (d) CCl_2 (e) Ca_2O

___   3. A metal (call it X) in Group IA of the periodic table forms a compound with an element (call it Y) of Group VIA. The compound would most likely have the formula _____ and would be _____.
(a) X_2Y, ionic   (b) X_2Y, covalent   (c) XY_2, ionic
(d) XY_2, covalent   (e) XY_6, covalent

___   4. Which of the following is the best description of covalent bonding?
(a) Bonding that occurs between elements with very different electronegativities, and with transfer of electrons
(b) Bonding that occurs between elements with very different electronegativities, and with sharing of electrons
(c) Bonding that occurs between elements with similar electronegativities, and with transfer of electrons
(d) Bonding that occurs between elements with similar electronegativities, and with sharing of electrons
(e) Bonding that occurs between ions and elements, with the sharing of electrons

___   5. Which of the following substances would be expected to be the best conductor of electricity in the liquid state (i.e., when melted or condensed if not already a liquid)?
(a) CH_4 (b) PCl_3 (c) SiO_2 (d) H_2O (e) BaF_2

___   6. Which of the following substances would be expected to have the highest melting point?
(a) NaF   (b) CH_4 (c) H_2O (d) HF   (e) BF_3

___   7. On the usual Pauling scale of electronegativities, the electronegativity of selenium (Se) is 2.4, while that of chlorine (Cl) is 3.0. Based on these data, we should expect the bonding between Se and Cl to be
(a) ionic.
(b) covalent and nonpolar.
(c) covalent and polar with the Se end of the bond a little negative.
(d) covalent and polar with the Se end of the bond a little positive.
(e) unstable in any circumstances.

___   8. Which of the following diagrams correctly indicates the polarity of the bond?

(a) $\overset{\longrightarrow}{\text{C—H}}$ (b) $\overset{\longleftarrow}{\text{C—Cl}}$ (c) $\overset{\longleftarrow}{\text{H—F}}$ (d) $\overset{\longleftarrow}{\text{C—F}}$
(e) None of the preceding answers is correct.

_____ 9. Nitrogen can form single covalent bonds with boron, carbon, nitrogen, oxygen, and fluorine. The bond would be expected to be polar, with the bonding electrons displaced most strongly away from the nitrogen in the case when it is bonded to
(a) boron.   (b) carbon.   (c) nitrogen.   (d) oxygen.
(e) fluorine.

_____ 10. Nitrogen and hydrogen can each exist as two isotopes. This means that molecules of ammonia, NH_3, could exist having several different masses. The number of different masses of ammonia molecules that would be possible is
(a) 1.   (b) 2.   (c) 4.   (d) 6.   (e) more than 6.

_____ 11. Which of the following contains both covalent and ionic bonding?
(a) KF   (b) CO_2 (c) CH_4 (d) NH_4F (e) C_2H_4

_____ 12. Which of the following compounds contains *no* polar bonds?
(a) HF   (b) CCl_4 (c) O_2 (d) NH_3 (e) PCl_5

_____ 13. The total number of electrons shared in the NH_3 molecule is
(a) 2.   (b) 3.   (c) 4.   (d) 6.   (e) 8.

_____ 14. What is the total number of valence electrons that should be shown in a Lewis dot formula for C_3H_5ClO? (Note that it is not necessary to draw the dot formula in order to figure this out!)
(a) 10   (b) 20   (c) 30   (d) 40   (e) 50

_____ 15. What is the number of shared electrons in the Lewis dot formula for C_3H_5ClO? (Again, it is not necessary to draw the formula or even to know in what order the atoms are connected.)
(a) 10   (b) 20   (c) 30   (d) 40   (e) 50

16. Which of the following is the best Lewis dot representation for the compound NF_3?

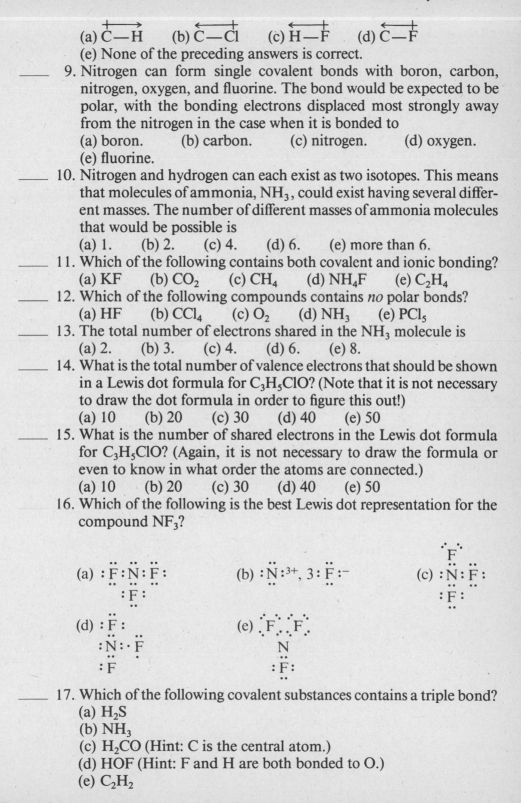

_____ 17. Which of the following covalent substances contains a triple bond?
(a) H_2S
(b) NH_3
(c) H_2CO (Hint: C is the central atom.)
(d) HOF (Hint: F and H are both bonded to O.)
(e) C_2H_2

_____ 18. The ion NH_4^+ can best be described as
(a) an anion.   (b) a cation.   (c) a Lewis dot ion.   (d) a monatomic ion.   (e) a homonuclear ion.

_____ 19. Which of the following is a polar molecule?
(a) CO_2 (a linear molecule)
(b) BF_3 (a planar triangular molecule)
(c) CH_4 (a tetrahedral molecule)
(d) NH_3 (pyramidal molecule)
(e) H_2

_____ 20. Which of the following statements concerning resonance is *not* correct?
(a) Resonance involves more than one formal Lewis formula to represent the bonding.
(b) Resonance involves the sharing of electrons in delocalized orbitals.
(c) The true energy of a molecule in which resonance is important is lower than that of any of the hypothetical molecules described by the contributing Lewis formulas.
(d) Resonance is important in understanding the structures of some ions as well as the structures of neutral molecules.
(e) An example of the use of the concept of resonance in understanding bonding is the rationalization of the observation that the two S—O bonds in SO_2 are not equivalent.

_____ 21. Which of the following contains *only* one unshared pair of valence electrons?
(a) H_2O (b) NH_3 (c) CH_4 (d) NaCl   (e) BF_3

_____ 22. Which one of the following statements regarding sp^3 hybrid orbitals is *not* correct?
(a) The process of sp^3 hybridization results in a set of orbitals of tetrahedral geometry.
(b) The process of sp^3 hybridization results in four orbitals, one of which is at lower energy, since one of them came from an s orbital.
(c) The angle between two sp^3 hybrid orbitals on the same atom is about 109.5°.
(d) If an atom has four electrons in a set of sp^3 hybrid orbitals, the lowest energy configuration would have all four electrons unpaired.
(e) The process of sp^3 hybridization results in four equivalent orbitals.

_____ 23. The main reason for describing the bonding around nitrogen in ammonia (NH_3) in terms of sp^3 hybrid orbitals on nitrogen is that
(a) the angle between two N—H bonds is closer to 109.5° than to any other ideal value.

(b) the angle between two N—H bonds is closer to 90° than to any other ideal value.

(c) the angle between two N—H bonds is closer to 120° than to any other ideal value.

(d) the hydrogen atoms attain the filled $1s^2$ configuration by bond formation.

(e) the ground-state configuration of nitrogen has four unpaired electrons.

_____ 24. Which of the following contains at least one atom that uses sp^3 hybridization in its bonding?

(a) H_2O

(b) NH_3

(c) CH_4

(d) All of the molecules listed

(e) None of the molecules listed

_____ 25. Which of the following contains at least one atom whose bonding may be described in terms of sp^2 hybridization?

(a) H_2O (b) NH_3 (c) C_2H_2 (d) C_2H_4 (e) H_2

_____ 26. In the compound hexachloroethane, C_2Cl_6, the angle between two C—Cl bonds on the same carbon atom is closest to which of the following values?

(a) 60°   (b) 90°   (c) 109.5°   (d) 120°   (e) 180°

_____ 27. The geometry of a molecule of silane, SiH_4, can be described as

(a) plane trigonal.   (b) octahedral.   (c) tetrahedral.

(d) linear.   (e) angular.

_____ 28. The shape of a molecule of phosphorus trichloride, PCl_3, can be described as

(a) tetrahedral.   (b) trigonal planar.   (c) trigonal bipyrami-dal.   (d) pyramidal.   (e) angular.

_____ 29. The hybrid orbitals on the central atom in PCl_3 are

(a) sp.   (b) sp^2.   (c) sp^3.   (d) sp^3d.   (e) sp^3d^2.

_____ 30. The hybrid orbitals on the central atom in PCl_5 are

(a) sp.   (b) sp^2.   (c) sp^3.   (d) sp^3d.   (e) sp^3d^2.

_____ 31. The shape of a molecule of phosphorus pentachloride, PCl_5, can be described as

(a) tetrahedral.   (b) trigonal planar.   (c) pyramidal.

(d) trigonal bipyramidal.   (e) angular.

_____ 32. In the compound SF_6, what is the arrangement of fluorine atoms around the sulfur atom, and what hybrid orbitals of the sulfur atom are used in bonding?

(a) hexagonal, sp^3 (b) tetrahedral, sp^3 (c) octahedral, sp^3d

(d) octahedral, sp^3d^2 (e) trigonal planar, sp^2

_____ 33. In the compound CH_3Cl, the bonding orbitals of the carbon atom are

(a) *p* orbitals.   (b) *sp* hybrid orbitals.   (c) *sp²* hybrid orbitals.
(d) *sp³* hybrid orbitals.   (e) *sp⁴* hybrid orbitals.

_____ 34. The compound tetrachloroethylene,

$$\begin{array}{ccc} Cl & & Cl \\ \diagdown & & \diagup \\ & C=C & \\ \diagup & & \diagdown \\ Cl & & Cl \end{array}$$

has a carbon-carbon double bond. The angle between two C—Cl bonds on the same C atom is expected to be closest to which of the following values?
(a) 60°   (b) 90°   (c) 109.5°   (d) 120°   (e) 180°

_____ 35. If an atom is attached to two other atoms and has no valence-shell nonbonding electrons, then the molecule's shape would be described as
(a) angular.   (b) linear.   (c) tetrahedral.   (d) trigonal planar.   (e) octahedral.

_____ 36. The water molecule, H_2O, is angular rather than linear, because
(a) the two hydrogen atoms attract one another.
(b) the bonding involves *s* orbitals of H, which are not linear.
(c) the bonding involves *sp²* orbitals of O.
(d) the bonding involves *sp³* orbitals of O.
(e) the *s* orbital of one H atom overlaps with the *s* orbital of the other H atom.

_____ 37. Propylene is a hydrocarbon with formula C_3H_6. The dash formula for propylene is

$$\begin{array}{ccc} H & H & H \\ | & | & | \\ H-C-C=C-H \\ | & | \\ 1 \quad H \quad 2 \quad \quad 3 \end{array}$$

Which of the carbon atoms in this molecule would we describe in terms of *sp²* hybrid orbitals?
(a) 1   (b) 2   (c) 3   (d) 2 and 3   (e) 1 and 3

_____ 38. A triple bond includes
(a) one σ and two π bonds.
(b) two π and one σ bond.
(c) three σ bonds.
(d) three π bonds.
(e) None of the preceding answers is correct.

_____ 39. The following five statements describe differences between a single bond and a double bond. One of the statements is incorrect. Which one?

(a) A double bond is the sharing of four electrons by two atoms, while a single bond is the sharing of two electrons by the two atoms.

(b) Atoms connected by a double bond are more difficult to rotate with respect to each other than atoms connected by a single bond.

(c) A double bond usually consists of a σ bond and a π bond, while a single bond is usually a π bond.

(d) In a single bond, the region of highest density of bonding electrons is directly between the two atomic centers, while in a double bond another region of high density of bonding electrons also exists on two sides of the line between the atomic centers.

(e) A double bond is stronger (harder to break) than a single bond between the same two atoms.

_____ 40. A π bond can be formed by the overlap of

(a) two s orbitals on different atoms.

(b) two p orbitals on the same atom.

(c) two p orbitals on different atoms, these p orbitals lying side-by-side in the same plane.

(d) two p orbitals on different atoms, these p orbitals lying end-to-end in the same plane.

(e) two p orbitals on different atoms, these p orbitals lying side-by-side in planes that are perpendicular to one another.

_____ 41. In order to understand the shape of H_2CO, we describe the hybridization of carbon (the central atom) as sp^2. In order to fully describe the double bond, we postulate that the hybridization of the oxygen atom is

(a) sp.   (b) sp^2.   (c) sp^3.   (d) sp^3d.   (e) sp^3d^2.

_____ 42. Which of the following is the formula for cobalt(II) nitrite?

(a) Co_2N (b) Co_2NO_2 (c) $Co(NO_2)_2$ (d) $CoNO_2$
(e) $Co(NO_3)_2$

_____ 43. Which of the following is the formula for iron(II) sulfite?

(a) $FeSO_4$ (b) FeS (c) Fe_2SO_3 (d) $FeSO_3$
(e) $Fe(SO_3)_2$

_____ 44. What is the name of the ion SO_4^{2-}?

(a) sulfide   (b) sulfite   (c) sulfate   (d) sulfur tetroxide
(e) None of the preceding answers is correct.

_____ 45. Which of the following is the formula for iron(II) oxide?

(a) FeO (b) FeO_3 (c) Fe_2O (d) Fe_2O_3 (e) Fe_3O_2

_____ 46. What is the name of the ion SO_3^{2-}?

(a) sulfide   (b) sulfite   (c) sulfate   (d) sulfur trioxide
(e) None of the preceding answers is correct.

_____ 47. Which of the following is the formula for nickel(II) sulfide?
(a) NiS   (b) Ni_2S (c) NiS_2 (d) $NiSO_4$ (e) Ni_2SO_4

_____ 48. What is the name of the ion NO_3^-?
(a) nitride   (b) nitrite   (c) nitrate   (d) nitrogen trioxide
(e) None of the preceding answers is correct.

_____ 49. Which of the following is the formula for manganese(II) hydroxide?
(a) MnO   (b) MnOH   (c) $Mn(OH)_2$ (d) $Mn_2(OH)$
(e) $Mn_3(OH)_2$

_____ 50. Which of the following is the formula for iron(III) sulfate?
(a) $Fe_2(SO_4)_3$ (b) Fe_3SO_4 (c) $Fe(SO_3)_2$ (d) Fe_3SO_3
(e) $Fe_3(SO_4)_2$

_____ 51. Which of the following is the formula for chromium (III) nitrate?
(a) $CrNO_3$ (b) Cr_3NO_3 (c) $Cr(NO_3)_3$
(d) $Cr_2(NO_2)_3$ (e) $Cr(NO_2)_2$

Answers to Preliminary Test

Do not just look up answers. Think about the reasons for the answers.

True-False

1. True. For all questions like this, you need to first draw the Lewis dot formula for the molecule or ion. Study this topic in Section 5–3.
2. True
3. True
4. False. This is false for two reasons: (1) Not all atoms obey the octet rule in their covalent bonding. Be familiar with the exceptions discussed in Section 5–6. (2) Even if the octet rule is satisfied, the bonding may involve double or triple bonds, which account for only *one* high electron density region each.
5. False. This is false for two reasons: (1) We only count regions of high electron density on one central atom at a time, and the formula $S = N - A$ refers to an entire molecule or ion. (2) Even if there is only one central atom, the term S in this formula tells the total number of shared electrons. These may be shared in single, double, or triple bonds, each of which counts as only *one* region of high electron density.
6. True
7. False. Such a molecule may have the central atom bonded to fewer than four other atoms, in which case the electronic geometry and the molecu-

lar geometry are different. For example, study the discussions of NH_3 in Section 5–13 and H_2O in Section 5–14.

8. True. This could occur if all of the regions of high electron density were electrons that bond the central atom to others. An example is PF_5, discussed in Section 5–16.

9. False. This could occur *only* if all of the regions of high electron density were bonding sets to other atoms, and this is not necessary. Suppose there were *six* regions of high electron density (octahedral electronic geometry), with one of these being a nonbonded electron pair. IF_5 or SF_5^- would be examples of such species.

10. True

11. True

12. True.

13. False. See the discussion in Sections 5–13 and 5–14.

14. False. The repulsion of the bonded pairs by the lone pairs causes the bond angles F—N—F to be less than the ideal tetrahedral value of 109° 28′.

15. False. Even though there are no lone pairs to account for, the angles in a trigonal bipyramidal arrangement are not all equal. Six are 90° (axial-equatorial), three are 120° (equatorial-equatorial), and one is 180° (axial-axial).

16. True

17. False. If any dipoles due to lone pairs are arranged so that their effects cancel, the molecule would still be nonpolar. A simple example is CO_2; other examples are encountered in Section 5–2 and in exercises at the end of the text chapter.

18. False. HCN is an example of such a molecule that is polar.

19. False. CO_2 is an example of such a molecule that is nonpolar.

20. False. If all four atoms (X) attached to the central atom (A) in a tetrahedral molecule AX_4 are the same, then the molecule would be nonpolar. Examples of this are CH_4, CF_4, and SO_4^{2-}.

21. False. If one or more of the atoms is different from the others, the molecule *could* still be polar. An example would be CH_3Cl.

Short Answer

1. the tendency of atoms to attain stable electronic configurations by overlapping their orbitals so as to share electrons

2. repulsion of the nuclei of the two atoms, repulsion of the nonbonded electrons of the two atoms

3. potential energy

4. 2 (or one pair of)

5. 4 (or two pairs of)

6. H_2, Cl_2, HCl. Remember that the term *"diatomic"* means that the

molecule consists of two atoms, whether or not they are the same kind of atom.

7. Homonuclear: He, H_2, Cl_2, S_8, P_4; heteronuclear: HCl, CS_2, NH_3, H_2O. Remember that the term "homonuclear" means "consisting of only one kind of atom," while the term "heteronuclear" means "consisting of more than one kind of atom."

8. nonpolar, polar

9. electronegativity

10. CF_4. It will be helpful to remember that C and H have almost the same values of electronegativity; you must also remember the trends in electronegativity with respect to position in the periodic table.

11. there must be at least some polar bonds, these polar bonds must be arranged in such a way that the bond polarities (or bond dipoles) do not cancel one another

12. Valence Shell Electron Pair Repulsion. This is often referred to, of course, as the VSEPR theory, but you should remember what those initials stand for, as it will help you to remember the central idea of the theory.

13. Valence Bond

14. hybridization

15. $180°$

16. $120°$

17. $109° \, 28'$ (or $109.5°$)

18.

Compound or Ion	N	A	S	Dot Formula	Dash Formula
CH_4	16	8	8	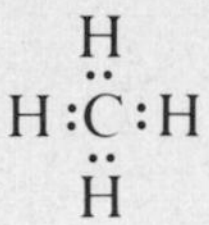 H H:C:H H	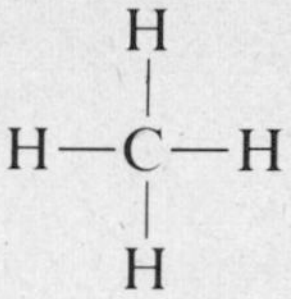 H | H—C—H | H
CCl_4	40	32	8	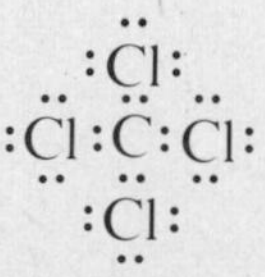 :Cl: :Cl:C:Cl: :Cl:	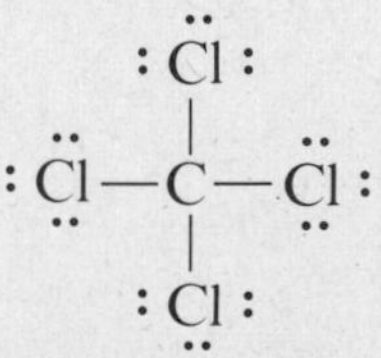 :Cl: | :Cl—C—Cl: | :Cl:
NH_3	14	8	6	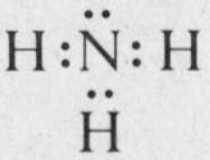 H:N:H H	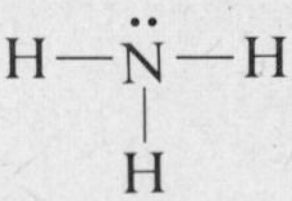 H—N—H | H
$NH_4{}^+$ (Remember to account for the + charge by decreasing A by 1)	16	8	8	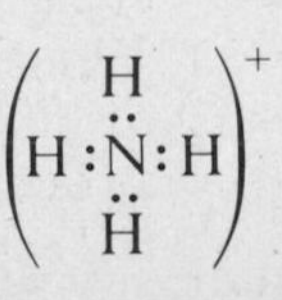 $\left(\begin{matrix} H \\ H:N:H \\ H \end{matrix} \right)^+$	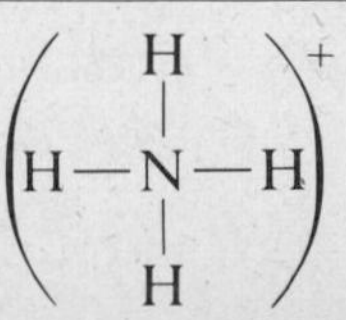 $\left(\begin{matrix} H \\ \| \\ H—N—H \\ \| \\ H \end{matrix} \right)^+$

CH_3Cl	22	14	8	H H:C̈:C̈l: H	H | H—C—C̈l: | H
CS_2	24	16	8	S̈::C::S̈	:S̈=C=S̈:
PF_3	32	26	6	:F̈:P̈:F̈: :F̈:	:F̈—P—F̈: | :F̈:
ClO_3^- (Remember to account for the − charge by increasing A by 1)	32	26	6	$\left(:\ddot{O}:\ddot{C}l:\ddot{O}:\atop :\ddot{O}:\right)^-$	$\left(:\ddot{O}-\ddot{C}l-\ddot{O}:\atop \|\atop :\ddot{O}:\right)^-$
SO_4^{2-} (Remember to account for the −2 charge by increasing A by 2)	40	32	8	$\left(:\ddot{O}:\atop :\ddot{O}:\ddot{S}:\ddot{O}:\atop :\ddot{O}:\right)^{2-}$	$\left(:\ddot{O}:\atop :\ddot{O}-S-\ddot{O}:\atop :\ddot{O}:\right)^{2-}$
HCN	18	10	8	H:C:::N:	H—C≡N
C_2H_2	20	10	10	H:C:::C:H	H—C≡C—H
N_2H_4	24	14	10	H:N̈:N̈:H H H	H—N̈—N̈—H | | H H
H_2CO	20	12	8	H:C:H :Ö:	H—C—H || :Ö:

19. linear, *sp*, linear
20. tetrahedral, *sp*³, pyramidal
21. trigonal planar, *sp*², trigonal planar
22. tetrahedral, *sp*³, angular
23. tetrahedral, *sp*³, tetrahedral
24. octahedral, *sp*³*d*², octahedral
25. (a) $CuCl_2$
    (b) $CuCl_2$
    (c) $NaCH_3COO$
    (d) SO_4^{2-} (Note that this is some-
         times written SO_4^{-2},
         SO_4^{--}, or $SO_4^{=}$)
    (e) NH_4^+
    (f) MnO_4^-
    (g) $NaHSO_4$
    (h) Na_2SO_4
    (i) Na_2SO_3
    (j) $NaNO_3$

(k) $NaNO_2$

(l) LiCN

(m) $Fe_2(SO_3)_3$

(n) $Na_2Cr_2O_7$

(o) Na_2CrO_4

(p) H_2SO_3

(q) H_2SO_4

(r) HBrO

(s) $HBrO_2$

(t) $HBrO_3$

(u) $HBrO_4$

(v) HBr (aq)

(w) H_2PO_4

(x) H_2CO_3

(y) $MgCO_3$

(z) $KHCO_3$

26. (a) calcium sulfate

(b) iron(II) sulfate, ferrous sulfate

(c) iron(III) sulfate, ferric sulfate

(d) sodium permanganate

(e) iron(III) cyanide, ferric cyanide

(f) calcium nitrite

(g) cadmium sulfide

(h) chromium(III) fluoride, chromic fluoride

(i) arsenate ion

(j) perchlorate ion

(k) zinc ion

(l) cobalt(II) sulfite, cobaltous sulfite

(m) barium thiocyanate

(n) acetate ion

(o) ammonium carbonate

(p) sodium hydrogen carbonate, sodium bicarbonate

(q) iron(II) phosphate, ferrous phosphate

(r) nickel(II) oxide, nickelous oxide

(s) silver chloride

(t) mercury(I) cyanide, mercurous cyanide

(u) phosphorous acid

(v) hydrofluoric acid

(w) hydroiodic acid

(x) iodic acid

(y) nitric acid

(z) mercury(II) nitrite, mercuric nitrite

Multiple Choice

1. (d). This is the pair of elements with the smallest electronegativity difference of any listed. Remember trends in electronegativity associated with position in the periodic table.

2. (c). In none of the others do all of the atoms attain a stable configuration.

3. (a)

4. (d)

5. (e). BaF_2 is the only ionic substance listed. Notice that pure water, which is covalent, is a poor conductor of electricity — its commonly observed ability to conduct electricity is due to small amounts of dissolved ions.

6. (a). NaF is the only ionic substance listed.

7. (d)

8. (e)

9. (e)

10. (e). There are eight possible combinations. Can you write all of them?

11. (d)
12. (c). Each of the other compounds listed contains covalent bonds between elements of unequal electronegativities.
13. (d). Use the formula $S = N - A$.
14. (c). This is A in the formula $S = N - A$.
15. (b). This is S in the formula $S = N - A$. $N = 50$, and $A = 30$ (Question 14).

16. (a)	34. (d)
17. (e)	35. (b)
18. (b)	36. (d)
19. (d)	37. (d)
20. (e)	38. (a)
21. (b)	39. (c)
22. (b)	40. (c)
23. (a)	41. (b)
24. (d)	42. (c)
25. (d)	43. (d)
26. (c)	44. (c)
27. (c)	45. (a)
28. (d)	46. (b)
29. (c)	47. (a)
30. (d)	48. (c)
31. (d)	49. (c)
32. (d)	50. (a)
33. (d)	51. (c)

6

Molecular Orbitals in Chemical Bonding

Chapter Summary

In Chapter 5, we saw that we could describe covalent bonding as resulting from the overlap of orbitals that remain on or between the atoms involved (Valence Bond or VB theory). We also saw that we could describe, or at least rationalize, the molecular geometry as resulting from the repulsions among valence shell electron pairs on the atoms (VSEPR theory). In Chapter 6, we are introduced to the **Molecular Orbital (MO)** theory, which simply provides an alternative description of covalent bonding. Recall that in VB theory, we proposed that the various orbitals on a single atom could mix and recombine (hybridize) to form hybrid orbitals, which then had different energies and shapes than the "pure" or isolated atomic orbitals would have had. Similarly, the MO theory assumes that in a molecule the orbitals can mix to form orbitals that are no longer the "property" of just one atom but extend over at least the pair of atoms involved, or, in some cases, over the entire molecule. These are termed molecular orbitals.

For many molecules, the two descriptions are equivalent, with the VB approach having the advantage of being easily visualized, while the MO theory has an advantage with respect to quantitative calculations of energies and geometry, description of electron distributions, and correlation with magnetic properties. In other cases, the MO theory can give a correct description of some molecular property (for example, the paramagnetism of O_2) when the VB approach fails.

When two atomic orbitals from different atoms combine, they produce the same number of molecular orbitals. Of these molecular orbitals, one (the **bonding orbital**) is at lower energy than the original orbitals while the other (the **antibonding orbital**) is at higher energy than the pure atomic orbitals. Section 6–1 describes the various ways in which atomic orbitals can combine to give molecular orbitals and pictures the relation between the shapes of the atomic orbitals and those of the bonding and antibonding orbitals. You should be sure that you understand the notation used to describe molecular orbitals. The notation **sigma (σ)** indicates that the molecular orbital is cylindrically symmetrical about a line through the internuclear axis, while the notation **pi (π)** means that the molecular orbital has mirror symmetry across a plane through the two nuclei. The **subscripts** indicate the type of atomic orbitals that went to give this molecular orbital — s if both were s orbitals, sp if one was s and one was p, and p if both were p. The **superscript asterisk (*)** means that the orbital is antibonding, while the absence of any superscript means that the orbital is bonding. Notice that the only way (at least using only s and p orbitals as we do in this chapter) that a π molecular orbital can be formed is by side-by-side overlap of p orbitals on two different atoms.

Section 6–2 extends the description of the molecular orbitals to include the relative energies of the various molecular orbitals; knowledge of the relative energies is then used to fill the orbitals with the correct number of electrons for the molecule. (If you will compare the approach here with that in Sections 3–14 and 3–15 of Chapter 3, you will see that we are now doing just the same thing with molecules that we did earlier with isolated atoms.) It is important to remember the **order** of the energy levels for the various homonuclear diatomic molecules of the first- and second-period elements; remember that for O_2, F_2, and Ne_2 (and their ions) the order of energies of the σ_p and the π_p orbitals is reversed from the order of these orbitals for the other molecules and ions.

Once the correct number of electrons has been put into the set of molecular orbitals (following the Aufbau Principle, Hund's Rule, and the Pauli Principle, just as for isolated atoms), the stability of the resultant arrangement can be described by the **bond order,** as defined in Section 6–3. The greater the bond order, the more stable we predict the molecular or ion to be, and the shorter the **bond length** and the greater the **bond energy.**

Section 6–4 covers in detail the neutral homonuclear diatomics of the first and second periods. A careful study of this section will familiarize you with the notation used and will help you to understand the approach and application of the MO theory. As you will see in this section, the MO theory can also be used to describe bonding in diatomic cations and anions by removing or adding the appropriate number of electrons. For many heteronuclear diatomic molecules, the general features of the molecular orbital diagrams already studied can just be adjusted to take into account the electronegativity difference between the atoms. This is discussed in Section 6–5, with CO (a slightly polar molecule) and HF (a quite polar molecule) used as examples.

The Molecular Orbital theory is also quite useful in discussions of bonding in molecules and ions in which electron delocalization is an important feature of the bonding. (These are the species that the Valence Bond theory describes with resonance structures.) Two important illustrations of this approach, the carbonate ion (CO_3^-) and benzene (C_6H_6), are discussed in Section 6–6.

Study Goals

As in other chapters, some typical textbook exercises related to each study goal are indicated.

1. Distinguish between the main concepts of the Valence Bond (VB) theory and the Molecular Orbital (MO) theory. (Introduction to Chapter 6 and Section 6–1; Exercises 1 through 4)
2. Describe and distinguish between molecular orbitals and atomic orbitals. (Section 6–1; Exercises 2 and 3)
3. Describe each of the following molecular orbitals: σ_s, σ_s^*, σ_{sp}, σ_{sp}^*, σ_p, σ_p^*, π_p, and π_p^*. Understand how each of these orbitals is related to the "pure" atomic orbitals from which it is formed. (Sections 6–1 and 6–5; Exercise 5)
4. Distinguish between sigma (σ) and pi (π) molecular orbitals. Distinguish between bonding and antibonding molecular orbitals. (Section 6–1; Exercises 5 and 7)
5. Remember the order of energies of the molecular orbitals for simple homonuclear diatomic molecules and ions. Construct molecular orbital diagrams for these molecules and ions. (Section 6–2; Exercises 6 and 8)
6. Apply the concepts of molecular orbital theory to determine bond orders and to predict relative stabilities of simple diatomic molecules and ions. (Sections 6–3 and 6–4; Exercises 7, 9 through 17, 19, 20, and 22)
7. Remember the order of energies of the molecular orbitals for simple heteronuclear diatomic molecules and ions. Relate the appearance of molecular orbital diagrams to polarities of bonds. Construct molecular orbital diagrams for these molecules and ions. (Section 6–5; Exercises 12, 18 through 21, and 23)
8. Sketch three-dimensional representations of molecular orbitals in some molecules and ions for which delocalization is important. (Section 6–6; Exercise 24)

Some Important Terms in This Chapter

Write the meanings *in your own words*. Check the Key Terms list and the chapter reading. Then rewrite your definitions, still in your own words, to improve them. Study other new terms, and review terms from preceding chapters if necessary.

molecular orbital

atomic orbital

bonding orbital

nonbonding orbital

antibonding orbital

sigma orbital

pi orbital

bond order

delocalization

Preliminary Test

As in other chapters, this test will check your understanding of basic concepts. Be sure to practice *many* of the additional textbook exercises, some of which are indicated in the Study Goals.

Short Answer

1. The maximum number of electrons that can occupy one molecular orbital is ___.
2. When two atomic orbitals combine, the number of molecular orbitals formed is ___.
3. When three atomic orbitals combine, the number of molecular orbitals formed is ___.
4. End-to-end overlap of two p orbitals in formation of the molecular orbitals ___ and ___.
5. Side-by-side overlap of two p orbitals results in formation of the molecular orbitals ___ and ___.
6. Molecular orbitals that are at lower energy than the atomic orbitals from which they are formed are called _____ orbitals.
7. Molecular orbitals that when occupied increase the stability of the bonding between two atoms are called _____ orbitals.
8. The criterion that uses the relative number of electrons in bonding and antibonding orbitals to predict the stability of bonds is called the _____.
9. The definition of bond order is _____ _____.
10. In order for a molecule to be stable, its bond order must be _____.
11. The amount of energy necessary to break a mole of bonds is called the _____.
12. Generally, the more stable a bond, the _____ is the bond order, the _____ is the bond length, and the _____ is the bond energy. (Answer with words like greater, shorter, etc.)
13. The order of energies of the molecular orbitals of the homonuclear diatomic molecules and ions of the first- and second-row elements (atomic numbers up to and including that of nitrogen) is _____ _____.
14. The order of energies of the molecular orbitals of the homonuclear diatomic molecules and ions of the second-row elements (atomic numbers greater than that of nitrogen) is _____ _____.
15. A molecule or ion with an odd number of electrons must be _____.
16. In order for a molecule to be paramagnetic, it must have _____ electrons.
17. Of the homonuclear diatomic molecules whose electron distributions are shown in Figure 6–7 of the text, the ones that are paramagnetic are _____.
18. In terms of its magnetic properties, F_2 would be described as _____.
19. Of the first- and second-row homonuclear diatomic molecules, the most stable one is predicted to be ___.
20. The electronic configuration of Li_2 would be _____.
21. The bond order of Li_2 is ___; thus we predict that the molecule of Li_2 would be _____.

22. For heteronuclear diatomics, the atomic orbitals of the more electronegative element are _____ in energy than the corresponding orbitals of the less electronegative element.

23. According to the molecular orbital theory, we predict that the order of stability of NO, NO^-, and NO^+ would be (from most stable to least stable) _____.

Multiple Choice

____ 1. When two s orbitals combine to form molecular orbitals, the orbitals formed are
(a) one σ_s and one σ_s^*.
(b) two σ_s.
(c) two σ_s^*.
(d) one σ_s and one π_s.
(e) one π_s and one π_s^*.

____ 2. When an s orbital and a p orbital combine to form molecular orbitals, the orbitals formed are
(a) one σ_s and one σ_p.
(b) one π_s and one π_p.
(c) one σ_{sp} and one σ_{sp}^*.
(d) one π_{sp} and one π_{sp}^*.
(e) one σ_{sp} and one π_{sp}^*.

____ 3. The molecular orbital with the following shape can best be described as
(a) σ_p.   (b) σ_s^*.   (c) π_p^*.   (d) π_p.   (e) σ_p^*.

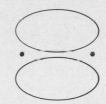

____ 4. The molecular orbital with the following shape can best be described as
(a) σ_p.   (b) σ_s^*.   (c) π_p^*.   (d) π_p.   (e) σ_p^*.

____ 5. Which of the following describes a diatomic molecule with bond order equal to zero?
(a) More electrons in bonding than in antibonding orbitals
(b) More electrons in antibonding than in bonding orbitals
(c) No electrons in bonding orbitals
(d) No electrons in antibonding orbitals
(e) Equal number of electrons in bonding and in antibonding orbitals

_____ 6. Which of the following molecules or ions would have a bond order equal to $2\frac{1}{2}$?
(a) He_2 (b) CO   (c) NO   (d) O_2 (e) Li_2^+

_____ 7. Which of the following molecules would be predicted to be the most stable?
(a) H_2 (b) Li_2 (c) B_2 (d) Be_2 (e) C_2

_____ 8. Which of the following molecules or ions would be most polar?
(a) B_2 (b) B_2^+ (c) NO   (d) NO^+ (e) CO

_____ 9. Which of the following would be described as being bonded with one σ bond plus two π bonds?
(a) B_2 (b) C_2 (c) N_2 (d) O_2 (e) F_2

Questions 10 through 12 refer to the following MO diagram.

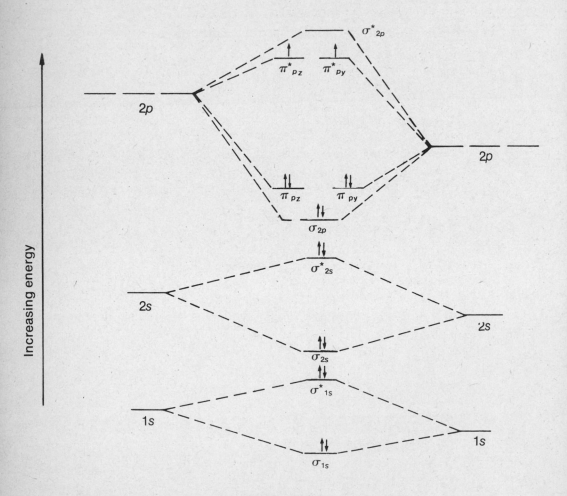

_____ 10. The bond order of the molecule or ion shown is
(a) 1.   (b) $1\frac{1}{2}$.   (c) 2.   (d) $2\frac{1}{2}$.   (e) 3.

_____ 11. Which of the following statements is true?

(a) The compound is diamagnetic.

(b) The compound does not have a dipole moment.

(c) The compound is a homonuclear diatomic.

(d) The compound is a heteronuclear diatomic.

(e) None of the preceding statements is true.

_____ 12. The MO diagram best describes which of the following molecules or ions?

(a) NO^- (b) O_2 (c) CO^- (d) NO^+ (e) CN^-

Answers to Preliminary Test

Do not just look up answers. Think about the reasons for the answers.

Short Answer

1. Two. Just as for pure atomic orbitals, a molecular orbital is a region in space that can hold a maximum of two electrons, and then only if they have opposite spin (i.e., are paired).
2. Two. The number of molecular orbitals formed is always the same as the number of atomic orbitals used to form them.
3. Three. See the answer to Question 2.
4. σ_p and σ_p^*. When two orbitals combine, one of the resultant molecular orbitals is bonding and one is antibonding. These are σ orbitals because they have cylindrical symmetry about the internuclear line. See Figure 6-3.
5. π_p and π_p^*. See Figure 6-4.
6. bonding
7. bonding
8. bond order. See Section 6-3.
9. (number of electrons in bonding orbitals − number of electrons in antibonding orbitals)/2. See Section 6-3.
10. greater than 0
11. bond energy. See Section 6-3.
12. greater, shorter, greater. See Section 6-3.
13. $\sigma_{1s}, \sigma_{1s}^*, \sigma_{2s}, \sigma_{2s}^*, \pi_{p_y} = \pi_{p_z}, \sigma_p, \pi_{p_y}^* = \pi_{p_z}^*, \sigma_p^*$. See Figure 6-5. You should know this order of orbitals.
14. $\sigma_{1s}, \sigma_{1s}^*, \sigma_{2s}, \sigma_{2s}^*, \sigma_p, \pi_{p_y} = \pi_{p_z}, \pi_{p_y}^* = \pi_{p_z}^*, \sigma_p^*$. See Figure 6-6. You should know this order of orbitals.
15. paramagnetic. Remember that the presence of unpaired electrons leads to paramagnetism—if an atom or molecule has an odd number of electrons, they cannot all be paired.
16. unpaired
17. B_2 and O_2. Only these have unpaired electrons.
18. diamagnetic

19. N_2. This molecule has the highest bond order.
20. $\sigma_{1s}^2 \, \sigma_{1s}^{*2} \, \sigma_{2s}^2$
21. 1, stable. The bond order is calculated as $(4 - 2)/2 = 1$
22. lower. One way to remember this is to recall that the electrons are drawn preferentially to the more electronegative element.
23. NO^+, NO, NO^-. To figure this out, use the energy level diagram (either the one in Figure 6–5 or the one in Figure 6–6 will work) to determine the configuration and then the bond order of each. NO has 15 electrons and a bond order of $2\frac{1}{2}$; NO^+ has 14 electrons and a bond order of 3 (same as N_2); NO^- has 16 electrons and a bond order of 2 (same as O_2). Higher bond order means higher stability.

Multiple Choice

1. (a). See Figure 6–1 and the discussion in Section 6–1.
2. (c). See Figure 6–9 and the discussion in Section 6–5.
3. (d). See Figure 6–3 and the discussion in Section 6–1.
4. (e). See Figure 6–2 and the discussion in Section 6–1.
5. (e)
6. (c). Be sure you know how to fill up the orbitals and then calculate bond order.
7. (e). The bond orders are $H_2 = 1$, $Li_2 = 1$, $B_2 = 1$, $Be_2 = 0$, $C_2 = 2$. Since C_2 has the highest bond order, it is predicted to be the most stable of the molecules listed here.
8. (e). Remember the electronegativity trends that you learned in Chapter 4. The larger the electronegativity difference, the more polar the bond (Section 5–2).
9. (c). Look at the electron distributions in Figure 6–7 (which you should be able to write down, remembering the order of the MOs). Remember that the presence of an electron pair in an antibonding orbital negates the bonding effect of an electron pair in the same type of bonding orbital. Thus, since F_2 has $\pi_{p_y}^2$ but also has $\pi_{p_y}^{*2}$, this does not count as a π bond. The same reasoning applies for $\pi_{p_z}^2$ and $\pi_{p_z}^{*2}$, so F_2 has only one σ bond.
10. (c). $(10 - 6)/2$
11. (d). We can tell because the atomic orbitals of the atom on the right are at lower energy than the orbitals of the atom on the left. Thus, these must be two different elements, with the one on the right the more electronegative. Since there are unpaired electrons, it could not be diamagnetic.
12. (a). Count the number of electrons in each of the species listed. Only NO^- has 16 electrons, the number shown in the diagram, and is also heteronuclear.

7

Chemical Reactions: A Systematic Study

Chapter Summary

Any study of chemistry must include attention to the reactions that elements and compounds undergo. This general area of a chemistry course is often termed "descriptive chemistry." Since there are more than a hundred elements and several million known compounds, each able to undergo many reactions, it might seem at first that a study of descriptive chemistry involves such a huge mass of information as to be hopelessly incomprehensible. Fortunately, there are several ways in which we can systematize this large amount of information to make it manageable. This chapter will help you get started in your study of descriptive chemistry by showing you several ways to organize the information and introducing you to some general terminology of descriptive chemistry.

You should organize your study of Chapter 7 around the following three principal lines, aided by the more explicit Study Goals in this guide. (1) Many new general concepts introduced in this chapter will be used throughout your subsequent studies. Included are general ideas of reactions in water (aqueous) solutions, acid-base behavior, neutralization, solubility, and oxidation-reduction processes. (2) Another way of organizing the variety of chemical information is by classifying the types of reactions that are encountered. Suggestions for study of this classification appear later in this Chapter Summary. (3) The periodic table is a guide to organizing information about reactivity and properties. This approach will be emphasized throughout the chapter, so watch for that thread. The chemistry of the common elements hydrogen and oxygen and their compounds, as presented in the last two sections of this chapter, will serve as an excellent illustration of all three of these approaches to descriptive chemistry.

It will be useful to you, before beginning your study of this chapter, to review the major ideas of chemical periodicity (Chapter 4), inorganic nomenclature (Sections 5–23 and 5–24), writing of chemical equations (Section 2–7), and oxidation numbers (Section 4–12).

Section 7–1 introduces you to many aspects of reactions and properties in **aqueous** solutions. Many substances dissolve in water by the formation of ions. Due to the mobility of these ions, such solutions are able to conduct electricity; these substances are called **electrolytes.** They range in their behavior from **strong** to **weak.** Aqueous solutions of other substances, **nonelectrolytes,** do not conduct electricity to any appreciable extent.

The second part of Section 7–1 is your first introduction to the behavior of the important substances known as **acids** and **bases,** with more detailed coverage of these substances and their reactions to come in Chapters 11, 16, and 17. According to the view presented here, in aqueous solution an acid acts as a source of **hydrogen ions, H^+,** and a base is a source of **hydroxide ions, OH^-.** The fundamental reaction that acids undergo is **ionization:**

$$H_nX \text{ (aq)} \rightarrow nH^+ \text{ (aq)} + X^{n-} \text{ (aq)},$$

where n is, for example, usually 1, but sometimes 2 (e.g., for sulfuric acid, H_2SO_4) or even 3 (e.g., phosphoric acid, H_3PO_4). Some acids are able to undergo this reaction essentially completely in dilute aqueous solution; these are referred to as **strong acids.** The seven common strong acids and their anions (H_nX and X^{n-} in the above general representation) are listed in Table 7–1. You should learn the names and formulas of these acids and their anions. Those acids that undergo this ionization reaction only slightly in dilute aqueous solution are referred to as **weak acids.** They are much more numerous, but the brief list of the common weak acids and their anions in Table 7–2 should also be learned. You should note that in solutions of strong acids, very little of the acid exists in solution, most of it having been converted to the anion; in weak acid solutions, the acid exists almost entirely as nonionized acid molecules, relatively little of the anion having been formed. This is an example of a reaction that is strongly **reversible.**

In like fashion, **bases,** compounds that produce OH^- in aqueous solutions, can be strong or weak. Since most common bases are metal hydroxides, many of which are not very soluble in water, only a few common bases need to be considered. The list of strong soluble bases in Table 7–3 should be learned. The fundamental reaction for the dissociation (ionization) of strong soluble bases can be written as

$$M(OH)_n \text{ (s)} \rightarrow M^{n+} \text{ (aq)} + nOH^- \text{ (aq)},$$

where n is an integer, equal to 1 for the alkali metals (Group IA) and equal to 2 for the alkaline earth metals (Groups IIA).

Do not confuse the terminology of "weak" and "strong" acids and bases with that of "dilute" and "concentrated" solutions. The terms "dilute" and "concentrated" refer to *how much* substance, acid or base, we put into the solution. Recall that we learned in Chapter 2 a couple of methods for describing the "concentrations" of solutions. The terms "strong" and "weak" refer to the *fraction* of acid or base that ionizes according to the reaction to give H_3O^+ or OH^-. In Chapter 16 we will learn about more quantitative ways to describe the strengths of acids and bases.

The rules that summarize the solubility of various common types of compounds in water (Section 7–1.5) are very important and should be learned. Understanding and use of these rules will depend on your grasp of inorganic nomenclature (Sections 5–23 and 5–24).

According to the scheme presented in this chapter, we categorize reactions in the following classes: (1) combination reactions, (2) displacement reactions, (3) decomposition reactions, (4) metathesis reactions, and (5) oxidation-reduction reactions. As we will see, some reactions, especially oxidation-reduction reactions, may fit into one or even two other categories. (That is why Study Goal 6 is worded as it is.)

(1) **Combination reactions,** those in which two or more substances combine to form a single compound, are discussed in Section 7–2. This class can be further subdivided according to the nature of the reactants. (Remember the terminology that you encountered in Chapter 2 — the reactants are the substances that are consumed as the reaction proceeds, while the products are those substances being formed by the reaction.) (a) In some such reactions, the two reactants are both elements. Typical reactions that are discussed in the text are the formation of **hydrides** by reaction of metals or nonmetals with hydrogen, formation of **oxides** by reaction of metals or nonmetals with oxygen, and other reactions of metals with nonmetals. Since all of the reactions discussed in this subsection involve only two elements, the compounds that are formed are referred to as **binary compounds** (Chapter 5). (b) Some other combination reactions have an element and a compound as reactants. A common example of this type is the reaction of a compound with oxygen. (c) In the third subclass of combination reactions, two compounds combine to form a single new compound.

(2) **Displacement reactions,** Section 7–3, are those in which one element displaces another from a compound. Examples of such reactions are the displacement of one metal from a compound by another, of hydrogen from a compound by a metal, and of one nonmetal by another. Notice the terminology by which we call the metal (or nonmetal) most able to displace hydrogen or other metals (or other nonmetals) from a compound the most **active.** A ranking of the ability of elements to displace one another from compounds is given in the **activity series.** A quantitative approach to this ranking will be studied in Chapter 19. In this section we also are introduced to several helpful ways of writing the chemical equation, depending on what feature of the reaction we wish to emphasize. The three ways are (a) the **molecular equation,** in which the formulas of all compounds are shown as neutral substances, whether they actually consist of ions or of molecules, (b) the **total ionic equation,** in which the formulas are written to show the form in which each substance exists in solution, and (c) the **net ionic equation,** which includes only those species that actually react, the **spectator ions** having been eliminated from the

equation. You should be aware, of course, that this formalism for writing equations is also useful for writing other types of reactions, not just displacement reactions.

(3) **Decomposition reactions,** which are discussed in Section 7–4, are just the reverse of combination reactions and can again be subclassified into three groups, this time in terms of the nature of the products. (a) In some decomposition reactions, both products are elements. (b) In other decomposition reactions, the products are an element and one or more compounds, although this type of reaction is not as common. (c) A third type of decomposition reaction is that in which the products are two or more compounds.

(4) **Metathesis reactions,** the topic of Section 7–5, are those in which two compounds react in a particular way to form two new compounds. The terminology of "changing partners" will help you to recognize such reactions. The **neutralization** reaction of an acid and a base to form a **salt** and water is a very common example of such a metathesis reaction. As you study this type of reaction, both here and in Chapter 11, it will help you to notice that the **net ionic equation** for all acid-base neutralization reactions between strong acids and strong soluble bases to form a soluble salt in water is always the same:

$$H^+ (aq) + OH^- (aq) \rightarrow H_2O (\ell)$$

while the spectator ions (and hence the salt that is formed) change depending on the identities of the acid and the base involved in the reaction. Similar net ionic equations for neutralizations involving weak acids, weak or insoluble bases, or insoluble salts are also discussed in this section.

Many reactions occurring in aqueous solution result in removal of ions from solution. Several ways in which this can occur are discussed in Section 7–6.

(5) **Oxidation-reduction reactions,** Section 7–7, are those in which some substances undergo changes in oxidation number. These are often called **redox** reactions. It is essential that you learn the terminology — **oxidation, reduction, oxidizing agent, reducing agent** — that is presented early in the section. You should be especially aware that oxidation cannot occur without a corresponding reduction, and vice versa. You have already encountered many oxidation-reduction reactions earlier in this chapter. A reaction in which one element is both oxidized and reduced is termed a **disproportionation reaction.** Another type of redox reaction is the **displacement reaction** (Section 7–3), in which one element displaces another from a compound. Examples of such reactions are the displacement of one metal from a compound by another, of hydrogen from a compound by a metal, and of one nonmetal by another. Acid-base neutralization reactions and other metathesis reactions are *not* oxida-

tion-reduction reactions, but many of the other types of reactions we have seen frequently are also redox reactions. In your study of redox reactions, in addition to being able to recognize such reactions, you should learn to identify which substance is oxidized and which is reduced. Be sure that you notice the terminology: we call the **compound** (or **polyatomic ion**) containing the element undergoing a *decrease* in oxidation number the oxidizing agent, and the compound that contains the element undergoing an oxidation number *increase,* the reducing agent.

A more detailed study of oxidation-reduction reactions will be encountered in Chapter 11, with systematic procedures for balancing such reactions and stoichiometric calculations based on redox reactions. In addition, the study of electron-transfer reactions (electrochemistry, electrolysis, voltaic cells, batteries, etc.), which is the subject of Chapter 19, also involves oxidation-reduction reactions.

Oxygen and hydrogen combine with more elements than any others. For this reason, a study of the reactions and compounds of these two elements provides a nice illustration of the concepts and classifications of this chapter. In Section 7–8, you learn about the properties of the element H_2 and some methods of its preparation. In its reactions, hydrogen combines with metals or with nonmetals to form binary (two-element) compounds called **hydrides.** These range in their properties from the ionic hydrides (with the more active metals) to the covalent hydrides (with nonmetals), through some compounds of intermediate character. The periodic table is the key to keeping track of the formulas and properties of these compounds.

Section 7–9 takes a similar approach to the properties, preparation, reactions, and compounds of oxygen. Most of the elementary oxygen exists in the familiar diatomic form, O_2, sometimes called **dioxygen,** but usually just referred to as **oxygen.** The other **allotropic** form of this element, O_3, called **ozone,** is an unstable, very reactive gas. Oxygen combines with more elements than any other element, forming binary compounds called **oxides** by direct reaction with all elements except the noble gases and a few of the less reactive metals, such as silver and gold. Oxygen does form compounds indirectly with several of these. It may seem to you that a rather short portion of the text is devoted to the descriptive chemistry of this important element. However, since oxygen combines with nearly every other element, you will study more about its reactions with the descriptive chemistry of other elements. The binary compounds of oxygen range in character from ionic (with metals) to covalent (with nonmetals). In the binary compounds with metals, oxygen can exist either as the **oxide ion (O^{2-})**, as the **peroxide ion (O_2^{2-})**, or as the **superoxide ion (O_2^-).** Though the first of these is the most common, the tendency to form the others is correlated to trends in the periodic table (Section 7–1.2). The three types of oxide reactions discussed here are (1) the reaction of metal oxides (basic anhydrides) with water to form bases, (2) the reaction of nonmetal oxides (acid anhydrides) with water to form **ternary** acids (three elements—H, O, and a nonmetal), and (3) the reaction of these two types of oxides with one another to form **salts.** We note that all three of these occur without change of oxidation number. The last two parts of Section 7–9 discuss **combustion reactions,** which are redox reactions in which oxygen combines rapidly with oxidizable materials in highly exothermic reactions with a visible flame (we call this "burning"). The atmospheric pollution that results from the combustion of fossil fuels is discussed.

Study the terminology introduced in this chapter and learn to recognize the various types of reactions. This will help you to systematize your study of subsequent descriptive chemistry chapters.

Study Goals

These goals should help you to organize your study of the chapter. Use them as a guide to summarize your class notes and chapter reading. Answering many of the suggested questions will help you to check your progress toward these goals.

1. Describe solutions of strong electrolytes, weak electrolytes, and nonelectrolytes, giving examples of each. (Section 7–1.1; Exercises 3 and 16 through 18)
2. Be familiar with the characteristics of acids and bases and their solutions. (Sections 7–1.1 through 7–1.4; Exercises 1 and 2)
3. Distinguish between strong acids and weak acids. Distinguish among strong soluble bases, weak bases, and insoluble bases. (Sections 7–1.2 through 7–1.4; Exercise 4)
4. Recognize and write the names and formulas of the seven common strong acids and their anions listed in Table 7–1. Recognize and write the names and formulas of the common weak acids and their anions listed in Table 7–2. Recognize and write the names and formulas of the eight strong soluble bases in Table 7–3. (Sections 7–1.2 and 7–1.4; Exercises 5 through 11)
5. Apply the water-solubility rules to identify relatively soluble and relatively insoluble compounds. (Section 7–1.5; Exercises 12 through 15)
6. Classify chemical reactions as one or more of the following types: (a) combination, (b) decomposition, (c) displacement, (d) metathesis, (e) oxidation-reduction. (Sections 7–2 through 7–7; Exercises 41 through 48)
7. Distinguish among molecular, total ionic, and net ionic equations. (Section 7–3; Exercises 27 through 38, 41, 43)
8. Be able to use the activity table to predict whether or not one element

would displace another from a compound. Write equations for displacement reactions. (Section 7–5; Exercises 44 through 46)

9. Be able to predict the products of metathesis reactions. (Section 7–5; Exercises 27 through 32)
10. Give several examples of balanced molecular equations, total ionic equations, and net ionic equations for neutralization reactions of acids and bases to form salts. Be able to name all compounds involved in these equations. (Section 7–5; review Sections 5–23 and 5–24 for naming; Exercises 27 through 39)
11. Know what is meant by each of the terms "oxidation," "reduction," "oxidizing agent," and "reducing agent." Identify oxidizing agents and reducing agents in equations for redox reactions. (Section 7–7; Exercises 40 through 47)
12. Know some preparations and properties of hydrogen (H_2) and oxygen (O_2). (Sections 7–8.1 and 7–9.1; Exercises 48, 49, and 55 through 57)
13. Know some of the reactions of hydrogen and oxygen (Sections 7–2.2 and 7–3.2; Exercises 50 and 58 through 63)
14. Recognize and give examples of the following classes of compounds: (a) metal hydrides, (b) nonmetal hydrides, (c) metal oxides (basic anhydrides), peroxides, and superoxides, (d) nonmetal oxides (acidic anhydrides). Give the preparations and reactions of these classes of compounds. (Sections 7–8 and 7–9; Exercises 50 through 54, 58 through 70)
15. Know the basic features of combustion reactions. (Sections 7–9.3 and 7–9.4; Exercises 71 through 76)

Some Important Terms in This Chapter

Write the meanings *in your own words*. Check the Key Terms list and the chapter reading. Then rewrite your definitions, still in your own words, to improve them. Study other new terms, and review terms from preceding chapters if necessary.

electrolyte

strong electrolyte

weak electrolyte

acid

base

neutralization

salt

molecular equation

total ionic equation

net ionic equation

oxidation

reduction

oxidation-reduction reaction

metathesis reaction

disproportionation reaction

displacement reaction

combustion reaction

combination reaction

decomposition reaction

hydride

oxide

acid anhydride

basic anhydride

activity series

Preliminary Test

This test will check your understanding and application of basic ideas. Be sure to practice many of the additional textbook exercises, as indicated in the Study Goals.

Short Answer

Answer with a word, a phrase, a formula, or a number with units as necessary.

1. An acid is a substance that produces _____ (name, formula) in aqueous solution.
2. An acid that does not very efficiently form H^+ in aqueous solutions is called a (an) _____.
3. The anion of nitric acid is _____ (name, formula).
4. The anion of acetic acid is _____ (name, formula).
5. The acid of which cyanide ion is the anion is _____ (name, formula).
6. All of the strong soluble bases listed in the text are hydroxides of the elements of _____ and _____.
7. Organic acids contain the atom grouping _____.
8. A base, when dissolved in water, produces _____ (name, formula).

9. When a strong acid is dissolved in water, its ionization takes place _____.

10. When a weak acid is dissolved in water, its ionization takes place _____.

11. Classify each of the following substances as soluble or insoluble in water.

(a) KNO_3 _____
(b) $SrCl_2$ _____
(c) SO_2 _____
(d) $Al(OH)_3$ _____
(e) $(NH_4)_2S$ _____
(f) FeS _____
(g) $CaCO_3$ _____
(h) HBr _____
(i) $PbCl_2$ _____
(j) NaSCN _____
(k) $Ca(OH)_2$ _____
(l) $AgNO_3$ _____
(m) $Mg(CH_3COO)_2$ _____
(n) $Zn(ClO_4)_2$ _____
(o) H_3PO_4 _____
(p) $Ba_3(PO_4)_2$ _____
(q) MgS _____
(r) $(NH_4)_2CO_3$ _____
(s) KOH _____
(t) Rb_2SO_4 _____

12. A binary compound is one consisting of _____ elements.

13. A ternary compound is one consisting of _____ elements.

14. A ternary acid is one containing hydrogen, oxygen, and _____ _____.

15. A reaction in which the elements or ions may be described as "changing partners" is called a _____ reaction.

16. A reaction in which one element reacts with a compound to give a new compound and an element is called a _____ reaction.

17. A reaction in which a compound breaks apart to produce one or more elements and one more compounds is called a _____ reaction.

18. A reaction in which one element and one compound come together to form a single new compound is called a _____ reaction.

19. When silver nitrate solution and sodium sulfate solution are mixed, silver sulfate precipitates (that is, solid silver sulfate is formed), leaving a solution containing sodium ions and nitrate ions. The balanced molecular equation for this reaction is _____. This reaction may be classified as a _____ reaction. This reaction _____ (is, is not) an oxidation-reduction reaction.

20. Solid lead(IV) chloride, when heated to 100°C, reacts to give solid lead(II) chloride and chlorine gas. The balanced molecular equation for this reaction is _____. This reaction may be classified as a _____ reaction. This reaction _____ (is, is not) an oxidation-reduction reaction.

21. When the ammonia fumes above a solution of ammonia are allowed to mix with the hydrogen chloride fumes above a hydrochloric acid solution, a "smoke" (actually a colloid of finely divided solid particles — see Chapter 10) of ammonium chloride forms. The balanced molecular equation for this reaction is _____. This reaction may be classified as a _____ reaction; it _____ (is, is not) a redox reaction.

22. In the following equations, A, B, X, and Y are hypothetical elements, while H and O are hydrogen and oxygen, respectively. Classify each of the following as a combination reaction, a displacement reaction, a decomposition reaction, or a metathesis reaction.
    (a) $XO + H_2O \rightarrow H_2XO_2$ _____
    (b) $A + X_2 \rightarrow AX_2$ _____
    (c) $A + BX \rightarrow AX + B$ _____
    (d) $2AX + Y_2 \rightarrow 2AY + X_2$ _____
    (e) $HX + BOH \rightarrow H_2O + BX$ _____
    (f) $AX \rightarrow A + X$ _____
    (g) $A + B \rightarrow AB$ _____
    (h) $AX + BX \rightarrow ABX_2$ _____
    (i) $2A_2O \rightarrow 2A_2 + O_2$ _____
    (j) $2HX + B(OH)_2 \rightarrow 2H_2O + BX_2$ _____
    (k) $AX + BY \rightarrow AY + BX$ _____
    (l) $AXO_3 \rightarrow AO + XO_2$ _____
    (m) $2A + 2HX \rightarrow 2AX + H_2$ _____
    (n) $2A + X_2 \rightarrow 2AX$ _____
    (o) $2AX + X_2 \rightarrow 2AX_2$ _____
    (p) $A_2 + 2BX \rightarrow 2AX + B_2$ _____
    (q) $AO + BO \rightarrow ABO_2$ _____
    (r) $2AXO_3 \rightarrow 2AX + 3O_2$ _____
23. When an acid and a base act to neutralize one another, the products are _____ and _____.
24. The name and formula of the salt that results from the neutralization of calcium hydroxide and nitric acid are _____.
25. The formula of magnesium acetate is _____.
26. The net ionic reaction for all neutralization reactions involving strong acids and strong soluble bases to form soluble salts in water is _____.
27. For the neutralization reaction of potassium hydroxide and sulfuric acid, the balanced molecular equation is _____ _____, the total ionic equation is _____ _____, and the net ionic equation is _____ _____. The spectator ions are _____.
28. When the oxides of nonmetals dissolve in water, they form _____ solutions.
29. Basic anhydrides are the oxides of _____.
30. Strong soluble bases, such as the Group IA metal hydroxides, can often be prepared by the reaction of _____ with water.
31. Many ternary acids can be prepared by dissolving the appropriate _____ in water.
32. A process in which electrons are lost in a reaction is termed _____.
33. A substance that loses electrons in a reaction is termed a (an) _____.

34. A substance that undergoes an increase in oxidation number in a reaction is termed a (an) _____ .

35. The substance that is reduced in a reaction is termed a (an) _____ .

36. In any reaction in which reduction occurs, _____ must also occur.

37. Another name for an oxidation-reduction reaction is a _____ .

The reaction in which nitrogen and hydrogen react to give ammonia is an oxidation-reduction reaction in which all substances are gases. Questions 38 through 41 refer to this reaction.

38. The unbalanced molecular equation that describes this reaction is _____ .

39. In this reaction, nitrogen undergoes a change in oxidation number from _____ to _____; hydrogen undergoes a change in oxidation number from _____ to _____ .

40. The balanced molecular equation that describes this reaction is _____ .

41. This reaction can also be classified as a _____ reaction.

42. A hydride is a compound composed of _____ and _____ .

43. A covalent hydride contains hydrogen and _____ , whereas an ionic hydride contains hydrogen and _____ _____ .

44. The general formula of the hydrides of the halogens is _____ (denoting a halogen as X).

45. The general formula of the hydrides of the Group VIA nonmetals is _____ (denoting a Group VIA nonmetal as Y).

46. The general formula for the *normal* oxides of the alkali metals is _____ (denoting an alkali metal as M).

47. The two binary compounds that oxygen forms with hydrogen are _____ and _____ . (Give name and formula of each.)

48. Of the two allotropic forms of oxygen, _____ is much more stable than _____ . (Give name and formula of each.)

49. Metal peroxides contain the _____ ion, with formula ____; in this ion, the oxidation number of oxygen is ____ .

50. Some nonmetallic oxides are referred to as _____ anhydrides, because they _____ .

51. Many ionic metal oxides are _____ anhydrides, so called because they _____ .

52. Oxides that can dissolve in either acids or bases are termed _____ .

53. The formula for sodium peroxide is _____ .

54. The formula for hydrogen peroxide is _____ .

55. The name of the ion O^{2-} is _____.
56. The name of the ion O_2^- is _____.
57. The name of the ion O_2^{2-} is _____.
58. The process in which oxygen combines rapidly with some materials in highly exothermic reactions, with a visible flame, is called _____.
59. The usual products of the complete combustion of hydrocarbons are _____ and _____. (Give name and formula of each.)
60. Combustion reactions always give off _____.
61. Combustion of fuels containing sulfur produces _____ _____ (name, formula), which is a very harmful atmospheric pollutant.
62. The substance produced in Question 61 is slowly oxidized in air to _____, which then combines with moisture in air to form _____. (Give name and formula of each.)

Multiple Choice

_____ 1. Which of the Group VIA elements is not a solid at room temperature and atmospheric pressure?
(a) oxygen   (b) sulfur   (c) selenium   (d) tellurium
(e) polonium

_____ 2. The element oxygen, in the form O_2, accounts for which of the following percentages, by volume, of dry air?
(a) about 20 percent   (b) about 40 percent   (c) about 50 percent   (d) about 60 percent   (e) about 80 percent

_____ 3. Which of the following Group VIA elements has the highest first ionization energy?
(a) O   (b) S   (c) Se   (d) Te

_____ 4. Which of the following is *not* a common strong acid?
(a) HF   (b) HCl   (c) HBr   (d) HI   (e) $HClO_4$

_____ 5. Which of the following is *not* a common weak acid?
(a) $HClO_4$ (b) $(COOH)_2$ (c) H_2SO_3 (d) HSO_3^-
(e) CH_3COOH

_____ 6. The salt that would be formed by the neutralization of HCl with $Mg(OH)_2$ is
(a) MgCl.   (b) $MgCl_2$.   (c) Mg_2Cl.   (d) HMg.   (e) ClOH.

_____ 7. The salt that would result from the complete neutralization reaction between sulfuric acid and potassium hydroxide is
(a) K_2SO_4.   (b) KSO_4.   (c) $K_2(SO_4)_2$.   (d) KS.   (e) K_2S.

_____ 8. The reaction

$$2HCl + Ca(OH)_2 \rightarrow 2H_2O + CaCl_2$$

can be described as

(a) a neutralization reaction.
(b) a displacement reaction.
(c) a disproportionation reaction.
(d) a precipitation reaction.
(e) an oxidation-reduction reaction.

_____ 9. The salt that would result from the neutralization reaction between phosphoric acid and calcium hydroxide is
(a) $CaPO_4$.   (b) $Ca_3(PO_4)_2$.   (c) $Ca_2(PO_4)_3$.   (d) $Ca(PO_4)_2$.
(e) Ca_3PO_4.

_____ 10. The following describe properties of substances. Which one is not a typical acid property?
(a) It has a sour taste.
(b) It reacts with metal oxides to form salts and water.
(c) It reacts with acids to form salts and water.
(d) Its aqueous solutions conduct an electric current.
(e) It reacts with active metals to liberate H_2.

_____ 11. Some soluble bases can be formed by the action of metals with water. For which of the following metals would this not be a likely way of preparing the corresponding hydroxide base?
(a) K   (b) Ca   (c) Na   (d) Ba   (e) Fe

_____ 12. Each of the following ions forms a stable hydroxide. For which of the ions would the hydroxide *not* be amphoteric?
(a) Sn^{2+} (b) Sn^{4+} (c) Cr^{3+} (d) Be^{2+} (e) Ba^{2+}

_____ 13. When heated in the presence of oxygen (O_2), the gas carbon monoxide (CO) is converted to carbon dioxide (CO_2). This reaction is best described as
(a) a displacement reaction.   (b) a decomposition reaction.
(c) a metathesis reaction.   (d) a redox reaction.   (e) a neutralization reaction.

_____ 14. The oxidation numbers (oxidation states) of the elements in $KClO_3$ are
(a) $K = +3$, $Cl = +3$, $O = -2$.
(b) $K = -1$, $Cl = -5$, $O = +2$.
(c) $K = +1$, $Cl = +5$, $O = -2$.
(d) $K = +1$, $Cl = +3$, $O = -1$.
(e) $K = +1$, $Cl = +2$, $O = -3$.

_____ 15. In the reaction

$$2Na\ (s) + 2H_2O\ (\ell) \rightarrow 2Na^+\ (aq) + H_2\ (g) + 2OH^-\ (aq)$$

sodium metal
(a) is acting as a transition element.
(b) is the oxidizing agent and is being reduced.
(c) is the oxidizing agent and is being oxidized.
(d) is the reducing agent and is being oxidized.
(e) is the reducing agent and is being reduced.

_____ 16. In the reaction

$$Cr_2O_7^{2-} (aq) + 3H_2S (aq) + 8H^+ (aq) \rightarrow 2Cr^{3+} (aq) \\ + 2S (s) + 7H_2O (\ell)$$

which element is being oxidized?
(a) Cr   (b) H   (c) O   (d) S   (e) None, since this is not an oxidation-reduction reaction.

_____ 17. In the reaction of Question 16, the reducing agent is
(a) $Cr_2O_7^{2-}$.   (b) H_2S.   (c) H^+.   (d) H_2O.   (e) There is no reducing agent, since this is not an oxidation-reduction reaction.

_____ 18. In the reaction

$$Mg (s) + Cl_2 (g) \rightarrow MgCl_2 (s)$$

chlorine gas acts as
(a) an anion. (b) a cation. (c) an oxidizing agent. (d) an acid.
(e) a reducing agent.

_____ 19. The reaction of Question 18 could be classified as
(a) a metathesis reaction.   (b) a neutralization reaction.
(c) a decomposition reaction.   (d) a combination reaction.
(e) a displacement reaction.

_____ 20. In the reaction

$$Ca_3(PO_4)_2 (s) + 3H_2SO_4 (aq) \rightarrow 2H_3PO_4 (aq) + 3CaSO_4 (s)$$

which element is being oxidized?
(a) Ca   (b) P   (c) S   (d) O   (e) None, since this is not an oxidation-reduction reaction.

_____ 21. The mineral fluorite is an ionic substance consisting only of calcium and fluorine. What are the oxidation numbers of Ca and F in fluorite?
(a) $Ca = -2$, $F = +1$ (b) $Ca = +1$, $F = +2$ (c) $Ca = +2$, $F = -2$ (d) $Ca = +2$, $F = -1$ (e) $Ca = +2$, $F = +9$

_____ 22. Consider the following equation that describes the rusting of iron:

$$4Fe + O_2 \rightarrow 2Fe_2O_3$$

Which one of the following statements is *not* correct?
(a) This is an example of an oxidation-reduction reaction.
(b) Metallic iron is a reducing agent.
(c) O_2 is an oxidizing agent.
(d) Metallic iron is reduced.
(e) The total gain in oxidation number of one element equals the total loss of oxidation number of another element.

_____ 23. Which of the following compounds contains an element with an oxidation number of $+5$?
(a) HClO   (b) HNO_2 (c) $HClO_3$ (d) $HBrO_4$ (e) H_2SO_4

_____ 24. Which of the following compounds contains an element with an oxidation number of $+3$?
    (a) HClO   (b) HNO_2 (c) $HClO_3$ (d) $HBrO_4$ (e) H_2SO_4

_____ 25. In the net ionic equation

$$5SO_3^{2-} + 6H^+ + 2MnO_4^- \rightarrow 5SO_4^{2-} + 2Mn^{2+} + 3H_2O$$

which element is being reduced?
(a) S   (b) O   (c) H   (d) Mn   (e) None, since this is not an oxidation-reduction reaction.

Answers to Preliminary Test

Short Answer

1. hydrogen ion, H^+
2. weak acid
3. nitrate, NO_3^-. Remember that the anion of an acid is what is left when the acid gives up H^+ to water.
4. acetate, CH_3COO^-. Formulas for anions written without the proper charge are incorrect.
5. hydrocyanic acid, HCN. Remember that you can find out the acid(s) corresponding to an anion by adding one (or more) H^+. Remember to adjust the charge.
6. Group IA (alkali metals), the heavier members of Group IIA (alkaline earth metals)

7. —COOH   or $-\overset{\overset{\displaystyle O}{\|}}{C}-O-H$
8. hydroxide ion, OH^-
9. completely
10. very slightly
11. (a) soluble   (k) soluble
    (b) soluble   (l) soluble
    (c) soluble   (m) soluble
    (d) insoluble   (n) soluble
    (e) soluble   (o) soluble
    (f) insoluble   (p) insoluble
    (g) insoluble   (q) soluble
    (h) soluble   (r) soluble
    (i) insoluble   (s) soluble
    (j) soluble   (t) soluble
You should _know_ and be able to apply the solubility rules in Section

7–1.5. You may need to review chemical nomenclature of inorganic compounds, Sections 5–23 and 5–24.

12. two
13. three
14. a nonmetal
15. metathesis
16. displacement
17. decomposition
18. combination
19. $2AgNO_3$ (aq) + Na_2SO_4 (aq) $\rightarrow$ Ag_2SO_4 (s) + $2NaNO_3$ (aq), metathesis, is not. Notice that you can always check to find out whether a reaction is a redox reaction by determining the oxidation numbers of all elements on both sides of the equation. In this equation, there are no oxidation number changes.
20. $PbCl_4$ (s) $\rightarrow$ $PbCl_2$ (s) + Cl_2 (g), decomposition, is. Both lead and part of the chlorine change in oxidation number.
21. NH_3 (g) + HCl (g) $\rightarrow$ NH_4Cl (s), combination, is not
22. (a) combination
    (b) combination
    (c) displacement
    (d) displacement
    (e) metathesis (a neutralization reaction)
    (f) decomposition
    (g) combination
    (h) combination
    (i) decomposition
    (j) metathesis (another neutralization reaction)
    (k) metathesis
    (l) decomposition
    (m) displacement
    (n) combination
    (o) combination
    (p) displacement
    (q) combination
    (r) decomposition

It would be helpful for you to find one or more examples of each of these reactions in the text.
23. water, a salt. Some salts are insoluble and precipitate from solution, while others are soluble, remaining in solution in ionized form. Be sure you understand that NaCl, which we commonly call "salt," is only one member of an entire class of compounds that are collectively called salts in correct chemical usage.
24. calcium nitrate, $Ca(NO_3)_2$. Review the names of the anions of the common weak acids (Table 7–3) and the common strong acids (Table 7–2). You must also be familiar with the usage of inorganic nomenclature that you studied in Chapter 5.
25. $Mg(CH_3COO)_2$
26. H^+ (aq) + OH^- (aq) $\rightarrow$ H_2O (ℓ)
27. molecular: H_2SO_4 (aq) + 2KOH (aq) $\rightarrow$ $2H_2O$ (ℓ) + K_2SO_4 (aq)
    total ionic: $[2H^+$ (aq) + SO_4^{2-} (aq)] + $2[K^+$ (aq) + OH^- (aq)] $\rightarrow$
    $$2H_2O \ (\ell) + [2K^+ \ (aq) + SO_4^{2-} \ (aq)]$$

net ionic: H^+ (aq) $+ OH^-$ (aq) $\rightarrow H_2O$ (ℓ)
spectator ions: K^+, SO_4^{2-}

28. acidic. See Section 7–9.
29. metals. See Section 7–9.
30. the metallic element. Some such reactions occur at dangerously explosive rates.
31. nonmetal oxide. See Section 7–9.
32. oxidation
33. reducing agent
34. reducing agent. Remember that a substance that undergoes an increase in oxidation number is said to be oxidized — the substance oxidized is the reducing agent.
35. oxidizing agent
36. oxidation
37. redox reaction
38. N_2 (g) $+ H_2$ (g) $\rightarrow NH_3$ (g). Note that it is incorrect to represent nitrogen gas as just N, or hydrogen gas as H, since they do not exist that way — each is diatomic.
39. 0, -3; 0, $+1$. Review oxidation numbers, Section 4–12.
40. N_2 (g) $+ 3H_2$ (g) $\rightarrow 2NH_3$ (g)
41. combination
42. hydrogen, another element
43. a nonmetal, an active metal. Remember that the hydrides of the less active metals are intermediate in character between the most ionic and the most covalent. See the classification of the hydrides of the representative elements in Figure 7–5.
44. HX
45. H_2Y
46. M_2O. But you should be aware that the alkali metals commonly form peroxides or superoxides in their direct reaction with O_2. See Table 7–6.
47. water (H_2O), hydrogen peroxide (H_2O_2)
48. dioxygen (O_2, often just called oxygen), ozone (O_3)
49. peroxide, O_2^{2-}, -1. Remember that in this text, the ionic charge is designated as $n-$ or $n+$, while the oxidation number or oxidation state is designated as $-n$ or $+n$. The peroxides are one of the rare classes of compounds in which oxygen exhibits an oxidation number other than -2.
50. acid, react with water to give acid solutions. How many examples of this behavior can you list?
51. basic, react with water to form bases. These are primarily the oxides of the alkali metals and those of the heavier alkaline earth metals.
52. amphoteric
53. Na_2O_2

54. H_2O_2
55. oxide
56. superoxide
57. peroxide
58. combustion
59. water (H_2O), carbon dioxide (CO_2)
60. heat. These are always exothermic; the usual reason for carrying out combustion reactions is to use the heat energy produced, rather than to make desirable products.
61. sulfur dioxide (SO_2)
62. sulfur trioxide (SO_3), sulfuric acid (H_2SO_4)

Multiple Choice

1. (a)
2. (a)
3. (a). This trend of decreasing first ionization energy going down the group prevails in all representative groups of the periodic table. Review Section 4–4.
4. (a). Remember that HF is the only one of the hydrohalic acids (binary acids involving halogens) that is not a strong acid.
5. (a). Notice that (b), (c), and (e) are listed as common weak acids. Sulfite ion, SO_3^{2-}, is listed as one of the anions derived from the weak acid H_2SO_3; this means that HSO_3^- must also be able to act as a weak acid.
6. (b)
7. (a)
8. (a)
9. (b)
10. (c)
11. (e). This method is applicable only to the Group IA metals and to the heavier Group IIA metals. Study Section 7–9.2.
12. (e)
13. (d). The oxidation number of C changes from $+2$ to $+4$, while the oxidation number of O changes from 0 (in O_2, the element) to -2. This is also a combination reaction.
14. (c)
15. (d)
16. (d). Determine the oxidation number of each element on both sides of the equation. Sulfur goes from -2 in H_2S to 0 in S (the free element).
17. (b). Remember that we often call the compound containing the element that is oxidized the reducing agent.
18. (c)
19. (d)

20. (e). No element undergoes a change in oxidation number. This is a metathesis reaction, and these are never oxidation-reduction reactions. However, the criterion of change in oxidation number is entirely foolproof and should always be used to determine whether a reaction is a redox reaction.
21. (d)
22. (d)
23. (c)
24. (b)
25. (d)

8

Gases and the Kinetic-Molecular Theory

Chapter Summary

For the past several chapters, we have been primarily concerned with the bonding, properties, and reactions of specific substances. In this chapter we begin a study of some aspects of the behavior of matter that are, to a certain extent, more dependent on the physical state of the substances than on their chemical identity. We are first concerned, in this chapter and the next, with pure substances in the three states of matter—gas, liquid, and solid—and then with a study of mixtures of substances. The introduction and first section of Chapter 8 point out some of the distinguishing characteristics of the gas, liquid, and solid states.

As you study this chapter, keep in mind the approach that we are following, outlined in Chapter 1 of this guide. We will first be concerned with the observable **macroscopic behavior** of gases, which we will then relate to proposed **molecular behavior.** As two examples of this approach, you see in Section 8–1 (1) that the characteristic observable property of gases having low density is taken as an indication that in gases the molecules are much further apart than in liquids or solids and (2) that the ability of gases to fill the container in which they are put and to diffuse and mix is interpreted as telling us that in gases the molecules, whatever else they might be doing, are in rapid motion. In Sections 8–2 through 8–12, we will be dealing almost entirely with measurable properties of gases and the observed relationships among these properties—such quantities as **density, pressure, volume,** amount of gas **(number of moles),** and **temperature.** Then in Section 8–13 we will try to interpret these relationships in terms of the kinetic-molecular theory. Throughout most of this chapter, we are helped in our study by the observation that, over many ranges of conditions, all gases behave the same. These are referred to as **ideal gases.** Only in Section 8–15 will we pay much attention to conditions for which this ideal behavior is not observed.

We begin our study of the properties pressure (P), volume (V), number of moles (n), and temperature (T) and the ways in which these are interrelated for typical gases. Of these properties, pressure is the one for which students often have the least prior understanding, so Section 8–3 gives an introduction to the concept of pressure and to some of the ways of measuring it. The general approach to interrelating such properties is to keep two of these variables constant and then to see how the other two are related. This means that many of the relationships in this chapter are valid only under certain conditions, so you *must* keep in mind the limitations of each one. As you study these various relationships, you should note the ways we represent them: (1) **In words.** You should be able to make a verbal statement of each relationship. It is of more importance that you understand this statement than that you just memorize it. Be certain that you know what you are saying when you use words like "proportional," "inversely," etc. (2) **In mathematical relationships.** Since we are dealing with quantitative relationships, we must be able to understand and use the equations that describe them. Thus, an important part of your understanding the relationships among the properties of gases is to learn to use them, in mathematical form, to solve problems. (3) **In graphs.** This pictorial way of representing mathematical relationships can also be a great help in understanding, remembering, and applying the relations.

In Section 8–4, we begin with the relationship between pressure and volume for a fixed amount of gas (constant n) at a fixed temperature (constant T), a relationship known as **Boyle's Law.** Of the various mathematical ways of representing this law, some are more useful than others. Since one of our uses of Boyle's Law is to relate some initial set of conditions of P and V to a final set of conditions of these two variables, one form that we usually find very useful is

$$P_1 V_1 = P_2 V_2 \qquad \text{(constant } n, T\text{)}.$$

Again, notice that the set of conditions to which this equation is limited must be observed. The relation $P_1 V_1 = P_2 V_2$ must not be expected to hold if the amount of gas changes (n not constant) or if the temperature changes (T not constant). Experimentally, we also find that the relationship

$$\frac{V_1}{T_1} = \frac{V_2}{T_2} \qquad \text{(constant } n, P\text{)},$$

known as **Charles' Law** (Section 8–6), describes the relation of volume and temperature of a gas, so long as we keep the amount of gas and the pressure of the gas constant. One important point to notice here is that in order for the relation to take this simple form, the temperature must be expressed on the **absolute** or **Kelvin scale** (Section 8–5). Be sure that you understand the rationale behind the establishment of this scale and its relation to other temperature scales. You should also keep in mind that the symbol T in chemistry always refers to the temperature measured on the Kelvin scale. The establishment of a set of conditions of T and P as **standard temperature**

and pressure (STP), as discussed in Section 8 – 7, facilitates a comparison of different gases.

In Section 8 – 8, we see how we can combine Boyle's and Charles' Laws into the **combined gas law,**

$$\frac{P_1 V_1}{T_1} = \frac{P_2 V_2}{T_2} \qquad \text{(constant } n\text{),}$$

which is quite convenient to use when several of the quantities P, V, and T change. A common use of this equation is to correct the description of a gas at some arbitrary set of conditions to those that would apply at STP.

One of the ways in which the behavior of gases is almost independent of the identity of the gas is that the volume occupied by 1 mole of the gas at STP, the so-called *standard molar volume,* is the same for all gases (Section 8 – 9). This is summarized in Avogadro's Law,

$$\frac{V_1}{n_1} = \frac{V_2}{n_2} \qquad \text{(constant } T, P\text{),}$$

which gives the basis for calculations relating volumes and amounts of gas at constant P and T. Since 1 mole of each different gas would have a different mass, different gases have different densities, even at the same conditions.

Each of the gas laws studied up until now is applicable only at certain conditions and covers only certain relationships. In addition, they are useful primarily to determine changes in one quantity, given changes in another. In Section 8 – 10, we see how we can combine all of these laws into a very useful relation, the **ideal gas law,** given by the equation

$$PV = nRT.$$

Be sure that you see the significance of the **gas law constant,** R. Its value does not depend on what gas the equation is being applied to, and it can be expressed in different sets of units (with, of course, different numerical values), depending on the units used to describe the other quantities in the equation. Since R is a constant, this equation allows us to predict the value of any one of the four quantities P, V, n, and T, given values for the other three.

An important use of the ideal gas equation, illustrated in Section 8 – 11, is the *experimental* determination of molecular weight by measurement of gas densities. Until now, you have seen the molecular weight, or formula weight, arrived at only by adding up the atomic weights of the atoms in the formula. This is the first of several methods you will learn for experimentally determining molecular weights even if the chemical formula is not known, so that we can determine formulas of unknown substances. (Watch for other such methods in this and succeeding chapters.) This determination may be carried out either by measuring the density at STP or by measuring it at some other condition and then correcting, via the gas laws already studied, to STP. This latter idea finds application in the Dumas method for determining molecular weights of **volatile** liquids, i.e., those that evaporate easily to form gases.

To this point, all that we have described about gases is independent of the identity of the gas, so we should not be too surprised that some aspects of the behavior of mixtures of gases (providing they do not react) are also quite simply described. **Dalton's Law** of partial pressures, Section 8 – 12, is such a description, based first on direct observation, but shown to be consistent with the ideal gas equation. One very useful application of this law is the calculation associated with the collection of a gas over water, which exerts a pressure by evaporating.

In Sections 8 – 4 through 8 – 12, we have been talking about observed properties of gases, with no reference to the properties or even the existence of molecules. We see that at the macroscopic level, all gases behave essentially the same. We now try to describe a molecular level of behavior — we assume that gas molecules behave in a certain way, to a good approximation, independently of chemical identity. We then see whether this molecular behavior is consistent with the observed macroscopic properties. The result is the **kinetic-molecular theory,** Section 8 – 13. Not only does this theory provide us with a molecular-level understanding of such quantities as pressure and temperature, it can be used to predict additional types of behavior. One such prediction is **Graham's Law** (Section 8 – 14), dealing with rates of diffusion of gases; this is the basis for another method of experimental determination of molecular weight of unknown gaseous compounds. Based on its consistency with observed macroscopic aspects of gases, we now believe that the kinetic-molecular theory gives a good description of how gas molecules act.

All of the discussion until now in this chapter has been applicable at high temperature (that is, quite a bit higher than the boiling point of the substances) and at low or moderate pressures. At those conditions, all gases behave alike. However, if the temperature is too low or the pressure too high, the gas molecules do not behave independently of one another, and this deviation from ideal behavior is different for different gases. To describe such **"real gases"** we must take two approaches (Section 8 – 15). One is to make up equations that "fit" the observed properties of such gases better at high P and low T than do the various ideal equations studied so far. One of these is the **van der Waals' equation,** which has in it two constants, a and b, that are different for every gas to which the equation is to be applied. The second approach, now at the molecular level, is to understand the deviations of different gases from ideal behavior in terms of molecular properties such as molecular size and intermolecular attraction, both of which are insignificant at low P and high T.

In our study of stoichiometry in Chapter 2, we saw that the fundamental relationship among amounts of reactants and products is in terms of the numbers of moles. At that stage, the only way we had to "measure" the number of moles was in terms of the weight of the substance. Now we have seen that the volume of a gas at specified conditions of temperature and pressure is a measure of the number of moles present. In the closing part of the chapter, we use this as a basis to extend our study of stoichiometry, by relating the volume change accompanying a reaction to the changes in numbers of moles of gaseous reactants and products.

The importance of such studies is shown by the use of **Gay-Lussac's Law of Combining Volumes** (Section 8–16) to predict the volumes of gases involved in chemical reactions. This law provided the basis for Avogadro's important deductions about the diatomic nature of some gas molecules. Using the molecular weight, we can extend these ideas to deal with mass-volume relationships in reactions involving gases (Section 8–17).

Study Goals

Remember to practice many of the exercises suggested at the end of the text chapter. Be systematic in your solutions to numerical problems, writing down all steps and reasoning.

1. Summarize the general physical properties of gases. (Sections 8–1 and 8–2; Exercises 1 through 4)
2. Explain what pressure is and illustrate its measurement with (a) an inverted-tube mercury barometer and (b) a mercury barometer connected to a container of gas. (Section 8–3; Exercises 5 through 9)
3. State in words and in mathematical relationships the Laws of (a) Boyle, (b) Charles, (c) Graham, (d) Avogadro, (e) Dalton, and (f) Gay-Lussac. (Sections 8–4 through 8–6, 8–9, 8–12, 8–14 and 8–16; Exercises 10 through 13, 21 through 23, 36, 37, 60, 70, and 84)
4. Explain the basis of the absolute temperature scale. Be able to convert temperatures from other scales to the absolute scale. (Section 8–5; Exercises 19 and 20)
5. Perform calculations using the relationships of Study Goal 3 to relate volume changes, pressure changes, temperature changes, and changes in number of moles of gas. (Sections as listed for Study Goal 3; Exercises 10 through 18, 21 through 29, 36 through 44, 60 through 66, 70 through 76, and 85 through 88)
6. State the combined gas law in mathematical terms. (Section 8–8; Exercise 30)
7. Given, for a gaseous system, any five out of six variables (P_1, P_2, V_1, V_2, T_1, T_2), be able to solve for the value of the missing sixth variable. (Section 8–8; Exercises 30 through 35)
8. Be able to calculate the molecular weight of a pure gaseous substance,

given the density of the gas at any condition of temperature and pressure. Use this information to help determine the molecular (true) formula of a gaseous substance. (Section 8–11; Exercises 56 through 59)

9. State the ideal gas equation and its assumptions; derive the ideal gas equation from the combined gas laws. Perform calculations relating the variables in the ideal gas law. Given any three of the variables P, V, n, and T for a sample of ideal gas, be able to solve for the value of the other variable. (Section 8–10; Exercises 45 through 55)

10. Know the standard molar volume of an ideal gas. Relate the volume of a gas at a given set of temperature and pressure conditions to the number of moles (and grams) of the gas present. (Sections 8–9 and 8–10; Exercises 36 through 44)

11. Given the total pressure and composition of a mixture of gases, be able to solve for the partial pressure of each gas present in the mixture. (Section 8–12; Exercises 60 through 63)

12. Given the vapor pressure of water at various temperatures, be able to correct volumes and pressures of wet gases at specified temperatures and barometric pressures for the vapor pressure of water. (Section 8–12; Exercises 64 through 66)

13. State the assumptions of the kinetic-molecular theory. Account for the laws listed in Study Goal 3 in terms of the kinetic-molecular theory. (Section 8–13; Exercises 67 through 69)

14. Distinguish between real gases and ideal gases. Relate the van der Waals' equation to the ideal gas equation. Relate the van der Waals' constants a and b to deviations of molecular properties of the gases using the assumptions of the kinetic-molecular theory. (Section 8–15; Exercises 77 through 81)

15. Be able to use the van der Waals' equation to carry out calculations relating n, P, V, and T for real gases. Understand both when and why these results differ significantly from those predicted by the ideal gas equation. (Section 8–15; Exercises 81 through 83)

16. Be able to carry out calculations involving (a) volumes of gases involved in chemical reactions, and (b) mass-volume relationships for chemical reactions involving gases. (Sections 8–16 and 8–17; Exercises 84 through 96)

Some Important Terms in This Chapter

Write the meanings *in your own words*. Check the Key Terms list and the chapter reading. Then rewrite your definitions, still in your own words, to improve them. Study other new terms, and review terms from preceding chapters if necessary.

fluids

equation of state

absolute zero

Boyle's Law

Charles' Law

Avogadro's Law

Law of Combining Volumes (Gay-Lussac's Law)

standard conditions (STP or SC)

standard molar volume

kinetic-molecular theory

ideal gas

ideal gas law

universal gas constant

partial pressure

Law of Partial Pressures (Dalton's Law)

real gases

van der Waals' equation

Preliminary Test

This test will check your understanding of basic concepts and types of calculations. Be sure to then answer *many* of the additional textbook exercises; since they are more challenging than these preliminary test questions, they will give you additional insight into the meaning and applications of the ideas of this chapter. For all Preliminary Test questions in this chapter, assume that the gas referred to is acting ideally, unless you are told otherwise.

True-False

Mark each statement as true (T) or false (F).

_____ 1. Because the noble gases do not easily react to form compounds, they are present in a very high amount in the atmosphere.
_____ 2. All substances are less dense as gases than as liquids.
_____ 3. For any ideal gas, doubling the pressure would always cause the volume to decrease by a factor of two.
_____ 4. For any gas, whether ideal or not, doubling the pressure of a fixed amount of gas at a fixed temperature would cause the volume to decrease by a factor of two.
_____ 5. Doubling the temperature always doubles the volume of a fixed amount of ideal gas at constant pressure.

We have two identical containers. One is filled with hydrogen fluoride gas (HF) and the other is filled with neon gas (Ne). The two containers are at the same temperature and pressure. Questions 6 through 14 all refer to these two samples of gas. The atomic weights to be used for these questions are as follows: H = 1, F = 19, Ne = 20. For all of these questions except number 14, you may consider the gases to be ideal.

_____ 6. The two gas samples have the same number of molecules.
_____ 7. The two gas samples have the same number of atoms.
_____ 8. The two gas samples have the same total mass of gas.
_____ 9. The two gas samples have the same density.
_____ 10. The molecules in the two gas samples have the same average kinetic energy.
_____ 11. The molecules in the two gas samples have the same average velocity.
_____ 12. If the same size hole were opened in each container, the pressure in the neon container would decrease faster than the pressure in the hydrogen fluoride container.
_____ 13. If we were to remove all of the Ne from one box and put it into the other box with the HF, the molecules would mix so as to cause no change in total pressure in the second box.
_____ 14. If the same two gases were taken to the same low temperature and

the same very high pressure, we would expect HF to behave more ideally than Ne.

Short Answer

1. The pressure of 1 atmosphere is equal to _____ torr.
2. Expressed mathematically, Charles' Law may be written as _____.
3. The statement "The volumes of gases, measured at constant pressures and temperatures, involved in chemical reactions are in the ratios of small whole numbers" is a statement of _____ Law.
4. The statement "Equal volumes of gases at the same conditions of pressure and temperature contain equal numbers of molecules" is a statement of _____ Law.
5. Tripling the absolute temperature (in K) and doubling the pressure of a given volume of an ideal gas would result in a different volume of gas, which could be calculated by multiplying the original volume of the gas by a factor of ___.
6. To cause an ideal gas sample to change from a volume of 1.4 L to 4.2 L at constant temperature, the pressure must be changed to ___ times its initial value.
7. To cause an ideal gas sample to change from a volume of 1.4 L to 4.2 L at constant pressure, the absolute temperature must be changed to ___ times its initial value.
8. The zero of absolute temperature is taken as that temperature at which all gases would exhibit _____. Actually, before this temperature is reached, the gases would form _____ and then _____.
9. If 1.00 L of an ideal gas at 50°C is heated at constant pressure to 100°C, the new volume would be _____ L.
10. For one mole of an ideal gas, $PV/T =$ _____. (The answer is to be a number, with correct units.)
11. The conditions we refer to as standard temperature and pressure are _____ and _____.
12. A mixture of H_2 and O_2 is in a 6.00 L vessel. The partial pressure of H_2 in this mixture is 500 torr, and the partial pressure of O_2 is 250 torr. The volume that H_2 would occupy alone at these conditions of temperature and total pressure is ___ L.
13. The vapor pressure of water at 30°C is 31.8 torr. We collect hydrogen over water at 30°C until the total pressure of wet hydrogen is 1 atm. If we dried the hydrogen at the same temperature, the pressure it would exert would be _____ torr.
14. At STP, 1.00 L of a pure gaseous substance has a mass of 4.00 grams. The molecular weight of this substance is _____.
15. At standard temperature and pressure, 14.007 grams of nitrogen gas (considered ideal) occupies _____ L.
16. A sample of a pure gaseous substance occupying 4.1 L at 760 torr and

227°C is found to weigh 16.4 grams. The density of the substance under these conditions is _____ .

17. The molecular weight of the substance in Question 16 is ____.

18. If 1 L of gas X weighs 44 times as much as 1 L of H_2 at the same temperature and pressure, then the molecular weight of the gas X is ____.

19. One mole of chlorine gas weighs ____ grams, contains _____ molecules, contains _____ atoms, and occupies ____ L at 0°C and 1 atm.

20. In the kinetic-molecular description of gas behavior, the pressure is a result of _____ .

21. In the kinetic-molecular description of gas behavior, temperature is a measure of _____ .

22. The formula weight of SO_2 is 64 g/mol, while that of oxygen, O_2, is 32 g/mol. The rate of diffusion of SO_2 would be expected to be ____ (a number) times as great as the rate of diffusion of O_2.

23. A real gas behaves most nearly like an ideal gas at conditions of _____ and _____ .

24. In the van der Waals' equation describing real (nonideal) gases, the a term is related to the molecular property of _____ _____ .

Carbon disulfide, CS_2, burns according to the equation

$$CS_2 (\ell) + 3O_2 (g) \rightarrow CO_2 (g) + 2SO_2 (g).$$

The following three questions, 25 through 27, refer to the complete combustion of 1 mole of CS_2, according to this reaction.

25. The volume of O_2, measured at standard temperature and pressure (STP), required for the reaction is _____ .

26. The volume of CO_2, measured at STP, that would be produced is _____ .

27. The volume of SO_2, measured at STP, that would be produced is _____ .

28. The commercial preparation of ammonia is carried out by reaction of nitrogen and hydrogen:

$$N_2 (g) + 3H_2 (g) \rightarrow 2NH_3 (g).$$

In order to form 1000 L of ammonia gas, we would have to supply ____ L of nitrogen and ____ L of hydrogen, with all gases measured at the same temperature and pressure. (Treat the reaction as if it goes to completion.)

Multiple Choice

____ 1. Each of the following plots refers to the behavior of a sample of an ideal gas. Which plot is *not* correct?

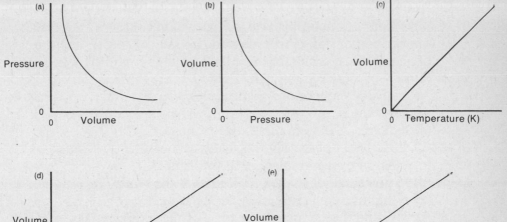

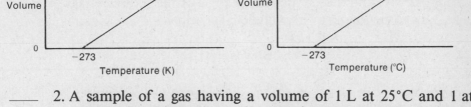

_____ 2. A sample of a gas having a volume of 1 L at 25°C and 1 atm pressure is subjected to an increase in pressure and a decrease in temperature. The density of the gas
   (a) decreases.
   (b) increases.
   (c) either increases or decreases, depending on the sizes of the pressure and temperature changes.
   (d) remains the same.
   (e) becomes zero.

_____ 3. A sample of a gas having a volume of 1 L at 25°C and 1 atm pressure is subjected to an increase in pressure and an increase in temperature. The volume of the gas
   (a) decreases.
   (b) increases.
   (c) either increases or decreases, depending on the sizes of the pressure and temperature changes.
   (d) remains the same.
   (e) becomes zero.

_____ 4. At the same temperature, the molecules of all gases have the same
   (a) average mass.
   (b) van der Waals' constants a and b.
   (c) average kinetic energies.
   (d) average velocities.
   (e) molecular diameters.

_____ 5. How many molecules of an ideal gas are contained in 8.2 L at −73°C and 0.5 atm?
   (a) 0.25   (b) 1.5×10^{23} (c) -4.1×10^{23} (d) 7.5×10^{23}
   (e) 4.2×10^{-25}

_____ 6. One liter of phosphorus gas reacts with 6 liters of hydrogen gas to form 4 liters of phosphine gas. All gas volumes are measured at the same conditions of temperature and pressure. What is the formula of phosphine? (Remember that the formula for phosphorus is P_4.)
(a) P   (b) P_2 (c) PH   (d) PH_2 (e) PH_3

_____ 7. At a given temperature, hydrogen molecules have an average velocity that is
(a) the same as oxygen molecules at the same T.
(b) 4 times that of oxygen molecules at the same T.
(c) $\frac{1}{4}$ that of oxygen molecules at the same T.
(d) 16 times that of oxygen molecules at the same T.
(e) $\frac{1}{16}$ that of oxygen molecules at the same T.

_____ 8. At 0°C and 1 atm pressure, which of the following gases would have the lowest average molecular velocity?
(a) NH_3 (b) CO_2 (c) Ar   (d) N_2 (e) H_2

_____ 9. Which of the following gases would diffuse most rapidly?
(a) CO_2 (b) O_2 (c) CH_4 (d) He   (e) N_2

_____ 10. Analysis of a gas gave 80% C, 20% H, by weight. A sample of the gas occupying 2.24 L at 0°C, 1 atm, is found to weigh 3.0 grams. Which one of the following substances could this gas be?
(a) Methane, CH_4 (b) Ethane, C_2H_6 (c) Ethylene, C_2H_4
(d) Acetylene, C_2H_2 (e) Benzene, C_6H_6

_____ 11. An 1120 mL sample of pure gaseous compound, measured at 0°C and 1 atm, is found to weigh 2.86 grams. The molecular weight of the compound is
(a) 2.86.   (b) 28.6.   (c) 5.72.   (d) 57.2   (e) 14.3

_____ 12. What volume of pure oxygen gas, O_2, measured at 546 K and 760 torr, is formed by complete dissociation of 0.200 mole of Ag_2O, according to the following reaction?

$$2Ag_2O \text{ (s)} \rightarrow 4Ag \text{ (s)} + O_2 \text{ (g)}$$

(a) 1.12 L   (b) 2.24 L   (c) 17.92 L   (d) 4.48 L
(e) 8.96 L

_____ 13. How many moles of $KClO_3$ are needed to form 2.8 L of O_2, measured at STP, according to the following reaction?

$$2KClO_3 \text{ (s)} \rightarrow 2KCl \text{ (s)} + 3O_2 \text{ (g)}$$

(a) $\frac{1}{12}$ mole   (b) $\frac{1}{6}$ mole   (c) $\frac{1}{3}$ mole   (d) $\frac{1}{4}$ mole   (e) $\frac{1}{2}$ mole

_____ 14. What volume of chlorine gas, measured at 0°C and 1 atm pressure, is needed to react completely with 5.61 grams of KOH in the following reaction?

$$Cl_2 \text{ (g)} + 2KOH \text{ (aq)} \rightarrow KCl \text{ (aq)} + KClO \text{ (aq)} + H_2O \text{ (}\ell\text{)}$$

(a) 0.56 L   (b) 1.12 L   (c) 2.24 L   (d) 4.48 L   (e) 22.4 L

_____ 15. One step in the industrial manufacture of nitric acid involves the production of nitric oxide by the oxidation of ammonia:

$$4NH_3 \text{ (g)} + 5O_2 \text{ (g)} \rightarrow 6H_2O \text{ (g)} + 4NO\text{(g)}.$$

We wish to produce 100 L of NO gas (measured at STP). How many liters of oxygen gas, also measured at STP, would be required?

(a) 100   (b) 125   (c) 22.4   (d) 100×22.4
(e) 125×22.4

Answers to Preliminary Test

True-False

1. False. See Table 8–2. In fact, these are sometimes referred to as the rare gases.
2. True
3. False. This is only true at constant temperature and for a fixed amount of gas.
4. False. Only for ideal gases. We cannot predict in general what the factor would be for other gases.
5. False. This is true only if the temperature is expressed on the absolute, or Kelvin, scale.
6. True
7. False
8. True. But only because these two particular gases have the same molecular weights.
9. True. Same comments as for Question 8.
10. True. This would be true even if the gases did not have the same molecular weights.
11. True. Same comments as for Question 8.
12. False. The two types of gas molecules have the same average velocity.
13. False. The pressure would double.
14. False. HF is more polar, so it would behave less ideally than Ne.

Short Answer

1. 760
2. $\dfrac{V_1}{T_1} = \dfrac{V_2}{T_2}$ (constant n, P). This is incorrect without the specification of its limitations.
3. Gay-Lussac's
4. Avogadro's

5. $\frac{3}{2}$. Remember that V is directly proportional to T and is inversely proportional to P.

6. $\frac{1}{3}$

7. 3

8. zero volume, liquids, solids

9. 1.15. Volume is proportional to Kelvin temperature, which changes from 323 K to 373 K. Either multiply old volume by 373/323 or use the mathematical formulation of Charles' Law with $V_1 = 1.00$ L, $T_1 = 323$ K, $T_2 = 373$ K.

10. 0.0821 $\dfrac{\text{liter atm}}{\text{K}}$. Other values, with the appropriate units, could also be correct.

11. 0°C, 1 atm

12. 4.00. Apply Dalton's Law. Since $\frac{2}{3}$ of the total pressure of the mixture is due to H_2, it must account for $\frac{2}{3}$ of the total number of moles. If we removed the O_2 ($\frac{1}{3}$ of the total moles) and adjusted to the same total pressure, the moles of H_2 would occupy $\frac{2}{3}$ of the original total volume.

13. 728.2. Of the total 760 torr (1 atm) exerted, 31.8 torr is due to water vapor, so only $760 - 31.8 = 728.2$ torr would be due to hydrogen.

14. 89.6. One mole is the amount that would occupy 22.4 L at STP. This would weigh 22.4×4.0 grams, or 89.6 grams.

15. 11.2. Remember that nitrogen is diatomic, so 14.007 grams is only $\frac{1}{2}$ mole. Each mole occupies 22.4 L at STP.

16. 4.0 g/L

17. 164. Apply $PV = nRT$, with $T = 227 + 273 = 500$ K; $P = 760$ torr $= 1$ atm; $V = 4.1$ liters; to find the amount of substance present in 0.10 mole. This weighs 16.4 grams, so molecular weight $= (16.4$ g$)/(0.1$ mole$) = 164$ g/mole.

18. 88

19. 71.0, 6.022×10^{23} (molecules), 1.204×10^{24} (atoms), 22.4

20. collision of molecules with the walls of the container

21. average molecular kinetic energy

22. $\sqrt{\frac{1}{2}}$

23. high T, low P

24. intermolecular attraction. The b term is related to the size of the molecules.

25. 67.2 L

26. 22.4 L

27. 44.8 L

28. 500, 1500. Apply Gay-Lussac's Law.

Multiple Choice

1. (d)
2. (b)

3. (c)

4. (c)

5. (b). Use the ideal gas law to determine the number of moles. Then remember that there are 6.0×10^{23} molecules/mole (Avogadro's number).

6. (e)

7. (b). Hydrogen molecules weigh $2.0/32.0 = \frac{1}{16}$ times as much as O_2 molecules. Thus their average velocity is proportional to

$$\sqrt{1/\text{molecular weight}}, \text{ or } \sqrt{1/(\tfrac{1}{16})} = \sqrt{16} = 4.$$

8. (b). All have the same average kinetic energy; CO_2 has the highest molecular weight, so it would be moving slowest at the same kinetic energy.

9. (d)

10. (b). You can answer this by determining the simplest formula (as in Chapter 2) to be CH_3. The data about gas volume can be used to show that the molecular weight is 30 g/mol.

11. (d)

12. (d). The 0.100 mole O_2 formed would occupy 0.100×22.4 L at 273 K, 1 atm. Corrected to 546 K and 1 atm, it would occupy 4.48 liters. Alternatively, use the ideal gas law to find the volume of the 0.100 mole of O_2 at the desired temperature and pressure.

13. (a). 2.8 L (at STP) is $2.8/22.4$ mol $= \frac{1}{8}$ mol. According to the stoichiometry of the reaction, this would require $\frac{1}{12}$ mole. Use unit factors.

14. (b)

15. (b)

9

Liquids and Solids

Chapter Summary

In the preceding chapter, we learned about the properties of gases, and then were able to understand these observed properties in terms of the behavior of the molecules that make up the gas—the kinetic-molecular theory. In Chapter 9, we will learn in the same way about the two **condensed phases** or states of matter, liquids and solids, and also about qualitative and quantitative aspects of changes among these three states of matter. The most important difference, in molecular terms, between gases on the one hand and liquids and solids on the other is that in liquids and solids the molecules are so close together that they can interact quite strongly, while in gases they are so far apart that their interactions are very slight. In these terms, using the kinetic-molecular theory, we will be able to understand differences in properties among these three states of matter, which were mentioned in Section 8–1 and are systematically listed in the introduction to Chapter 9.

As you learn about solids and liquids in this chapter, notice that we have several different goals in mind. One is to understand the properties of liquids by describing what the molecules are doing and how they interact. Another is to gain a similar understanding of properties of solids relative to their molecular and ionic interactions. A third aspect of our study deals with phase changes—liquid $\rightleftharpoons$ gas, solid $\rightleftharpoons$ liquid, and solid $\rightleftharpoons$ gas. Notice that in discussing this last aspect, either just descriptively or quantitatively, we use our understanding of molecular properties in the individual states involved. For example, we have concluded from a study of their observed properties (Chapter 8) that in gases the molecules are far apart and have very little attraction for one another. In this chapter, we will see that properties such as high density, surface tension, and viscosity tell us that in liquids the molecules are so close together that their attractions for one another are very strong and very important in determining properties. When we then try to understand evaporation or boiling, which both involve a substance changing from a liquid to a gas, we must think about the amount of energy that we have put in to overcome the attractive forces in the liquid and so convert it to a gas.

The extension of the ideas of the kinetic-molecular theory to apply to liquids and solids (Section 9–1) will provide us with the basis for our discussion of Chapter 9. In the first few sections of the chapter, we see the relation of such observed macroscopic properties of a liquid as **viscosity**

(9–2), **surface tension** (9–3), and **capillary action** (9–4) to the intermolecular attractions. The next several sections are concerned primarily with a descriptive presentation of changes from liquid to gas. When the kinetic energy of a molecule near the surface of a liquid is great enough to overcome the attraction of its neighbors, it can **evaporate** or **vaporize;** conversely, gas molecules with little enough kinetic energy can **condense** (Section 9–5). If the container is closed, the two processes eventually occur at equal rates, and the **vapor pressure** (Section 9–6) characteristic of the liquid at that temperature is established. Pay very close attention to the ideas of **dynamic equilibrium** and the **LeChatelier's Principle** that are presented here, because these will be central to our understanding of many equilibrium situations, including chemical reactions. Section 9–7 deals with a related phenomenon — **boiling** — and with the use of differences in boiling point from one substance to another to separate components of a liquid mixture — **distillation.**

We now begin a quantitative consideration of some of the energy changes involved in heating substances and in their phase changes. Why, in molecular terms, does the energy change? Remember that increasing the temperature of a substance means increasing the average kinetic energy of its molecules. So to raise the temperature of a substance, we must put in energy, often in the form of heat (we speak of "heating the substance"). Likewise, in order for a liquid to evaporate, the kinetic energy of its molecules must be raised sufficiently to overcome the attractive forces between molecules. Again, this is done by putting in heat. In Section 9–8, we learn to do several kinds of calculations with heat transfer involving liquids. Before beginning that section, you will probably want to review the units and measurement of heat, Section 1–13. The amount of heat required to raise the temperature of a substance by a certain amount is expressed as the **specific heat** or the **molar heat capacity** of the substance; the quantity of heat needed to cause vaporization of a liquid is the **heat of vaporization,** which may be expressed on a molar basis.

The properties of liquids and solids depend on **intermolecular** forces of attraction. These forces may be classified (Section 9–9) as **ion-ion interactions, dipole-dipole interactions, hydrogen bonding,** and **London forces.** The different types of forces vary greatly in their strengths, but they have a great influence on melting and boiling points, heats of fusion, vaporization, and many other physical properties of substances, as summarized in Table 9–5. An understanding of these attractive forces will also aid in understanding properties of solutions as discussed in Chapter 10.

In a similar way, the process of melting (and the reverse, freezing) involves a change of state between liquid and solid. When these two processes are in equilibrium, again a dynamic one, the substance is at its **melting point** (Section 9–10). Melting must be accomplished, in molecular terms, by putting in enough heat energy for the molecules or ions to overcome the strong attractions that hold them in their fixed positions in the solid. Terms analogous to those we have already seen are used to describe the heat transfer involving solids — the **specific heat** and **molar heat capacity** of a solid, as well as its **heat of fusion,** again often on a molar basis (Section 9–11). The corresponding transitions from solid to gas **(sublimation)** and gas to solid **(deposition)** and the related idea of the vapor pressure of solids are discussed in Section 9–12. One very useful way of summarizing much data regarding phase transitions for any pure substance is the **phase diagram,** Section 9–13. As you learn to interpret this diagram for various substances, it will help to remember that all points along any horizontal line in the diagram are at the same pressure, while all points along any vertical line are at the same temperature.

As discussed in Section 9–14, solids may be either **amorphous** (lacking internal regularity) or **crystalline.** This latter class, which is characterized by a regularly repeating pattern of molecules or ions, somewhat like a three-dimensional wallpaper pattern, comprises most solids. Because of the regularity of crystalline solids, they are rather easy to describe and understand in a systematic way. Much of our information about the structure of solids comes from studying them by the technique of x-**ray diffraction.** In this method, the scattering of the x-rays (very short-wavelength light) by the regularly repeating arrays of atoms leads to interference of the rays. Analysis of the directions and intensities of these scattered rays has led us to an understanding of the three-dimensional structure of solids. Because many solids are composed of molecules or complex ions, this method has provided one of our major sources of information about the three-dimensional structures of molecules and polyatomic ions, which we learn about in Chapter 5.

Section 9–15 discusses the various patterns by which atoms, ions, or molecules may be arranged in crystals. The principal point here is that even though there are many different kinds of particles to be arranged in different solids, the requirement that they be regularly arranged in a repeating pattern in the crystal means that only a few types of *arrangements* are possible. These are the seven crystal systems, given in Table 9–8, which lists the restrictions on the shapes of the possible box **(unit cell)** by which the structure repeats. It is important to realize that this is just an imaginary box that describes the size and shape of the repeating unit — the repeating unit itself consists of atoms, molecules, or ions arranged in a particular way.

We often classify crystalline solids depending on the types of particles making up the lattice and the type and strength of the bonding or interactions among them. These categories are summarized in Table 9–9 and discussed in detail with examples in Section 9–16.

(1) In **molecular solids,** the fundamental unit of the crystal is a molecule. Each molecule contains strong covalent bonds, but the molecules interact in the solid only weakly, giving these solids their characteristic properties.

(2) **Covalent solids** are those in which the atoms are covalently bonded

together over many unit cells. Examples of these are diamond, graphite, quartz, and many minerals.

(3) **Ionic solids** consist of extended arrays of ions, with very strong attractions for one another, because of the arrangement in which each positive ion has as its nearest neighbors negative ions, and vice versa. As has already been emphasized in Chapter 4, these substances do not consist of molecules. A determination of the size and shape of the repetitive pattern of such substances can often give information about ionic sizes, as shown in the various examples of the section.

(4) In **metallic solids,** the metal atoms occupy lattice sites, with valence electrons free to move throughout the array of atoms. The details of the resulting properties of these metallic solids are well understood in terms of this electronic structure, formalized as the **band theory** of metallic solids (Section 9 – 17).

Study Goals

There are many important ideas and skills in this chapter. If you concentrate on them in the following groups, it will help you to organize your study. Answer as many of the text questions as you can.

1. Compare and contrast the properties of gases, liquids, and solids. (Introduction; Exercises 1, 8, and 9)
2. Apply the kinetic-molecular theory to explain the similarities and differences in properties of the three states of matter. (Section 12 – 1; Exercises 2, 7, and 13)
3. Describe and illustrate the following terms concerning liquids: (a) viscosity, (b) surface tension, (c) cohesive and adhesive forces, (d) capillary action, (e) evaporation and condensation, (f) vapor pressure, (g) boiling point, and (h) distillation. (Sections 9 – 2 through 9 – 7; Exercises 10 through 14 and 17 through 19)
4. Describe each of the following kinds of intermolecular interactions: (a) ion-ion interactions, (b) dipole-dipole interactions, (c) hydrogen bonding, and (d) London forces. (Section 9 – 9; Exercise 3)
5. Understand the significance of the types of intermolecular forces in Study Goal 4 in determining such properties as those listed in Study Goal 3. (Section 9 – 9; Exercises 4 through 6, 15 through 17, and 20 through 22)
6. Describe and illustrate the following terms concerning solids: (a) melting point, (b) fusion and solidification, and (c) sublimation and deposition. Understand the significance of the types of intermolecular forces in Study Goal 4 in determining these properties of solids. (Sections 9 – 10 through 9 – 12)

7. Be able to write equations for reactions that are phase transitions. (Section 9–7, 9–10, and 9–12; Exercise 24)

8. Be able to use the kinetic-molecular theory to describe the heat flow that accompanies changes of temperature and phase transitions. (Sections 9–8 and 9–11; Exercise 23)

9. Given the appropriate heat capacities or heats of fusion, vaporization or sublimation of a substance, be able to relate energy (heat) gain or loss to the temperature changes and phase transitions of the substance. (Sections 9–8 and 9–11; Exercises 25 through 35)

10. Be able to interpret phase diagrams. (Section 9–13; Exercises 36 through 40)

11. Distinguish between amorphous and crystalline solids. Describe a glass as a supercooled liquid, as distinguished from a true solid. (Section 9–14; Exercises 41, 43, and 44)

12. Illustrate the fundamental ideas underlying X-ray diffraction by crystals. (Section 9–14; Exercises 45 and 53)

13. Characterize the seven crystal systems by names and patterns of axial lengths and interaxial angles. (Section 9–15)

14. Given a picture or description of a unit cell and its contents, determine the number of atoms, ions, or molecules per unit cell. (Section 9–15; Exercises 50 through 52)

15. Sketch the three kinds of cubic lattices. (Section 9–15; Exercises 55 through 57)

16. Classify solids into one of the following four categories and summarize the distinguishing characteristics of these classes: (a) molecular solids, (b) covalent solids, (c) ionic solids, and (d) metallic solids. (Section 9–16; Exercises 47 through 49)

17. Describe and distinguish between the close-packed crystal structures. (Section 9–15; Exercise 56)

18. Perform calculations to relate unit cell data to such quantities as atomic and ionic radii and volumes, densities of solids, and the number of particles per unit cell. (Section 9–16; Exercises 60 through 70)

19. Describe metallic bonding in terms of band theory. (Section 9–15; Exercises 71 through 73)

20. Use band theory to describe electrical conductors, nonconductors (insulators), and semiconductors. (Section 9–16); Exercises 71 through 73)

Some Important Terms in This Chapter

This chapter has a very large number of new terms, many of which will be used in subsequent chapters. This is only a partial list, so be sure you study others as well. Write the meanings *in your own words*. Check the Key Terms list and the chapter reading. Then rewrite your definitions, still in your own words, to improve them. Study other new terms, and review terms from preceding chapters if necessary.

vapor pressure

boiling point (distinguish from normal boiling point)

intramolecular forces

intermolecular forces

ion-ion interactions

dipole-dipole interactions

hydrogen bond

London forces

crystalline solid

molecular solid

covalent solid

ionic solid

metallic solid

enthalpy of fusion (and molar enthalpy of fusion)

enthalpy of vaporization (and molar enthalpy of vaporization)

LeChatelier's Principle

dynamic equilibrium

metallic bonding

band

conduction band

forbidden zone

Preliminary Test

As in other chapters, this test will check your understanding of some basic concepts and types of calculations. Be sure to practice *many* of the additional textbook exercises.

Short Answer

1. The much lower compressibility of solids and liquids compared with gases tells us that in these condensed phases the molecules are _____ than in gases.
2. Forces between molecules within a liquid are called _____ forces.
3. Forces between molecules of a liquid and its container are called _____ forces.
4. Because the forces acting on molecules at the surface of a liquid are not equal in all directions, the liquid exhibits a property known as _____.
5. The movement of a liquid up a tube of small diameter is called _____; this occurs when the _____ exceed the _____.
6. Forces between particles of a substance are referred to, in general, as _____ forces, while those within molecules are called _____ forces.

7. Two liquids that are able to mix and produce a homogeneous solution are referred to as being _____ .

8. When two liquids mix spontaneously, the process is called _____ .

9. The process of diffusion is much _____ in liquids than it is in gases.

10. When a liquid is evaporating just as fast as its vapor is condensing, a state of _____ is said to exist; the pressure exerted by the gas at this condition is said to be the _____ of the liquid.

11. For a pure substance at any pressure, the temperature at which the vapor pressure is equal to the applied pressure is called the _____ of the liquid; if the pressure is 1 atm, this temperature is termed the _____ .

12. The vapor pressure of a liquid at 25°C is 200 torr. If the atmospheric pressure over the liquid is lowered to 200 torr at 25°C, the liquid will _____ .

13. Substance A has a greater tendency to evaporate at a given temperature than does substance B. We describe substance A as being more _____ than substance B. We also expect that the _____ _____ of A would be higher and that its _____ _____ would be lower.

14. The amount of heat required to melt 1 gram of a substance is called the _____ of the substance; the amount of heat required to melt 1 mole of the substance would be called the _____ _____ of the substance.

15. For any substance at a given temperature, the molar heat of vaporization must equal the _____ .

16. In order to convert the specific heat of a substance into its molar heat capacity, we would have to _____ by the _____ .

17. Because of the highly polar nature of the bonds, we should expect the molar heat of vaporization of HF to be considerably _____ than that of F_2 .

18. Even though both are gases at room temperature, we would expect the temperature at which CH_4 would condense to a liquid to be _____ than that for NH_3 .

19. The abnormally high boiling and melting points of water compared with H_2S, H_2Se, and H_2Te are attributable to the presence of _____ _____ in water.

20. Consider the substances $CaCl_2$, PH_3, N_2, Cl_2, and NH_3. The order of increasing boiling points of these substances is _____ _____ .

21. The two substances CO and N_2 have the same molecular weight, 28. It is observed that the molar heat of fusion of carbon monoxide is higher than that of nitrogen. The reason for this is the _____ of the CO molecules.

22. Hydrogen bonds are really a very strong form of _____ _____ .

23. The temperature at which the solid and liquid phases of a substance are in equilibrium with one another is called the _____ of the substance.
24. The set of conditions, at a particular pressure, at which the solid and gaseous states of a substance can exist in equilibrium is called the _____ of the substance.
25. The set of conditions at which a substance can exist simultaneously as solid, liquid, and gas in equilibrium is called the _____ of the substance.
26. A solid that shows no, or only limited, order on the molecular scale is called _____.
27. The melting points of ionic crystals are generally _____ than those of molecular crystals.
28. Two examples of substances that form covalent crystals are _____ and _____.
29. A method that is used for the study of atomic arrangements in solids is _____.
30. In a single layer of spheres of equal size, arranged in a close-packed arrangement, the number of nearest neighbors of each sphere is ____.
31. In a three-dimensionally close-packed arrangement of spheres of equal size, each sphere has ____ nearest neighbors.
32. In the NaCl structure, each Cl^- ion is surrounded by ____ nearest neighbors, each of which is a _____.
33. Two types of defects in the structures of crystalline solids that affect the properties of the solids are _____ and _____ _____.

Multiple Choice

____ 1. A drop of liquid has a spherical shape due to the property of
(a) surface tension.   (b) capillary action.   (c) viscosity.
(d) vapor pressure.   (e) close packing.

____ 2. As a liquid is heated, its vapor pressure
(a) does not change.   (b) increases.   (c) decreases.
(d) disappears.   (e) may increase or decrease, depending on the liquid.

____ 3. When the external pressure is decreased, the boiling point of a liquid
(a) does not change.   (b) increases.   (c) decreases.
(d) disappears.   (e) may increase or decrease, depending on the liquid.

____ 4. If energy, in the form of heat, is added to a pure liquid substance at its boiling point, while keeping the pressure constant, the
(a) temperature will increase.
(b) temperature will decrease.

(c) temperature will remain constant until all of the liquid has vaporized.

(d) temperature of the vapor will be greater than the temperature of the liquid.

(e) temperature of the liquid will be greater than the temperature of the vapor.

5. As we increase the temperature of a liquid, its properties change. Which of the following would *not* be an expected change in the properties of a liquid as we increase its temperature?

(a) decrease in viscosity

(b) decrease in density

(c) increase in surface tension

(d) increase in vapor pressure

(e) increase in tendency to evaporate

6. The vapor pressure of all liquids

(a) is the same at 100°C.

(b) is the same at their freezing points.

(c) increases with volume of liquid present.

(d) decreases with the increasing volume of the container.

(e) increases with temperature.

7. On a relative basis, the weaker the intermolecular forces in a substance,

(a) the larger its heat of vaporization.

(b) the more it deviates from the ideal gas law.

(c) the greater its vapor pressure.

(d) the larger its molar heat capacity as a liquid.

(e) the higher its melting point.

8. It is found that 600 joules of heat are required to melt 15 grams of a compound. What is the heat of fusion of this compound?

(a) 600×10 J/g   (b) $\dfrac{600 \times 15}{1000}$ kJ/g   (c) $\dfrac{600 \times 1000}{15}$ kJ/g

(d) 600/15 J/g   (e) cannot be answered without knowing the specific heat of solid substance

9. Substances have properties that are related to their structures. Which of the following statements regarding properties of substances is *not* expected to be correct?

(a) Molten KBr should be a good conductor of electricity.

(b) Diamond should have a high melting point.

(c) Solid sodium should be a good conductor of electricity.

(d) Solid CO_2 should have a low melting point.

(e) Solid K_2SO_4 should sublime readily.

10. Which of the following, in the solid state, would be an example of a molecular crystal?

(a) carbon dioxide   (b) diamond   (c) barium fluoride

(d) iron   (e) none of the preceding

_____ 11. Which of the following, in the solid state, would be an example of a covalent crystal?
(a) carbon dioxide   (b) diamond   (c) barium fluoride
(d) iron   (e) none of the preceding

_____ 12. Which of the following, in the solid state, would be an example of an ionic crystal?
(a) carbon dioxide   (b) diamond   (c) barium fluoride
(d) iron   (e) none of the preceding

_____ 13. Which of the following, in the solid state, would be an example of a metallic crystal?
(a) carbon dioxide   (b) diamond   (c) barium fluoride
(d) iron   (e) none of the preceding

_____ 14. The number of nearest neighbors of each atom in the face-centered cubic crystalline arrangement is
(a) 4.   (b) 6.   (c) 8.   (d)12.   (e) 16.

_____ 15. The unit-cell constants for a particular crystalline compound were determined by x-ray diffraction to be $a = 12.52$ Å, $b = 5.67$ Å, $c = 12.88$ Å, $\alpha = 90.8°$, $\beta = 98.2°$, $\gamma = 101.3°$. What is the crystal system for this compound?
(a) cubic   (b) orthorhombic   (c) tetragonal
(d) monoclinic   (e) triclinic

_____ 16. A hypothetical metal, atomic weight 60, forms a simple cubic crystal. The nearest distance between centers of adjacent atoms is 2.0 Å. What is the density of the crystalline material?
(a) 12.43 g/cm³   (b) 2.54 g/cm³   (c) 62.16 g/cm³
(d) 124.3 g/cm³   (e) 1.24 g/cm³

Questions 17 through 20 refer to the following phase diagram, which is for a hypothetical substance.

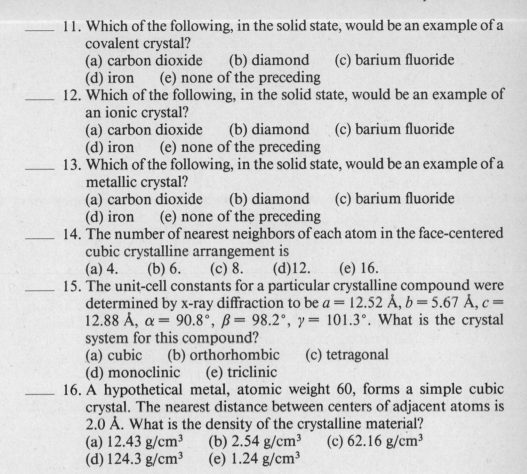

_____ 17. Where would you find the conditions necessary for the existence of a solid as a single phase?
(a) Region F   (b) Region G   (c) Region H
(d) Along line AE   (e) Along line AC

_____ 18. The normal boiling temperature of the substance is indicated in the figure by which of the following letters?
(a) A   (b) B   (c) C   (d) J   (e) L

_____ 19. In the figure, the point A is the
(a) triple point.   (b) critical point.   (c) normal freezing point.
(d) normal boiling point.   (e) point of maximum density.

_____ 20. Which of the following represents a pressure below which the substance cannot exist as a liquid?
(a) K   (b) B   (c) L   (d) D   (e) I

_____ 21. Which of the following is the band theory explanation for the conduction of electricity by metals?
(a) The occupied band of molecular orbitals overlaps a vacant conduction band of lower energy.
(b) The forbidden zone becomes polarized.
(c) Addition of electron-rich impurities by doping causes the conduction.
(d) The conduction band is fully occupied.
(e) The occupied band is either partially filled or overlaps a conduction band of higher energy.

Answers to Preliminary Test

Short Answer

1. much closer together
2. cohesive
3. adhesive
4. surface tension
5. capillary action, adhesive forces, cohesive forces
6. intermolecular, intramolecular
7. miscible
8. diffusion
9. slower
10. equilibrium, vapor pressure
11. boiling point, normal boiling point
12. boil
13. volatile, vapor pressure, boiling point
14. heat of fusion, molar heat of fusion

15. molar heat of condensation
16. multiply, formula weight (or molecular weight)
17. higher
18. lower. NH_3 is polar, with strong intermolecular attractions due to hydrogen bonds. Remember that the temperature at which the gas condenses to a liquid is the same as that at which the liquid boils. Thus, you can apply the reasoning of Section 9–9 to questions such as this.
19. hydrogen bonding
20. $N_2 < Cl_2 < PH_3 < NH_3 < CaCl_2$. Reason as follows: $CaCl_2$ is ionic, so it has the highest boiling point. NH_3 and PH_3 are both covalent molecules, but NH_3 is more polar and can undergo hydrogen bonding, so it boils at a higher temperature than PH_3. Nonpolar N_2 boils at a lower temperature than the heavier nonpolar Cl_2.
21. polar nature. This causes us to have to supply more energy to overcome the dipole-dipole interactions between CO molecules.
22. dipole-dipole interaction
23. melting point. Note that the melting point of a substance changes with pressure much less than the boiling point. Can you see that in the phase diagram of Figure 9–16?
24. sublimation point
25. triple point
26. amorphous
27. higher
28. Several answers would be correct here. Among these are diamond, graphite, quartz, and many minerals.
29. x-ray diffraction
30. 6
31. 12
32. 6, Na^+ ion
33. vacancies, substitutions of different types of atoms

Multiple Choice

1. (a)
2. (b)
3. (c)
4. (c)
5. (c). In general, at higher temperature, the molecules are less able to attract one another. This *would* cause the results listed in (a), (b), (d), and (e) to occur, along with a decrease in surface tension.
6. (e)
7. (c). Weaker forces between molecules would make it easy to evaporate (*lower* heat of vaporization, *higher* vapor pressure), would make it obey the ideal gas law better, would make it easier to move the molecules past

one another in the liquid (smaller molar heat capacity), and would make it easier to melt.

8. (d)

9. (e). KBr and K_2SO_4 are ionic solids, diamond is a covalent solid, Na is a metallic solid, and CO_2 is a molecular solid. See the characteristics of these types of solids listed in Table 9–9.

10. (a)

11. (b)

12. (c)

13. (d)

14. (d)

15. (e)

16. (a). This problem is similar to Example 9–9, except that the simple cubic cell contains only one metal atom (eight corners, each with only $\frac{1}{8}$ atom).

17. (a)

18. (b)

19. (a)

20. (e)

21. (e)

10

Solutions

Chapter Summary

Much of our study of substances and their properties has been of pure elements and compounds. However, since substances usually occur in mixtures, their properties are often affected by the presence of other substances, and so in Chapter 10 we will study solutions and their properties. The importance of solutions in some common processes is indicated in the chapter introduction, along with a reminder of some of the terminology by which we refer to the components of the solution (review Section 2–13). The first major portion of the chapter, Sections 10–1 through 10–7, deals descriptively with the ways in which substances interact to form solutions. While in general terms, a solution can be in any phase—solid, liquid, or gas—most of our study in this chapter will be of liquid solutions.

Throughout this chapter, we continue our general theme of attempting to understand macroscopic properties as resulting from the properties and interactions of molecules and ions. The general ideas introduced in Section 10–1, that a process is favored (1) by a **decrease in energy** and (2) by an **increase in randomness or disorder,** will be the subject of a much more detailed consideration in Chapter 13. As we see in the generalities of this section, we can better understand the dissolution process if we keep in mind the various kinds of attractions that occur on the molecular level: solute-solute attractions, solvent-solvent attractions, and solute-solvent attractions. Thus, the stronger the solute-solute interactions and the stronger the solvent-solvent interactions, the more each kind of species will tend to stay together, and the less **soluble** or **miscible** the substances will be. Conversely, very strong solvent-solute interactions can favor the dissolution process. To mention just one example here, the strong electrostatic attractions in an ionic solid and the strong attractions due to hydrogen bonding in water can be overcome by the even stronger interactions (**hydration**) between ions and water, so that many ionic substances are quite soluble in water. On the other hand, even though the molecules of a nonpolar hydrocarbon like benzene have relatively weak attractions for one another, they are not able to **solvate** the ions (strong solute-solute interaction, weak solvent-solvent interaction, very weak solvent-solute interaction), so that ionic substances are generally quite insoluble in benzene and other hydrocarbons. This general approach will help you to systematize the material in Sections 10–2 through 10–4, which deals with the dissolution of solids, liquids, and gases in liquids.

Throughout these sections, pay attention to the various factors that help to determine the strengths of the interactions — such features as charge density of ions, hydrogen bonding in liquids, dipole-dipole interactions, relative sizes of solute and solvent particles, and the tendency of some covalent substances to ionize in solution.

In Section 10–5 we see another application of some ideas first encountered in Chapter 9 regarding equilibrium. The **rate of dissolution** of a solute in a solvent, which depends on such factors as surface area, is opposed by the **rate of crystallization,** the rate at which dissolved solute particles form crystals of undissolved solid. When these two rates are equal, a state of **dynamic equilibrium** exists. At that point, the solution is **saturated.** Again, be sure you realize that it is incorrect to describe this state of equilibrium as a situation where "nothing is happening"; on the molecular and ionic level, much is happening, but there is *no net change* in the amount of dissolved solute.

The effects of temperature and pressure on solubility are summarized and related to molecular-level behavior in Sections 10–6 and 10–7. Pressure changes generally have a significant effect only on the solubility of gases in liquids; this relationship is quantitatively summarized in **Henry's Law.** It is important to understand the effects of temperature and pressure on solubility in terms of *LeChatelier's Principle,* which was introduced in Chapter 9.

We have now dealt descriptively with the factors that affect solubility. The next several sections of the chapter are concerned (1) with describing how much solute is contained in a certain amount of solution or solvent and (2) with studying some solution properties that are closely related to concentration. Before beginning this portion of the chapter, you should review Section 2–13, which discusses some methods for expressing solution concentrations. Two of these methods are further explained in Sections 10–8 and 10–9. Two more methods, **molality** and **mole fraction,** are introduced in Sections 10–10 and 10–11. All of the various methods for expressing concentrations must be learned, and you should become comfortable with the mathematical manipulations associated with each, since different methods are useful in different applications in chemistry.

A number of physical properties of solutions depend on the *number* and not on the *kind* of solute particles; these are called **colligative properties.** The four colligative properties are **vapor pressure lowering, freezing point depression, boiling point elevation,** and **osmotic pressure.** Be sure you notice that vapor pressure, melting (freezing) point, and boiling point are *not* colligative properties — *changes* in these, depression of the first two, elevation of the latter, are considered colligative properties. As you study the next several sections dealing with the colligative properties, it will be helpful for you to notice the various reasons for the study. Certainly, one reason is to be able to *describe* the behavior, both verbally and mathematically where possible. A second reason is to be able to *understand* this behavior in terms of the interactions between molecules and ions. A third objective of this study is to be able to *use* these properties. Uses such as separation of mixtures by **fractional distillation** and **reverse osmosis,** intentional alteration of the freezing and boiling points of fluids such as the coolant in automobile radiators, experimental determination of the degree of ionization (relative strength) of electrolytes, and additional methods for the experimental determination of molecular weight are discussed in this chapter. Notice that the latter two uses really illustrate the utility of the colligative properties: that they depend quantitatively on the particles in solution and not on the kind of particles. Sections 10-11 through 10-20 discuss the colligative properties, their interpretation, and their uses.

The last portion of the chapter, Sections 10-21 through 10-24, discusses **colloids,** those mixtures that may be viewed as intermediate between homogeneous and heterogeneous. In colloids, the dispersed particles are larger than in true solutions, so the mixture is not entirely homogeneous, but they are too small to settle out, so it is not truly heterogeneous either. These dispersed particles may be either collections of molecules or ions, or may be individual large molecules such as proteins. Table 10-4 summarizes the various types of colloids and important examples of each. Colloids are frequently recognized by their ability to scatter light, the Tyndall effect discussed in Section 10-21. Since colloids really consist of finely divided particles with much surface area, their properties are understood in terms of surface phenomena, such as **adsorption,** Section 10-22. The interactions that keep the colloidal particles suspended or dispersed depend on what the colloidal particle is composed of. Thus, we often classify colloids as **hydrophilic** or **hydrophobic,** depending on whether or not they interact with water so as to remain suspended. Examples of these two important classes of colloids are discussed in Section 10-23, which emphasizes some useful characteristics of the colloidal state. Removal of colloidal particles from unwanted colloids, such as smoke and water supplies containing large amounts of clay, is discussed in Section 10-24. As you study this last segment of the chapter, you will recognize that colloids are involved in many problems of biological and ecological significance.

Study Goals

Write your own outline of the ideas presented in each study goal. Exercises at the end of the text chapter are indicated for your study.

1. Describe and distinguish among (a) solvent, solute, and solution; (b) solution and colloid. (Introduction to chapter; introduction to colloids; Exercise 75)
2. Give several examples of various kinds of solutions and colloids, involv-

ing different combinations of solids, liquids, and gases as dispersing medium and dispersed substance. (Introduction to chapter; introduction to colloids; Sections 10–1 through 10–4; Exercises 1 and 76)

3. Describe the relative effects on solubility of the following kinds of interactions: (a) solute-solute attractions, (b) solvent-solvent attractions, and (c) solvent-solute attractions. Be able to discuss these effects for solid-liquid, liquid-liquid, and gas-liquid solutions. (Sections 10–1 through 10–4; Exercises 2 through 6)

4. Describe and illustrate the mechanism of dissolution of ionic solids and polar covalent substances in water. (Section 10–2; Exercises 7 through 10)

5. Know the effects of exo- or endothermicity and of an increase in disorder on the spontaneity of the dissolution process. (Sections 10–1 and 10–6; Exercise 6)

6. Distinguish among unsaturated, saturated, and supersaturated solutions. (Section 10–5; Exercises 10 through 14)

7. Distinguish between exothermic and endothermic dissolution processes. Describe the effects of exothermicity or endothermicity on the temperature dependence of water solubility of a compound. (Section 10–6; Exercises 14 and 15)

8. Describe the effect on solubility of changing the pressure when the solute is (a) a gas, (b) a liquid, or (c) a solid. (Section 10–7; Exercise 16)

9. Relate specific amounts of solute dissolved in specific amounts of solvent or solution to concentration expressed as (a) percent by mass, (b) molarity, (c) mole fraction, and (d) molality. (Review Sections 2–13, 10–8, and 10–9; Exercises 17 through 37, 42 through 45, 50, and 51)

10. Name the colligative properties of solutions. Tell on what factors they depend. (Sections 10–11, 10–13, 10–14, and 10–19; Exercises 46 through 49)

11. Use Raoult's Law to describe the lowering of vapor pressure for solutions of nonvolatile solutes. (Section 10–11; Exercises 38 through 41)

12. Relate Study Goal 11 to the purification technique of fractional distillation. (Section 10–12)

13. Carry out calculations involving freezing point depression, boiling point elevation, and osmotic pressure in order to relate these physical properties of solutions to the amount of solute dissolved in a given amount of solvent. (Sections 10–11 through 10–14, and 10–19; Exercises 52 through 58, and 70 through 74)

14. Use the colligative properties to determine molecular weights of solutes. (Sections 10–15 and 10–19; Exercises 55, 56, 61, and 74)

15. Describe solutions of strong electrolytes, weak electrolytes, and nonelectrolytes, giving specific examples of each. (Review Section 7–1; Section 10–15; Exercise 8)

16. Understand how the properties of electrolyte solutions depend on such

factors as ion association and degree of ionization. (Sections 10–16 through 10–18; Exercises 59 through 67)

17. Describe and illustrate osmosis and reverse osmosis. (Sections 10–19 and 10–20; Exercises 68 and 69)
18. Distinguish among, and give common examples of, the kinds of colloids listed in Table 10–4, such as gels, sols, foams, and so on. (introduction to colloids; Exercises 75 through 77)
19. Describe and distinguish between hydrophilic and hydrophobic colloids. (Section 10–23; Exercise 78)
20. Describe and illustrate the action of an emulsifying agent, a soap, and a detergent. (Section 10–23; Exercises 79, 81, and 82)
21. Explain methods for removing colloidal particles from suspension. (Section 10–24; Exercises 80 and 83)

Some Important Terms in This Chapter

This is another chapter with *many* important new terms, some of which are listed here. Remember to study many others too. Write the meanings *in your own words*. Check the Key Terms list and the chapter reading. Then rewrite your definitions, still in your own words, to improve them. Study other new terms and review terms from preceding chapters if necessary.

solvation

hydration

Henry's Law

saturated solution

mole fraction

molality

colligative properties

Raoult's Law

distillation (including fractional)

boiling point elevation

freezing point depression

apparent ionization

percentage ionization

osmosis

osmotic pressure

van't Hoff factor

activity

activity coefficient

colloid

hydrophilic colloids

hydrophobic colloids

coagulation

emulsification

Preliminary Test

As in other chapters, this test will check your understanding of basic concepts and types of calculations. Be sure to practice *many* of the additional textbook exercises, including those indicated in the Study Goals.

True-False

Mark each statement as true (T) or false (F).

_____   1. When one substance dissolves in another the result is a situation of greater disorder.

_____   2. All cases of solids dissolving in water are endothermic.

_____   3. All cases of gases dissolving in water are exothermic.

_____   4. It is impossible, under any conditions, to dissolve more solute in a solvent than the amount to saturate it.

_____   5. Ions are usually dissolved in water without any interaction with the solvent.

_____   6. In general, the larger the charge and the smaller the size of an ion, the more easily it can be hydrated.

_____   7. An ionic substance such as KCl is able to dissolve in water because in the solution each K^+ ion can be surrounded closely by several Cl^- ions, while each Cl^- ion has several close K^+ neighbors.

_____   8. The larger the lattice energy for a solid substance, the less likely that it is able to dissolve in a specific solvent.

_____   9. Gases can dissolve in liquids only if they react.

_____ 10. Increasing the pressure usually makes solids more soluble in liquids.

_____ 11. The degree to which a substance is ionized in solution is greater for more concentrated solutions.

_____ 12. In order for a substance to be very soluble in water, it must be a strong electrolyte.

_____ 13. Nitric acid is a weak electrolyte solution.

_____ 14. Strong electrolytes are those that are mostly ionized in dilute aqueous solutions.

_____ 15. A solution that is described as concentrated would have a higher molarity than a dilute solution.

_____ 16. Before we can answer any question regarding a solution we must decide which component is the solute and which is the solvent.

_____ 17. A solution that is 20% A dissolved in B must have a mole fraction of B greater than that of A.

_____ 18. A solution that is described as a strong acid solution would have a higher molarity than a weak acid solution.

_____ 19. For a given solution, it would probably be easier to measure the freezing point depression than the boiling point elevation.

_____ 20. It is not necessary to use measurements such as colligative properties to determine the degree of ionization of $CaCl_2$ in solution since
we can predict from the formula that 1 mole of $CaCl_2$ must dissolve
to give 3 moles of solute particles.

_____ 21. All colloid particles are collections of molecules or ions, just small
enough to keep from settling out.

Short Answer

Answer with a word, a phrase, a formula or a number with units as
necessary.

1. A solution is an example of a _____ mixture.
2. When we describe a solution of a little sugar in water, we describe sugar as
the _____ and water as the _____ .
3. The reverse of the dissolution process is called _____ .
4. A solution that contains dissolved solute in equilibrium at a given
temperature with excess undissolved solute is said to be _____ .
5. The ease of the dissolution process depends on two factors: (a) the change
in _____ and (b) the change in _____ .
6. A process in which the substances involved decrease in energy is called
_____ .
7. The three types of interactions that are useful to consider in assessing the
change in heat content on dissolution are _____ ,
_____ , and _____ .
8. The dissolution process is favored by _____ solute-solute forces, by
_____ solvent-solvent forces, and by _____ solute-solvent forces.
9. The close clustering of solvent molecules around a solute particle is
generally called _____ ; when the solvent is water it is called
_____ .
10. Classify each of the following substances as soluble or insoluble in water
(for review).

   (a) KNO_3 _____ (k) $Ca(OH)_2$ _____
   (b) $SrCl_2$ _____ (l) $AgNO_3$ _____
   (c) SO_2 _____ (m) $Mg(CH_3COO)_2$ _____
   (d) $Al(OH)_3$ _____ (n) $Zn(ClO_4)_2$ _____
   (e) $(NH_4)_2S$ _____ (o) H_3PO_4 _____
   (f) FeS _____ (p) $Ba_3(PO_4)_2$ _____
   (g) $CaCO_3$ _____ (q) MgS _____
   (h) HBr _____ (r) $(NH_4)_2CO_3$ _____
   (i) $PbCl_2$ _____ (s) KOH _____
   (j) $NaSCN$ _____ (t) Rb_2SO_4 _____

11. In order to have a solution of acetone and water that has a mole fraction
of acetone equal to 0.20, we must add _____ moles of acetone to 6.0 moles
of water.

12. The lowering of the vapor pressure of a solvent due to the presence of dissolved solute is described by _____ Law, which states in words that _____

_____.

13. The vapor pressure of pure water is always _____ the vapor pressure of an aqueous solution of a nonvolatile solute at the same temperature.

We make up two solutions. Solution A contains 0.1 mole of NaBr dissolved in 1000 grams of water, while solution B contains 0.1 mole of sugar dissolved in 1000 grams of water. The next four questions, 14 through 17, refer to these two solutions.

14. We expect that the vapor pressure of solution A would be _____ that of solution B.

15. We expect that the freezing point of solution A would be _____ that of solution B.

16. We expect that the boiling point of solution A would be _____ that of solution B.

17. If each solution is put in contact through a semipermeable membrane with a sample of pure water, solution A would exhibit _____ osmotic pressure compared to solution B.

18. We prepare a solution by dissolving 0.01 mole of $MgCl_2$ in 1.0 kg water and observe the freezing point experimentally. We also calculate the freezing point depression, using $\Delta T_b = K_b m$, with $m = 0.01$ molal. The ratio of observed freezing point depression to calculated freezing point depression would be about _____.

19. The passage of solvent molecules selectively through a membrane is called _____.

20. Liquids diffuse through a membrane from regions of high solvent concentration to regions of low solvent concentration due to a force known as _____.

21. When we distill a mixture of the very volatile substance A and the moderately volatile substance B, the first distillate (liquid obtained by condensing the first vapor to boil off) should be richer in substance _____.

22. Of the four colligative properties of a solution, the one that would give the most easily determined measurement from which to calculate the solute molecular weight would be _____.

23. In order to carry out "reverse osmosis," the pressure that we exert on the solution must exceed the _____.

24. The "effective concentration" of ions in a solution is described as their

_____.

25. A fog is an example of a(n) _____.

26. The only combination of phases that cannot lead to formation of a colloid would be _____ dispersed in _____.
27. Colloids consisting of solids or liquids dispersed in a gas medium are called _____.
28. The process by which ions and molecules stick to the surface of a particle is called _____.
29. Colloid particles that readily attract water molecules to their surfaces are called _____.
30. The process in which the particles of the dispersed phase are coated with something to keep them from coming together to form a separate phase is called _____.
31. The bringing together of colloid particles to allow separation of phases is called _____, which is the opposite of dispersion.

Multiple Choice

____ 1. For gases that do not react chemically with water, the solubility of the gas in water generally
    (a) increases with increasing gas pressure and decreases with increasing temperature.
    (b) decreases with increasing gas pressure and decreases with increasing temperature.
    (c) increases with increasing gas pressure and increases with increasing temperature.
    (d) decreases with increasing gas pressure and increases with increasing temperature.
    (e) does not change appreciably with change in either gas pressure or temperature.

____ 2. The formation of tiny bubbles when a beaker of water is mildly heated is indicative that
    (a) the boiling point is being approached.
    (b) water is being decomposed into hydrogen and oxygen.
    (c) water is extensively hydrogen bonded.
    (d) air is less soluble in water at higher temperatures.
    (e) the lattice energy of water is large.

____ 3. Hydrogen chloride in the gaseous state is in the form of covalent molecules, yet in aqueous solution it behaves as a strong electrolyte, conducting electricity. The explanation for this solution behavior is that
    (a) HCl forms ionic crystals in the solid state.
    (b) HCl reacts with water to form ions.
    (c) although it is covalent, the molecule of HCl is polar and stays in solution as a polar molecule, conducting electricity.

(d) there is more than one form of gaseous HCl.

(e) at lower temperatures, HCl becomes ionic.

_____ 4. Which of the following alcohols would be the *least* miscible with water?

(a) Hexanol, $CH_3CH_2CH_2CH_2CH_2CH_2OH$

(b) Pentanol, $CH_3CH_2CH_2CH_2CH_2OH$

(c) Propanol, $CH_3CH_2CH_2OH$

(d) Ethanol, CH_3CH_2OH

(e) Methanol, CH_3OH

_____ 5. In four of the following groups, the three substances are either all strong electrolytes, all weak electrolytes, or all nonelectrolytes. Which group has one member that is not like the others in the group?

(a) H_2SO_4, NaOH, HCl

(b) NH_3, CH_3COOH, HCN

(c) NaCl, $Ca(OH)_2$, HNO_3

(d) O_2, $CO(NH_2)_2$, CH_3OH

(e) $BaCl_2$, $NaNO_3$, HF

_____ 6. Hydrogen chloride is observed to be soluble in benzene, although not to the extent that it is in water. We would expect that

(a) the HCl in benzene would be ionized, as in water.

(b) the solution of HCl in benzene would be a good conductor of electricity.

(c) the HCl molecules would be largely intact in benzene.

(d) the benzene molecules would solvate the HCl molecules very well.

(e) the limited solubility of HCl in benzene is due to the very strong interaction between benzene molecules.

_____ 7. Three of the following are colligative properties of solutions. Which one is not a colligative property?

(a) molality   (b) vapor pressure lowering   (c) osmotic pressure   (d) freezing point depression   (e) boiling point elevation

_____ 8. A 1-molar solution has

(a) 1 mole of solute per 1 liter of solvent.

(b) 1 mole of solute per 1 liter of solution.

(c) 1 mole of solute per 1 kilogram of solvent.

(d) 1 mole of solute per 1 kilogram of solution.

(e) 1 mole of solute per 1 mole of solvent.

_____ 9. A 1-molal solution has

(a) 1 mole of solute per 1 liter of solvent.

(b) 1 mole of solute per 1 liter of solution.

(c) 1 mole of solute per 1 kilogram of solvent.

(d) 1 mole of solute per 1 kilogram of solution.

(e) 1 mole of solute per 1 mole of solvent.

_____ 10. We dissolve 7.5 grams of urea (a nonelectrolyte, molecular weight = 60) in 500 grams of water. At what temperature would the solution boil? Additional useful data may be found in Table 10–2.
(a) 100.46°C   (b) 100.13°C   (c) 0.13°C   (d) 99.54°C
(e) 99.87°C

_____ 11. An aqueous solution of compound X is described as "a 10% X solution." Its density is 1.10 g/mL. Which of the following statements about this solution is not true?
(a) 1 liter of the solution would weigh 1.10 kg.
(b) 1 liter of the solution would contain 100 grams of compound X.
(c) 1 kg of the solution would contain 100 grams of compound X.
(d) The molality of the solution would be greater than the molarity.
(e) The boiling point of the solution would be higher than 100°C.

_____ 12. How many mL of a 0.320-molar solution of sucrose in benzene (density = 0.8787 g/mL) are needed to have 0.160 moles of sucrose?
(a) 500 mL   (b) 498.5 mL   (c) 438 mL   (d) 567.3 mL
(e) 219 mL

_____ 13. Which of the following aqueous solutions would exhibit the highest boiling point?
(a) 0.1 m urea   (b) 0.1 m NaCl   (c) 0.1 m CaCl$_2$
(d) 0.1 m HCl   (e) All would show the same boiling point.

_____ 14. According to Raoult's Law, the lowering of vapor pressure of the solvent in dilute solutions of a nonvolatile solute is proportional to the
(a) molarity of the solute.
(b) molarity of the solvent.
(c) mole fraction of the solute.
(d) mole fraction of the solvent.
(e) None of the preceding answers is correct.

Answers to Preliminary Test

True-False

1. True. The two kinds of molecules are mixed in the solution, so they are less ordered.
2. False. Some are exothermic, including those examples listed in Section 10–2.
3. True. See the discussion in Section 10–4.
4. False. Read about supersaturated solutions, Section 10–5.
5. False. Hydration must occur.

6. True. Remember the definition of charge density and known how it relates to solubility of ionic substances, Section 10–2.

7. False. The solubility of KCl in water is due to the ability of water to surround each ion and thus to *prevent* the kind of interaction described.

8. True. Lattice energy is a measure of the attraction of the ions (or molecules) in the solid. The higher it is, the more strongly these particles are held in the solid.

9. False. If they do react (e.g., HCl, SO_2, CO_2 to a limited extent) they are often much more soluble, but some nonreacting gases are slightly soluble in water (O_2, N_2).

10. False. Changing the pressure usually has no appreciable effect on the solubilities of either solids or liquids in liquids, but it does greatly alter the solubility of gases in liquids.

11. False. Higher concentration encourages "clumping" of ions, rather than a separate existence for each ion.

12. False. Many substances that are quite soluble in water are either weak electrolytes (e.g., HCN, HNO_2, acetic acid, ammonia) or are nonelectrolytes (e.g., sugar, alcohol, urea).

13. False. Remember that nitric acid is one of the common strong acids (Chapter 7) and is thus essentially completely ionized.

14. True

15. True

16. False. This terminology is a convenience, but sometimes it is neither easy nor necessary to identify one component as solute.

17. False. This would depend on the molecular weights of A and B. Suppose that A had a much lower molecular weight than B, so that the fewer number of grams were a greater number of moles — then the mole fraction A would be greater than that of B.

18. False. It may or may not. Remember that the terms "strong" and "weak" describe the efficiency of ionization of the solute, not the concentration.

19. True. From Table 10–2, you can see that for all solvents listed (in fact, for all solvents) the value of K_f is greater than that for K_b. Thus, a solution of a given concentration would undergo a bigger change in freezing point than in boiling point. Another factor is that freezing points are much less sensitive to external atmospheric pressure.

20. False. The actual degree of ionization depends on concentration — the more dilute the solution, the greater the degree of ionization of a particular solute.

21. False. Some are individual macromolecules, such as proteins.

Short Answer

1. homogeneous
2. solute, solvent

3. crystallization (or precipitation)
4. saturated
5. energy, disorder
6. exothermic
7. solute-solute, solvent-solvent, solute-solvent
8. weak, weak, strong
9. solvation, hydration
10. (a) soluble
    (b) soluble
    (c) soluble
    (d) insoluble
    (e) soluble
    (f) insoluble
    (g) insoluble
    (h) soluble
    (i) insoluble
    (j) soluble
    (k) soluble
    (l) soluble
    (m) soluble
    (n) soluble
    (o) soluble
    (p) insoluble
    (q) soluble
    (r) soluble
    (s) soluble
    (t) soluble

You should *know* and be able to apply the solubility rules in Section 7–1.5. You may need to review chemical nomenclature of inorganic compounds, Sections 5–23 and 5–24.

11. 1.5. We want 0.20 of the total number of moles to be acetone, so the total number of moles $(6.0 + x)$ can be calculated (letting $x =$ number of moles of acetone) as $x = 0.2(6.0 + x)$, or $x = 1.5$.

12. Raoult's, the vapor pressure of a solvent above a solution, is equal to the mole fraction of the solvent in the solution times the vapor pressure the solvent would have if pure.

13. higher than

14. lower than. NaBr dissolves to give ions in solutions, resulting in 2 moles of solute particles per mole, while sugar gives only 1 mole of solute particles per mole. The *lowering* of the vapor pressure depends on the total concentration of solute particles.

15. lower than. Freezing point is depressed, again by an amount depending on the total concentration of dissolved solute particles.

16. higher than. Boiling point is elevated, by an amount depending on the total concentration of dissolved solute particles.

17. higher. Osmotic pressure, like all colligative properties, depends on the total concentration of solute particles.

18. 3. Each mole of $MgCl_2$ dissolves to give 1 mole of Mg^{2+} and 2 moles of Cl^-, or 3 moles total of solute particles per mole of $MgCl_2$ dissolved. This would probably be a pretty good prediction for such a dilute solution.

19. osmosis

20. osmotic pressure

21. A. The more volatile substance evaporates better, so the vapor is richer in the more volatile substance.

22. osmotic pressure. See the discussion in Section 10–19.
23. osmotic pressure of the solution
24. activity
25. colloid (or aerosol, which is a type of colloid)
26. gases, gases. This is because gas mixtures are always homogeneous.
27. aerosols
28. adsorption. Note the spelling of this word. Do you know the difference between adsorption and absorption?
29. hydrophilic
30. emulsification. See Section 10–24 regarding favorable and unfavorable examples of emulsification.
31. coagulation or flocculation

Multiple Choice

1. (a)
2. (d)
3. (b)
4. (a). The three alcohols propanol, ethanol, and methanol are miscible with water in all proportions, but the alcohols with larger nonpolar hydrocarbon ends are much less so. Of the alcohols listed, hexanol is the most hydrocarbon-like, and hence least miscible with water.
5. (e). In (a), all substances are strong electrolytes; in (b), all are weak electrolytes; in (c), all are strong electrolytes; in (d), all are nonelectrolytes. In answer (e), $BaCl_2$ and $NaNO_3$ are strong electrolytes and HF is a weak electrolyte. You may need to review the strong and weak electrolytes discussed in Section 7–1.
6. (c). Benzene, a nonpolar solvent, cannot solvate very well, so the ionization process does not readily occur, as it does in water.
7. (a)
8. (b)
9. (c)
10. (b). $K_b m = \Delta T_b$. Molality (m) is $\dfrac{7.5 \text{ g}}{0.500 \text{ kg solvent}} \times \dfrac{1 \text{ mole}}{60 \text{ g}} =$ 0.25 molal. From Table 10–2, K_b is 0.512°C/molal, so $\Delta T_b = 0.13°C$. Remember that the boiling point is raised from its normal value by this amount.
11. (b). One liter would weigh 1100 grams, of which 10%, or 110 grams, would be compound X.
12. (a). Molarity directly relates moles of solute to volume of solution. Density is not needed to answer this question.
13. (c). Consider the number of dissolved particles in each solution. Urea is a nonelectrolyte.
14. (c)

11

Acids, Bases, and Salts

Chapter Summary

This chapter continues and broadens the descriptive chemistry associated with acids, bases, and salts that was introduced in Chapter 7. As you can see from the brief historical notes in Section 11–1, the most important overall feature of acids and bases, common to all of the studies in this chapter, is the essential *opposite nature* of these two classes of compounds. You see that the *Arrhenius* view of acids and bases is the approach that you already learned about in Chapter 7 — that acids are substances that produce H^+ in aqueous solution, whereas bases act to produce OH^- ions. We now know that H^+ exists in aqueous solution as the **hydrated hydrogen ion,** usually represented as the **hydronium ion, H_3O^+** (Section 11–2). One of the drawbacks of the Arrhenius approach, however, is that it does not emphasize sufficiently the "oppositeness" of acids and bases; it just says that acids do one thing and that bases do something else. Much of the remainder of this chapter is devoted to several other ways of looking at acids and bases. You should view each of these "theories" about acids, bases, and salts as a different way of describing and attempting to systematize the behavior of these substances.

One of the most useful descriptions of acid-base behavior is the **Brønsted-Lowry theory,** which developed from the Arrhenius description. The fundamental ideas and terminology of this theory are presented in Section 11–3. The Brønsted-Lowry theory is then used often in Sections 11–4 through 11–11 to describe a broad range of reactions. Sections 11–12 and 11–13 introduce two alternative views of acid-base behavior. The chapter then closes with some quantitative considerations of acid-base reactions in aqueous solution.

According to the Brønsted-Lowry view of acid-base behavior, an acid is a substance that **donates** H^+ (referred to as a proton, even though it is hydrated in aqueous solution), and a base is a substance that **accepts H^+.** Thus we see that this approach does emphasize the opposite nature of these two classes of substances. You should pay close attention at this stage to the terminology used to describe behavior and properties so that these terms will be useful and not confusing to you later in the chapter. Once we see that reactions are reversible, we can write a variety of reactions in the general form

$$acid_1 + base_2 \rightarrow acid_2 + base_1.$$

Each acid, when it gives up H^+ (as acids are supposed to do), becomes capable of accepting H^+ (as bases are supposed to do). Thus, we talk of **conjugate acid-base pairs** of substances — a pair of substances differing by an H^+. Notice that such apparently diverse reactions as the **autoionization** of water, the dissolving of hydrogen chloride in water to form hydrochloric acid, and the dissolving of ammonia in water to give a basic solution may all be described in this same set of terms. The ready recognition of conjugate acid-base pairs will be helpful in your study of this chapter. We also see in this section that the stronger an acid, the weaker is its conjugate base. It is also useful to notice that in order for any base to "accept" H^+, it must have available an unshared electron pair; this will be a basis for a different acid-base classification later in the chapter.

The general properties of aqueous solutions of protonic acids and soluble bases are summarized in Section 11–4. The list of properties presented there again emphasizes several aspects of their behavior in which acids and bases are said to be opposite.

One of our continuing goals in chemistry, beyond just learning and classifying the reactions, is to understand trends in properties in terms of electronic and structural features of the molecules — in other words, in terms of the bonding. Section 11–5 emphasizes such an understanding, dealing with the correlation of relative strengths of **binary** protonic acids with their bonding properties. As can be seen in this section, trends in strengths of acids (and of course the reverse trends in strengths of their conjugate bases) can be related to such features as electronegativity differences. The important notion of the **leveling** effect is introduced in this section.

Section 11–6 deals in a systematic way with the neutralization reactions between acids and bases. You will find it useful to review Section 7–5 before beginning your study of this section. It will also be necessary to familiarize yourself with the writing of **total ionic equations** and **net ionic equations** (Chapter 7) to represent reactions. A review of the generalizations regarding solubilities of inorganic compounds in water, Section 7–1.5, will assist you in understanding this section. As you go through the various subcategories of neutralization reactions in this section, you will see that the useful forms of the equations (that is, the important aspects of the reaction that we wish to emphasize) depend on several factors: (1) the strength of the acid involved, (2) the strength and solubility of the base involved, (3) the solubility of the salt in water, and (4) the ionic or covalent nature of the soluble substances. Try to see the distinguishing features of each category of reaction in these terms. Another recurrent theme in these reactions is the **driving force** for the reaction — usually the formation of the very stable covalent substance H_2O, sometimes accompanied by the formation of very stable insoluble salts.

When the salts formed by neutralization of acid and base contain no unreacted H^+ or OH^-, they are referred to as **normal salts.** But if other than stoichiometric amounts of acid and base are used, the product may be an **acidic salt** (i.e., may still have ionizable H^+) or a **basic salt** (may still have ionizable OH^-). The acidic and basic salts are the subject of Section 11 – 7. As you notice, these can be formed when the acid is **polyprotic** (more than one H^+ per acid molecule) or when the base is a **polyhydroxy** base (more than one OH^- per base formula unit).

In Section 11 – 8 we return to the correlation of observed reactive properties, acid strengths, with the bonding features of the acid molecules: structure, oxidation state of the central element, position in the periodic table, etc. In this section we are primarily concerned with **ternary** acids, those containing H, O, and one other element, usually a nonmetal. The generalizations regarding trends in acid strength presented in this section should be learned. The related topic of the structural basis for **amphoterism,** the ability of a substance to act either as an acid or as a base, is also discussed in this section. It will be useful to remember the formulas of some amphoteric hydroxides and the complex ions to which they are related (Table 11 – 3).

The next three sections, 11 – 9 through 11 – 11, deal with the methods of preparing various acids, strong soluble bases, and insoluble bases.

As we observed earlier, a Brønsted-Lowry base must have a lone pair available for bond formation with the H^+ that it accepts. The generalization of this behavior leads to the **Lewis theory** (Section 11 – 12), the broadest of all acid-base theories. In this theory, any substance that supplies an electron pair for bond formation, whether to H^+ or to any other species, is classified as a base; the substance that accepts a share in this lone pair is then classified as an acid. Notice that the Lewis theory includes all acid-base behavior previously discussed but extends the acid-base terminology to include reactions that do not involve H^+. This view of acid-base chemistry then serves to systematize additional types of reactions, such as the formation and reactions of coordination compounds (Chapter 27).

The final theory regarding acids and bases, the **solvent system theory,** is discussed in Section 11 – 13. According to this theory, an acid is any substance that produces the cation characteristic of the solvent (H^+ for water as the solvent, NH_4^+ for ammonia as the solvent, etc.) whereas a base is any substance that produces the anion characteristic of the solvent (OH^- for water, NH_2^- for ammonia, etc.). This theory is not as broadly useful as the Lewis theory, nor is it as descriptive for aqueous solutions as the Brønsted-Lowry theory. Its advantage is that it systematizes, under the same acid-base terminology, many reactions that occur in solvents other than water.

The last two sections of Chapter 11 deal with some quantitative aspects of acid-base reactions in aqueous solutions. As you study this portion of the chapter, you will see that the terminology of the Brønsted-Lowry and Arrhenius theories is used. Before beginning your study of Sections 11 – 14 and 11 – 15, you should review the methods for expressing concentrations of solutions—weight percent (Section 2–13.1) and molarity (Section 2–13.2). A brief review of calculations involving molarity also appears in Section 11–14.

The central chemical reaction of acid-base (neutralization) reactions is

$$H^+ \text{ (aq)} + OH^- \text{ (aq)} \rightarrow H_2O \text{ } (\ell).$$

The central idea behind neutralization calculations is that equal numbers of moles of H^+ and OH^- are required to reach neutrality, no matter what acid or base is involved. When this condition of neutrality has been reached, the solution contains only water, the anion of the acid, and the cation of the base. If the salt that is formed is insoluble, it precipitates from the reaction mixture as a solid; if it is soluble, it remains in solution as dispersed ions.

The essential criterion for neutralization—that equal numbers of moles of H^+ and OH^- (or **equivalent** amounts of acid and base) are required—is difficult to assess directly since we do not directly measure number of moles. Thus, a solution concentration that relates *number of moles* (which is hard to measure) to *volume of solution* (which is easy to measure) is quite useful. The calculation methods presented in Section 11–15 describe acid-base reactions in various convenient solution units.

Section 11–15.1 uses molarities to describe the amounts of acid and base solutions that are necessary to attain neutralization. The thing to watch for in this approach is that some acids (e.g., HCl) supply 1 mole of H^+ per mole of acid, whereas others (e.g., H_2SO_4) supply 2 moles of H^+ per mole of acid. Comparable difficulties exist for bases with different numbers of moles of OH^- per mole of base. This difficulty is overcome by the introduction, in Section 11–15.2, of the idea of the **equivalent weight of an acid.** This is defined as the weight of the acid, expressed in grams, that will furnish 1 mole of H^+. In a parallel description, the **equivalent weight of a base** is the amount of the base, expressed in grams, that will furnish 1 mole of OH^-. In these terms, one equivalent weight (usually called one **equivalent**) of *any acid* will neutralize one equivalent of *any base.* Once this has been established, the definition of **normality** of a solution as the number of equivalents of solute per liter of solution provides a convenient basis for calculation of the volumes of acid and base solutions involved in a reaction. Sometimes, for convenience, normality is expressed in terms of **milliequivalents** per milliliter of solution. Study carefully the examples in Section 11–15.2, noting particularly the relation between formula weight and equivalent weight for various acids and bases and between molarity and normality for various acid or base solutions.

Section 11–15 also discusses some of the practical matters associated with measuring volumes of solutions and relating these to amounts of solutes contained therein. Be sure that you first understand the terminology of **standard solutions, primary** and **secondary standards, titration,** and **indicators.**

After you understand the ideas of this section, get lots of practice by working comparable problems at the end of the chapter. Remember that the basis for all of these calculations is the following relationship at the point of neutralization (called the **equivalence point**):

$$\text{no eq acid} = \text{no eq base,}$$

or

$$\text{no meq acid} = \text{no meq base.}$$

Another useful relation using solution concentrations is that

$$\text{no eq} = N \times L, \text{ or no meq} = N \times mL.$$

These may be combined to get still another useful form:

$$\text{vol}_{acid} \times N_{acid} = \text{vol}_{base} \times N_{base},$$

where the two volumes must be expressed in the same units, i.e., both L or both mL.

This chapter brings together many of the concepts of earlier chapters and applies them to a discussion of the chemistry of important related classes of compounds—acids, bases, and salts. In addition, it introduces you to ways of viewing such reactions and to terminology commonly used in discussing the reactions. As you study the chapter, try to become comfortable with the terminology by being aware of the precise meanings of the terms, and try also to relate this material to what you already know from earlier chapters.

Study Goals

Be sure to review the ideas and skills from indicated sections of earlier chapters. Several of the study goals in this chapter take much practice, so be sure you answer many of the questions in the text. Be systematic in your study.

1. Review the fundamental ideas of acids and bases from earlier chapters. Memorize the lists of the common strong acids (Table 7–1) and the common strong soluble bases (Table 7–3). Classify common acids as strong or weak; classify common bases as strong soluble, insoluble, or weak. (Review Section 7–1; Section 11–1; Exercises 3 through 5, 15 through 17, and 21 through 23)
2. Define acid, base, and neutralization in terms of the Arrhenius theory. Give specific examples with formulas. (Section 11–1; Exercise 2)
3. Be familiar with the description of the hydrated hydrogen ion. (Section 11–2; Exercise 6)

4. Understand the Brønsted-Lowry acid-base theory. Be able to identify the Brønsted-Lowry acids and bases in reactions. (Section 11–3; Exercises 7 through 14)

5. Understand and apply the Brønsted-Lowry terminology of conjugate acid-base pairs and their relative strengths. (Section 11–3; Exercises 8, 15, and 16)

6. Be familiar with the characteristics of acids, bases, and their solutions. (Section 11–4; Exercises 1, 13, and 14)

7. Explain the trends in acid strengths of the binary acids. Understand the factors that determine the strengths of ternary acids. (Sections 11–5 and 11–8; Exercises 18 through 20, and 37 through 40)

8. Review the solubility rules for ionic substances in water. (Review Section 7–1.5)

9. Be able to write balanced molecular equations, total ionic equations, and net ionic equations for neutralization reactions of acids and bases to form salts. Be able to name all compounds involved in these equations. (Sections 11–5 and 11–6; Exercises 24 through 32, 76, and 77)

10. Tell what is meant by each of the following terms: (a) normal salt, (b) acidic salt, and (c) basic salt. Give examples of each and be able to tell by what kinds of reactions each type of salt could be formed. (Section 11–7; Exercises 33 through 36)

11. Know the identity, properties, and characteristic reactions of the amphoteric hydroxides. Correlate amphoteric behavior of metal hydroxides with the relative strengths of (a) metal-oxygen and (b) oxygen-hydrogen bonds associated with coordinated water molecules. (Section 11–8; Exercises 41 through 43)

12. Write equations illustrating the preparations of (a) binary acids, (b) ternary acids, (c) strong soluble bases, and (d) insoluble bases. (Sections 11–9 through 11–11; Exercises 44 through 47)

13. Understand the Lewis acid-base theory. Be able to recognize Lewis acid-base reactions and classify their acids and bases. (Section 11–12; Exercises 48 through 52)

14. Understand the solvent system theory of acids and bases. Understand how properties and processes such as amphoterism, neutralization, etc. are described through this theory. (Section 11–13; Exercises 53 through 58)

15. Review earlier calculations involving molarity. (Review Sections 2–14, 2–15, and 10–9; Section 11–14; Exercises 59 through 65, and 73 through 79)

16. Using specified concentrations of solutions, be able to calculate (a) whether a specified mixture of acid and base solutions results in neutralization and (b) the amounts of salts formed and acid or base remaining when an acid and a base solution are mixed. (Sections 11–14 and 11–15; Exercises 66 through 72)

17. Using molarity, be able to calculate (a) the concentration of an acid (or base) solution from information about the amount of base (or acid) required to neutralize it (standardization), (b) the volume of an acid (or base) solution required to neutralize a specified amount of base (or acid), and (c) the amount of acid or base in an unknown sample, by titration with a solution of known concentration. (Section 11 – 15.1; Exercises 76 through 94)

18. Define equivalent weight and normality for an acid or a base solution. Be able to carry out calculations relating these quantities (a) to one another and (b) to formula weight and molarity. (Section 11 – 15.2; Exercises 95 through 99)

19. Be able to carry out the calculations of Study Goal 17 using normality to express solution concentration. (Section 11 – 15.2; Exercises 100 through 107)

Some Important Terms in This Chapter

Write the meanings *in your own words.* Check the Key Terms list and the chapter reading. Then rewrite your definitions, still in your own words, to improve them. Study other new terms and review terms from preceding chapters if necessary.

Arrhenius acid

Arrhenius base

salt

molecular equation

total ionic equation

net ionic equation

Brønsted-Lowry acid

Brønsted-Lowry base

conjugate acid-base pair

ionization

autoionization

neutralization

normal salt

acidic salt

basic salt

binary acid

ternary acid

amphoterism

standardization

titration

standard solution

primary standard

molarity

normality

equivalent weight

Preliminary Test

As in other chapters, this test will check your understanding of basic concepts and types of calculations. Be sure to practice *many* of the additional textbook exercises, including those indicated with the Study Goals.

Short Answer

1. Write the definitions of acids and bases according to each of the following theories:

Theory	Definition
Arrhenius	(a) acid — (b) base —
Brønsted-Lowry	(c) acid — (d) base —
Lewis	(e) acid — (f) base —
Solvent System	(g) acid — (h) base —

2. The essential feature of bases, according to all theories considered here, is that they act to _____ acids.

3. In either the Arrhenius or the Brønsted-Lowry view of aqueous acid-base neutralization reactions, one of the products of the neutralization is molecules of _____. (Give name and formula.)

4. According to the Brønsted-Lowry description of acids and bases, when an acid acts to donate H^+, it is transformed into its _____.

5. The conjugate base of HCl is _____. (name, formula)

6. The conjugate base of acetic acid is _____. (name, formula)

7. The conjugate acid of ClO_4^- is _____. (name, formula)

8. The conjugate acid of HSO_4^- is _____. (name, formula)

9. The conjugate base of HSO_4^- is _____. (name, formula)

10. The conjugate acid of water is _____. (name, formula)

11. The conjugate base of water is _____. (name, formula)

12. The process of water ionizing to produce an equal number of hydrated hydrogen ions (that is, hydronium ions, H_3O^+) and hydroxide ions OH^- is called the _____ of water.

13. A substance that can act as either an acid or a base is termed _____.

14. The stronger an acid, the _____ is its conjugate base.

15. Since HCl is a stronger acid than HCN, we know that CN^- must be a _____ base than Cl^-.

16. Even though it is not included in the formal definition, we see that in order for a substance to act as a Brønsted-Lowry base, it must have _____.

17. We can attribute the weaker acidity of HF compared with the other hydrohalic acids to the _____ between H and F than between H and the other halogens.

18. "The strongest acid that can exist in aqueous solution is H_3O^+. Acids stronger than this react with water to produce H^+ and their conjugate bases." This is often referred to as the _____ of water.

19. All neutralization reactions in aqueous solution produce _____ and _____.

20. Nearly all soluble salts produce _____ when they dissolve in water.

21. The net ionic equation for the reaction of all strong acids with strong soluble bases to form soluble salts and water is _____.

22. An acid that contains only one acidic (ionizable) hydrogen atom per formula unit is termed _____; one that contains two is called _____.

23. The most common soluble weak base is ammonia. The net ionic equation for the reaction of strong acids with aqueous ammonia is _____.

24. The usual driving force for neutralization reactions in aqueous solution is the formation of _____; a secondary factor favoring such neutralizations might be the formation of _____.

25. Salts that contain no unreacted H^+ or OH^- ions are referred to as _____ salts; those with excess available H^+ are termed _____ salts, whereas those with remaining OH^- are called _____ salts.

26. An acid that is composed of hydrogen, oxygen, and one other element is referred to as a _____ acid.

27. For various ternary acids containing the same central element (i.e., the element other than H and O), strength of the acid increases as the _____ of the central atom _____.

28. For ternary acids containing different elements from the same group in the periodic table in the same oxidation state, acid strength increases with _____ of the central element.

29. Due to the formation of complex hydroxy-anions, many amphoteric metal hydroxides are soluble in _____.

30. Strong soluble bases, such as the Group IA metal hydroxides, can often be prepared by the reaction of _____ with water.

31. Many ternary acids can be prepared by dissolving the appropriate _____ in water.

32. When CO_2 is dissolved in water, as in carbonated drinks, the acid formed is _____. (name, formula)

33. In the Lewis acid-base theory, a neutralization reaction is described as always involving _____ bond formation.

34. In liquid ammonia as a solvent, we would consider NH_4^+ as _____ and NH_2^- as _____.

35. In liquid ammonia, the net ionic equation for all neutralization reactions that form soluble ionic salts would be _____.

36. One millimole of HCl would neutralize exactly ___ millimole(s) of KOH.

37. One millimole of HCl would neutralize exactly ___ millimole(s) of $Ba(OH)_2$.

38. One meq of HCl would neutralize exactly ___ meq of KOH.

39. One meq of HCl would neutralize exactly ___ meq of $Ba(OH)_2$.

40. One meq of H_2SO_4 would neutralize exactly ___ meq of KOH.

41. In terms of concentration and volume of solution, the number of millimoles of solute can be calculated as _____.

42. In terms of concentration and volume of solution, the number of meq of solute can be calculated as _____.

43. The formula weight of nitric acid is 63.02. The weight of one equivalent weight of nitric acid is _____ gram(s).

44. The weight of 1 meq of nitric acid is _____.

45. The formula weight of oxalic acid is 90.04. The weight of one equivalent weight of oxalic acid is _____ gram(s).

46. The formula weight of calcium hydroxide is 74.10. The weight of one equivalent weight of calcium hydroxide is _____ gram(s).

47. A solution of hydrochloric acid is described as 0.15 molar (0.15 M). In terms of normality, the concentration of this solution would be described as _____.

48. A solution of phosphoric acid is described as 0.15 molar (0.15 M). In terms of normality, the concentration of this solution would be described as _____.

49. The volume of 0.200 N HNO$_3$ required to exactly neutralize 50.0 mL of a 0.150 N solution of Ca(OH)$_2$ is _____.

50. A solution whose concentration is accurately known is referred to as a _____ solution.

51. The process by which we determine the volume of a solution required to react with a specific amount of a substance is called _____.

52. A substance that is of sufficient purity and ease of handling that the number of moles (or equivalents) present may be determined by direct weighing is referred to as a _____.

Multiple Choice

____ 1. According to the Brønsted-Lowry concept of acids and bases, which of the following statements about a base is *not* correct?
   (a) A base accepts a hydrogen ion by sharing a previously unshared electron pair with H$^+$.
   (b) A base accepts a hydrogen ion by forming a coordinate covalent bond to H$^+$.
   (c) If a base is weak, its conjugate acid will be a strong acid.
   (d) A base can be formed only by ionization of a compound containing a hydroxide group.

____ 2. Which of the following could not be a Brønsted-Lowry acid?
   (a) H$_2$O   (b) HN$_3$ (c) H$_3$O$^+$ (d) NH$_4^+$ (e) BF$_3$

____ 3. Which of the following could not act as a Lewis base?
   (a) PCl$_3$ (b) CN$^-$ (c) I$^-$ (d) CH$_4$ (e) H$_2$O

____ 4. When a salt such as sodium acetate is dissolved in water, the acetate ion acts according to the reaction

$$CH_3COO^- (aq) + H_2O (\ell) \rightarrow CH_3COOH (aq) + OH^- (aq).$$

In this reaction, acetate ion is acting as
   (a) an acid.   (b) a base.   (c) an amphoteric substance.
   (d) an oxidizing agent.   (e) a reducing agent.

____ 5. What substance is acting as a Lewis acid in the following reaction?

$$BF_3 + F^- \rightarrow BF_4^-$$

   (a) BF$_3$
   (b) F$^-$
   (c) BF$_4^-$
   (d) All of the substances listed.
   (e) None of the substances listed.

____ 6. Cupric ion, Cu^{2+}, is pale blue in water solution. When ammonia is added to the solution, the deep-blue complex ion [Cu(NH$_3$)$_4$]$^{2+}$ is formed. In the formation of this complex ion, Cu^{2+} is acting as
   (a) a Lewis acid.   (b) a Lewis base.   (c) an Arrhenius acid.
   (d) a Brønsted-Lowry acid.   (e) a Brønsted-Lowry base.

_____ 7. In the reaction

$$CN^- + NH_4^+ \rightarrow HCN + NH_3,$$

the cyanide ion acts as
(a) a base.   (b) an acid.   (c) an oxidizing agent.   (d) a reducing agent.   (e) an amphoteric substance.

_____ 8. The following describe properties of substances. Which one is not a typical acid property?
(a) It has a sour taste.
(b) It reacts with metal oxides to form salts and water.
(c) It reacts with acids to form salts and water.
(d) Its aqueous solutions conduct an electrical current.
(e) It reacts with active metals to liberate H_2.

_____ 9. In water solution, HCN is only very slightly ionized according to the reaction

$$HCN\ (aq) + H_2O\ (\ell) \rightarrow H_2O^+\ (aq) + CN^-\ (aq).$$

This observation shows that CN is a _____ than is water.
(a) stronger acid   (b) stronger base   (c) weaker acid
(d) weaker base

_____ 10. What is the conjugate base of HI?
(a) H^+ (b) HI   (c) I^- (d) HIO_3 (e) H_2I

_____ 11. HBr is a strong acid when dissolved in water. HF is a weak acid when dissolved in water. Which of the following is the strongest base?
(a) H^+ (b) Br^- (c) F^- (d) H_2O (e) Insufficient information is given to answer the question.

_____ 12. Some soluble bases can be formed by the action of metals with water. For which of the following metals would this not be a likely way of preparing the corresponding hydroxide base?
(a) K   (b) Ca   (c) Na   (d) Ba   (e) Fe

_____ 13. Which of the following is an example of an acidic salt?
(a) KNO_3 (b) $KHSO_4$ (c) H_3PO_4 (d) $Mg(OH)_2$
(e) $Al(OH)Cl_2$

_____ 14. Which of the following is an example of a basic salt?
(a) KNO_3 (b) $KHSO_4$ (c) H_3PO_4 (d) $Mg(OH)_2$
(e) $Al(OH)Cl_2$

_____ 15. Which of the following is an example of a normal salt?
(a) KNO_3 (b) $KHSO_4$ (c) H_3PO_4 (d) $Mg(OH)_2$
(e) $Al(OH)Cl_2$

_____ 16. Each of the following ions forms a stable hydroxide. For which of the ions would the hydroxide not be amphoteric?
(a) Sn^{2+} (b) Sn^{4+} (c) Cr^{3+} (d) Be^{2+} (e) Ba^{2+}

_____ 17. Which of the following statements is true?

(a) The equivalent weight of an acid is always less than its formula weight.

(b) The equivalent weight of an acid is always equal to its formula weight.

(c) The equivalent weight of an acid is always greater than its formula weight.

(d) The equivalent weight of an acid is always greater than or equal to its formula weight.

(e) The equivalent weight of an acid is always less than or equal to its formula weight.

_____ 18. Which of the following statements is true?

(a) The normality of an acid solution is always less than its molarity.

(b) The normality of an acid solution is always equal to its molarity.

(c) The normality of an acid solution is always greater than its molarity.

(d) The normality of an acid solution is always greater than or equal to its molarity.

(e) The normality of an acid solution is always less than or equal to its molarity.

_____ 19. The formula weight of the base NaOH is 40.0 g/mol. What is the equivalent weight of NaOH?

(a) 40.0 g/eq   (b) 20.0 g/eq   (c) 80.0 g/eq   (d) The answer depends on the reaction undergone by NaOH.

_____ 20. The formula weight of the base $Sr(OH)_2$ is 121.6 g/mol. What is the equivalent weight of $Sr(OH)_2$?

(a) 121.6 g/eq   (b) 60.8 g/eq   (c) 243.2 g/eq   (d) The answer depends on the reaction undergone by $Sr(OH)_2$.

_____ 21. What is the normality of a 0.40-M NaOH solution?

(a) 0.40 N (b) 0.20 N (c) 0.80 N (d) The answer depends on the reaction undergone by NaOH.

_____ 22. What is the normality of a 0.40-M $Sr(OH)_2$ solution?

(a) 0.40 N (b) 0.20 N (c) 0.80 N (d) The answer depends on the reaction undergone by $Sr(OH)_2$.

_____ 23. In which of the following pairs is the order of acid strength *incorrect*?

(a) HF < HCl   (b) $H_2SeO_4 < H_2SO_4$ (c) $HNO_2 < HNO_3$
(d) $H_2SO_4 < H_2SO_3$ (e) HCl < HI

Note: It takes a great deal of practice to learn to use the material in this chapter. You will need much more practice at working with molarity and normality than the questions in this guide provide. You should work many of the text Exercises suggested in the Study Goals.

Answers to Preliminary Test

Short Answer

1. (a) acts to produce H^+ (or H_3O^+)
   (b) acts to produce OH^-
   (c) a proton (H^+) donor
   (d) a proton (H^+) acceptor
   (e) accepts a share in an electron pair
   (f) makes available a share in an electron pair
   (g) produces the cation characteristic of the solvent
   (h) produces the anion characteristic of the solvent
2. neutralize
3. water, H_2O
4. conjugate base
5. chloride, Cl^-
6. acetate, CH_3COO^-. Perhaps you should review the names, formulas, and anions (here called conjugate bases) of common acids, Tables 7–1 and 7–2.
7. perchloric acid, $HClO_4$
8. sulfuric acid, H_2SO_4
9. sulfate, $SO_4{}^{2-}$
10. hydronium, H_3O^+
11. hydroxide, OH^-
12. autoionization
13. amphoteric
14. weaker
15. stronger
16. an unshared electron pair
17. greater electronegativity difference. See Section 11–5.
18. leveling effect. See Section 11–5.
19. water, a salt
20. ions
21. H^+ (aq) + OH^- (aq) → H_2O (ℓ). See Sections 7–5 and 11–6.
22. monoprotic, diprotic. Be sure you understand the term polyprotic.
23. H^+ (aq) + NH_3 (aq) → $NH_4{}^+$ (aq)
24. nonionized water molecules, an insoluble salt
25. normal, acidic, basic
26. ternary
27. oxidation state, increases. Notice that this also corresponds to an increasing number of oxygen atoms. For example, the order of increasing acid strengths of the *ternary* acids of chlorine is $HClO < HClO_2 < HClO_3 < HClO_4$. Be sure that you remember that this only applies when comparing *ternary* acids of the same *element*.

28. increasing electronegativity
29. bases
30. the metallic element. Some of these reactions occur at dangerously explosive rates.
31. nonmetal oxide. See Section 11–9.
32. carbonic acid, H_2CO_3
33. coordinate covalent. Be sure that you know what this term means. It refers to the formation of a covalent bond by one atom supplying both electrons for the bond.
34. an acid, a base. Review Section 11–13 for the terminology of the solvent system theory.
35. $NH_4^+ + NH_2^- \rightarrow 2NH_3$
36. 1
37. $\frac{1}{2}$
38. 1
39. 1
40. 1. The convenience of the use of equivalent weights is seen in Questions 38 through 40, compared with the use of moles in 36 and 37.
41. molarity $\times$ mL
42. normality $\times$ mL
43. 63.02
44. 63.02 mg or 0.06302 g
45. $90.04/2 = 45.02$
46. $74.10/2 = 37.05$
47. 0.15 N. This is because the equivalent weight and the formula weight of HCl are the same, since HCl produces 1 mole H^+ per mole HCl.
48. 0.45 N. The equivalent weight of H_3PO_4 is only one-third as great as its formula weight. Thus, a given weight of H_3PO_4 would contain three times as many equivalent weights of H_3PO_4 as moles of H_3PO_4. Normality is always equal to or greater than molarity.
49. 37.5 mL. Compare this problem with Example 11–11.
50. standard
51. titration
52. primary standard

Multiple Choice

1. (d)
2. (e). A Brønsted-Lowry acid acts as a source of H^+, BF_3 does not contain H.
3. (d). A Lewis base provides an unshared electron pair for bond formation. Of the compounds listed, only CH_4 has no unshared valence electron pairs.

4. (b). It accepts H^+.
5. (a). It accepts the electron pair from F^- (the base) in the formation of a coordinate covalent bond.
6. (a). Ammonia (the Lewis base) provides electron pairs to Cu^{2+}.
7. (a). In this case, as a Brønsted-Lowry base, accepting H^+
8. (c)
9. (b). The observation that most of the HCN is still present in undissociated form tells us that CN^- wins the competition for H^+ much more often than does H_2O.
10. (c)
11. (c). Reason as in Question 9. F^- must be a stronger base than H_2O, which must in turn be a stronger base than Br^-.
12. (e). This method is applicable only to the Group IA metals and to the heavier Group IIA metals. Study Section 11–10.
13. (b)
14. (e)
15. (a)
16. (e)
17. (e). This is also true for bases. Study the application of the idea of equivalent weight in Section 11–15.2.
18. (d). This too applies to bases as well as to acids.
19. (a)
20. (b)
21. (a)
22. (c)
23. (d). You should know the common strong acids. In addition, you should be able to use generalizations about strengths of binary and ternary acids discussed in Sections 11–5 and 11–8 to predict trends, even if you do not recognize the acids as strong or weak.

12

Oxidation-Reduction Reactions

Chapter Summary

In our first general survey of reaction types in Chapter 7, we saw that many reactions of differing types had one thing in common—they involved changes in oxidation numbers for at least some of the elements in the reaction. This class of reactions, called **oxidation-reduction reactions** or **redox reactions,** is now the object of a more detailed study in Chapter 12. Skill in recognizing and handling such reactions, both qualitatively and in terms of the amounts of substances involved, will aid in the study of many other topics of chemistry, especially electrochemistry, Chapter 19.

Section 12–1 reminds you of some of the basic concepts and terminology associated with redox reactions and provides additional breadth and detail in examples of applying these concepts and terms. An **oxidizing agent** (1) **gains** (or appears to gain) **electrons,** (2) is **reduced** (that is, undergoes a decrease in oxidation number), and (3) **oxidizes other substances.** A **reducing agent** (1) **loses** (or appears to lose) **electrons,** (2) is **oxidized** (that is, undergoes an increase in oxidation number), and (3) **reduces other substances.** You should practice determining the oxidation number of each element in any substance given its formula (review Section 4–12 for rules of assigning oxidation numbers). Then you should practice analyzing chemical reactions, whether balanced or not, to find out whether or not the reaction involves oxidation and reduction. You should be able to determine this whether the reaction is written as a molecular equation, as a total ionic equation, or as a net ionic equation. For those that are redox reactions, you will need to learn how to tell which substance is the oxidizing agent and which is the reducing agent.

As you study this portion of the chapter, be careful to learn both to recognize and to correctly apply the conventions for words and for formula representation. For instance, remember that the two terms **oxidation number** and **oxidation state** mean the same thing and are used interchangeably. Also be sure that you understand that the oxidation number is a quantity that is determined "per atom," and is represented in the text by the notation $+n$ or $-n$ *directly above* the *element* symbol. On the other hand, the ionic charge is the actual net electrical charge (in units of electronic charge) on the total ion, even if the ion is polyatomic; ionic charge is represented in the text by the notation $n+$ or $n-$ above and to the right of the formula for the ion.

Many applications of chemical reactions require that we write the equation to conform to the Law of Conservation of Matter (Chapter 1), that is, that the equation be **balanced.** Many redox equations are quite difficult to balance by inspection. However, recognition that these reactions involve electron transfer and that electrons are neither created nor destroyed in ordinary chemical reactions leads to the useful principle that the *total increase in oxidation numbers must equal the total decrease in oxidation numbers.* This, in turn, leads us to two very useful methods for balancing redox equations. Of course both methods for balancing redox equations lead to the same answer. It would be good to be familiar with both methods, though your instructor may prefer that you concentrate on becoming proficient in one or the other. In any case, be sure that you know how to carry out a completely reliable check on whether the resulting equation is balanced based on mass balance (*all* elements in the reaction!) and charge balance.

Section 12–2 describes the **change-in-oxidation-number** method, based on the equality of total increase and decrease in oxidation numbers. Whenever you apply this method, try to be systematic, following the recommended procedures until they are a habit.

The easiest type of equations to practice on first are those in which all reactants and products are given. This includes all equations given in Questions 8 through 11 at the end of the chapter in the text. However, for many reactions in aqueous solutions, it is necessary to add enough H and O to complete the mass balance if all reactants and products are not specified in the equation as given. Section 12–3 discusses this step, which is accomplished by adding *two of the three species* H^+, OH^-, and H_2O to the appropriate side of an equation. Since the preceding chapter covered acids and bases, it should be easy for you to remember which of these species you add, reasoning as follows: In acidic solutions, there is a lot of water (the solvent) and a large amount of H^+, but very little OH^- can be present. Thus, in acidic solutions there is essentially no OH^- to act as a reactant, and it cannot be written on the left-hand side of the equation; likewise, it should not be written on the right-hand side of the equation in acidic solution, since it would immediately be consumed by the excess H^+ to form water. So we conclude that in **acidic solution** we can add **only H^+ or H_2O** on either side as needed, but **we never add OH^-.** Similar reasoning (can you go through it?) regarding **basic solutions** (excess OH^-, very little H^+) leads to the conclusion that in basic solutions we can add **only OH^- or H_2O,** but **never H^+.** Questions 12 through 15 at the end of the text chapter will give you practice in this aspect of balancing redox equations.

Another method, equally valid and sometimes easier to apply, is the **ion-electron** method, frequently called the **half-reaction** method, discussed in Section 12–4. This method is based on the approach of separating the oxidation (electron loss) and reduction (electron gain) portions of the reaction into half-reactions, balancing each one separately, equalizing the numbers of electrons lost and gained in these two half-reactions, and then adding the balanced half-reactions to give the overall balanced equation. Again, as you learn this method, always apply the foolproof check of whether the final equation is balanced. Also, always check to be sure that no electrons remain on either side of the reaction! You can see that to apply this method you need to identify which species are changing in oxidation numbers, but the actual values of the oxidation numbers are not used in the balancing process. The same approach described earlier for adding H_2O and either H^+ or OH^- is applied in this method, but now to each half-reaction separately before recombining them.

Just as we were able to describe acid-base neutralization reactions by using the quantitative relationships associated with the balanced equations, we now take the same approach for redox reactions. The remaining two sections of this chapter deal with **redox titrations.** As before, we can carry out the calculations using the mole relationships indicated in the balanced equation, with solution concentrations expressed as molarity; in Section 12–5 this approach is illustrated with several examples. In Section 12–6, we see how to extend the idea of chemical equivalence and equivalent weight to oxidizing and reducing agents. First, recall how this was done for acids and bases. In an acid-base neutralization reaction, the essential thing was the transfer of H^+ from acid to base, so we defined the equivalent weight of an acid or base as that amount that could provide or accept, respectively, 1 mole of H^+. Now, in redox reactions, the essential transfer is that of electrons from one species to another, so we define the equivalent weight in those terms. The **equivalent weight** (also called 1 **equivalent**) **of a reducing agent** (which supplies electrons) is defined as the mass of the substance, measured in grams, that **supplies 1 mole of electrons; 1 equivalent weight of an oxidizing agent** (which accepts electrons) is likewise the mass of the substance that **gains 1 mole of electrons.** (Of course it is more convenient to think of 1 mole of electrons in terms of Avogadro's number, the number of any kind of items in 1 mole, than in terms of any "formula weight" of electrons.)

Once we have established these conventions, we find the same conveniences as before:

$$\text{no eq oxidizing agent} = \text{no eq reducing agent}$$

and

$$\text{no meq oxidizing agent} = \text{no meq reducing agent.}$$

Defining normality in just the same way as acids and bases, we see that

$$\text{no eq}_O = L_O \times N_O \text{ and no eq}_R = L_R \times N_R,$$

where the subscripts O and R mean oxidizing agent and reducing agent, respectively. All of the types of calculations presented in the remainder of Section 12–6 are just applications of these ideas. You must keep in mind that the equivalent weight of a redox reagent depends on the specific reaction that it undergoes—that is, how many electrons it accepts or supplies in that particular reaction. You should also notice that a substance may have one value for its equivalent weight when it acts as a redox reagent and another when it acts as an acid or as a base. An example of this is nitric acid; in redox reactions such as that in Question 7(c) in the text, its equivalent weight is equal to one-half its formula weight, since it undergoes a change of 2 in oxidation number. In acid-base reactions, the equivalent weight of HNO_3 is equal to its formula weight, since it is a monoprotic acid.

Study Goals

Be sure to review the ideas and skills from indicated sections of earlier chapters. Several of the study goals in this chapter take much practice (especially balancing redox reactions), so be sure you answer many of the questions in the text. Be systematic in your study.

1. Be able to assign oxidation numbers to elements, either free, in compounds, or in ions. Be able to recognize oxidation reactions and to distinguish them from reactions that do not involve oxidation-reduction. (Review Sections 4–12, 7–7; Exercises 2 through 7)
2. Be familiar with the terminology used to qualitatively describe redox reactions. Define and illustrate, with examples, each of the following terms: (a) oxidation, (b) reduction, (c) oxidizing agent, and (d) reducing agent. (Section 12–1; Exercises 1, 6, and 7)
3. Balance molecular and net ionic equations for redox reactions by either the *change-in-oxidation-number* method or the *ion-electron* method. Be able to add H^+, OH^-, and H_2O, as appropriate, to achieve mass balance of H and O. (Sections 12–2 through 12–4; Exercises 8 through 17)
4. Using molarity, perform stoichiometric calculations involving redox reactions in which one or more of the reactants is in solution. (Section 12–5; Exercises 18 through 25)
5. Given the reaction in which it participates, determine the equivalent weight and the normality of an oxidizing agent or a reducing agent in solution. (Section 12–6; Exercises 26 through 30)
6. Perform stoichiometric calculations as in Study Goal 14, using normality to express solution concentrations. (Section 12–6; Exercises 31 through 36)

Some Important Terms in This Chapter

Write the meanings *in your own words*. Check the Key Terms list and the chapter reading. Then rewrite your definitions, still in your own words, to

improve them. Study other new terms and review terms from preceding chapters if necessary.

oxidation

reduction

redox reaction

oxidizing agent

reducing agent

redox titration

equivalent weight (of oxidizing or reducing agent)

Preliminary Test

As in other chapters, this test will check your understanding of basic concepts and types of calculations. Be sure to practice *many* of the additional textbook exercises including those indicated with the Study Goals.

Short Answer

1. An oxidizing agent is a species that _____ electrons.
2. When an element in a substance undergoes an algebraic decrease in oxidation number, we say that the substance is being _____. In such a reaction it acts as the _____ agent.
3. The usual product formed when sulfuric acid acts as an oxidizing agent is _____ (name, formula); in this process, the oxidation number of sulfur changes from ___ to ___.
4. When permanganate ion acts as an oxidizing agent in acidic solution, the usual product formed is _____ (name, formula); during this process, the oxidation number of manganese changes from ___ to ___.
5. When permanganate ion acts as an oxidizing agent in basic solution, the usual product formed is _____ (name, formula); during this process, the oxidation number of manganese changes from ___ to ___.
6. When we need additional hydrogen and oxygen to balance the equation for a redox reaction that is carried out in acidic solution, we may add ___ or ___ to either side of the equation as needed, but we must not add ___.
7. The "change-in-oxidation-number" method for balancing redox equations is based on the idea that the _____ in oxidation numbers by all species being _____ must equal the _____ in oxidation numbers by all species being _____.
8. The "ion-electron" method for balancing redox equations is based on the idea that the ___ of electrons by all species being _____ must equal the ___ of electrons by all species being _____.
9. In applying the ion-electron method we formally separate the oxidation and the reduction processes, and write these as two separate _____, which we later recombine after balancing each separately.
10. When $Sn(OH)_3^-$ is converted to $Sn(OH)_6^{2-}$ the element tin is being _____, from oxidation number ___ to ___.
11. In the conversion of Question 10 the equivalent weight of $Sn(OH)_3^-$ is ___ grams.
12. When zinc metal is oxidized according to the reaction (not balanced)

$$Zn + NO_3^- \quad Zn^{2+} + N_2$$

its equivalent weight is _____ grams.
13. The equivalent weight of $KMnO_4$, used as an oxidizing agent in acidic solution, is _____.
14. The equivalent weight of $KMnO_4$, used as an oxidizing agent in basic solution is _____.
15. A solution of $KMnO_4$ is described as being 0.200 M. If this solution is to

be used as an oxidizing solution in acidic medium, its normality would be expressed as ———, while if it were to be used in basic medium the appropriate value for its normality would be ———.

Multiple Choice

1. In the reaction

$$2SO_2 + O_2 \rightarrow 2SO_3,$$

what is the oxidizing agent? (a) SO_2 (b) O_2 (c) SO_3 (d) none, since this is not a redox reaction.
2. In the reaction

$$Mg + H_2O \rightarrow MgO + H_2,$$

what is the reducing agent? (a) Mg (b) H_2O (c) MgO (d) H_2 (e) none, since this is not an oxidation-reduction reaction.
3. One of the reactions that takes place in a copper smelter to remove unwanted compounds from the ore is

$$CaCO_3 + SiO_2 \rightarrow CaSiO_3 + CO_2.$$

In this reaction, what is the oxidizing agent? (a) $CaCO_3$ (b) SiO_2 (c) $CaSiO_3$ (d) CO_2 (e) none, since this is not an oxidation-reduction reaction.
4. Copper(I) oxide may be prepared by boiling cuprous chloride with a metal hydroxide. The net ionic equation for this reaction is

$$2CuCl + 2OH^- \rightarrow Cu_2O + 2Cl^- + H_2O$$

In this reaction, what is the oxidizing agent? (a) CuCl (b) OH^- (c) Cu_2O (d) Cl^- (e) none, since this is not an oxidation-reduction reaction.
5. The reaction (not balanced)

$$SO_3^{2-} + MnO_4^- \rightarrow SO_4^{2-} + Mn^{2+}$$

is carried out in acidic solution. Which element is being reduced? (a) S (b) O (c) Mn (d) H (e) none, since this is not a redox reaction.
6. In the reaction of Question 5 which species is described as the reducing agent?
(a) SO_3^{2-} (b) MnO_4^- (c) SO_4^{2-} (d) Mn^{2+} (e) none since this is not a redox reaction.
7. In order to balance the equation in Question 5 the number that must be put in front of SO_3^{2-} and Mn^{2+} are, respectively, —— and ——
(a) 5 and 3. (b) 2 and 6. (c) 5 and 2. (d) 6 and 5. (e) 3 and 1.

8. The reaction

$$Cr_2O_7^{2-} + H_2S \rightarrow Cr^{3+} + S$$

is carried out in acidic solution. What element is being oxidized?
(a) Cr   (b) H   (c) O   (d) S   (e) none since this is not an oxi-dation-reduction reaction.

9. In the reaction of Question 8 which substance is described as the oxidiz-ing agent?
(a) $Cr_2O_7^{2-}$ (b) H_2S (c) Cr^{3+} (d) S   (e) none since this is not an oxidation-reduction reaction.

10. When the equation of Question 8 is completed and balanced the coeffi-cients in front of $Cr_2O_7^{2-}$ and S are, respectively, ___ and ___
(a) 1 and 3.   (b) 3 and 2.   (c) 2 and 7.   (d) 1 and 6.   (e) 10 and 4.

11. When the equation

$$NO_3^- + I_2 \rightarrow NO + IO_3^-$$

(acidic solution) is completed and balanced the coefficients in front of I_2 and NO are, respectively, ___ and ___
(a) 3 and 6.   (b) 3 and 10.   (c) 10 and 3.   (d) 1 and 2.   (e) 4 and 7.

> Note: It takes a great deal of practice to learn to deal comfort-ably with the kind of material in this chapter. This is especially true for recognizing and balancing oxidation-reduction reac-tions. Likewise, you will need much more practice at working molarity and normality problems than the questions in this guide have presented. You should work many of the text exercises suggested with the Study Goals.

Answers to Preliminary Test

Do not just look up answers. Think about the reasons for the answers.

Short Answer

1. gains
2. reduced, oxidizing
3. sulfur dioxide, SO_2, $+6$, $+4$
4. manganese (II) or manganous ions, Mn^{2+}, $+7$, $+2$
5. manganese dioxide, MnO_2, $+7$, $+4$
6. H^+, H_2O, OH^-
7. total increase, oxidized, total decrease, reduced
8. gain, reduced, loss, oxidized

9. half-reactions
10. oxidized, $+2, +4$
11. 84.9. The formula weight of $Sn(OH)_3^-$ is 169.7; the equivalent weight is equal to half that since it transfers two electrons (see Question 10).
12. 32.7. This is 65.4 (zinc's atomic weight) divided by 2 since the zinc atom transfers two electrons (undergoes a change in oxidation number of 2) in the reaction. Notice that it is not necessary to balance the equation to answer questions such as these.
13. 31.6. In acidic solution manganese undergoes a change of 5 in oxidation number, so the equivalent weight is $\frac{1}{5}$ the formula weight or $158.0/5 = 31.6$.
14. 52.7. In basic solution the change of oxidation number of manganese is 3, so the equivalent weight is $158.0/3 = 52.7$.
15. 1.000 N, 0.600 N. Since the equivalent weight is lower than the formula weight in the two cases by factors of 5 and 3 respectively, the same amount of solute would correspond to 5 and 3 times as many equivalent weights, respectively.

Multiple Choice

1. (b)
2. (a)
3. (e)
4. (e)
5. (c)
6. (a)
7. (c). The balanced equation is

$$5SO_3^{2-} + 6H^+ + 2MnO_4^- \rightarrow 5SO_4^{2-} + 2Mn^{2+} + 3H_2O.$$

Notice that we must add H^+ and H_2O since the reaction takes place in acidic solution.

8. (d)
9. (a)
10. (a). The balanced equation (remember that it is in acidic solution) is

$$Cr_2O_7^{2-} + 3H_2S + 8H^+ \rightarrow 2Cr^{3+} + 3S + 7H_2O.$$

11. (b). The balanced equation is

$$10NO_3^- + 3I_2 + 4H^+ \rightarrow 10NO + 6IO_3^- + 2H_2O.$$

13

Chemical Thermodynamics

Chapter Summary

At many stages so far in our study of chemistry, we have been concerned with questions such as these: Which is more stable: situation A or situation B? Will the chemical reaction occur? Will the gas expand or contract if we decrease the pressure? Which is more stable at the stated conditions: solid, liquid, or gas? Will the substance dissolve in water? Is the dissolution process exothermic or endothermic? What energy changes are associated with the process of melting or vaporization? All of these questions, varied as they seem, are really just applications of the question, "Is a proposed process, at a specified set of conditions, spontaneous?" A general approach to answering this question, based on the study of energy changes that accompany a process, is supplied by **chemical thermodynamics,** the subject of Chapter 13. In the course of this chapter, we will also learn how to understand and predict the amount of heat produced or absorbed when a change takes place—the topic called **thermochemistry.**

As we saw briefly in Chapter 10, the spontaneity of a process is favored by two factors: (1) a lowering of the energy (exothermicity) and (2) an increase in the disorder. It may help you to remember that rocks roll *down* hills (lower potential energy), not up, and that it is easier to *mix* things (scrambling an egg) than to unmix them. It is the intent of this chapter to study these two factors quantitatively and to show how both factors must be considered in understanding whether a particular process can occur. These ideas, which may seem somewhat abstract at this point, are exemplified in Section 13-1. Be sure that you understand that just because a process is **exothermic** (gives off energy to its surroundings) it is not necessarily spontaneous; exothermicity favors, but does not guarantee, spontaneity.

Section 13-2 introduces you to some thermodynamic terms, a few of which have been used earlier in the text, and you will encounter others throughout the chapter. In order to really understand the logic of chemical thermodynamics, you must be careful to pay close attention to the terms used and interpret them as they were meant to be. In the terminology of thermodynamics, a **process** may be any proposed change in the **system** under observation—a change of state, an expansion or contraction of the sample, the absorption or evolution of heat with or without a change of state, a chemical reaction, and so on.

As we saw above, one factor that helps to make a process spontaneous is a lowering of the energy. In thermodynamics, we express the change in the amount of energy that a sample (the system) contains as ΔE. Be sure that you remember that Δ (any property) is defined as the final value of the property minus the initial value of the property; therefore, the change is positive if the property increases. That is, if the final energy is greater than the initial energy, ΔE is positive. Because the total amount of energy in the universe is constant, in order for the system to increase its energy it must absorb energy from its surroundings.

The fundamental relationship among ΔE, heat, and work is explained in Section 13–3. One way of understanding this important relationship is as follows. If we put heat into a system it can (1) increase the internal energy of the system, (2) cause the system to do some work (for example, by expanding against an external force), or it can cause some combination of (1) and (2). Since energy can be neither created nor destroyed, the total amount of heat absorbed by the system (q) must show up as either an increase in the energy (ΔE) or as work done by the system (w). Thus, $q = \Delta E + w$, or as it is usually written, $\Delta E = q - w$. You *must* remember the conventions for when the values of q, w, and ΔE are positive.

One very useful comment about notation can be made here. We are using a symbol that will become quite common. Whenever we write Δ (any quantity) we mean the change in that quantity. This is always calculated as (the final value of the quantity) − (the initial value of the quantity). As an analogy, suppose your bank balance last Thursday was $450 and today it is $300. We could express the *change* in your bank balance as $\Delta \$ = \$_{final} - \$_{initial} = \$300 - \$450 = -\$150$. Do you see why we subtract them in the order we do? The negative answer indicates a *decrease* in the quantity being described. You will also notice that it does not matter how many deposits or withdrawals your bank balance had during the time elapsed—the *net change* is still a decrease of $150. This is the idea of a state function; all of the Δ values we will see, ΔE, ΔH, and so on, can be considered in this same way.

Heat energy can only be given up by one body if it is absorbed by another. The measurements of chemical thermodynamics involve heat changes, so we must have methods for measuring the flow of heat from one body to another. We can use the methods of **calorimetry** (Section 13–4) to measure the changes in energy of a sample. In addition to learning how to carry out the calculations associated with calorimetry, you will see in this section that different reactions liberate (ΔE negative) or absorb (ΔE positive) different amounts of heat. One practical use of liberated heat is to cause work to be done, e.g., to cause an automobile to roll, so some reactions such as combustion reactions are better than others for such applications. The discussion of gasohol exemplifies a practical application of these factors.

In calorimetry as discussed so far, the heat is released or absorbed at constant volume so it is a measure of ΔE for the process (no work done). However, not many reactions take place at constant volume under convenient laboratory conditions. In order to overcome this disadvantage we can use another thermodynamic quantity (or state function), the **enthalpy change** (ΔH), Section 13–5, as a description of the heat change at constant **pressure.** The relation between ΔH and ΔE for a reaction is described in this section. In general terms, ΔH is easier to measure than ΔE, and a lowering of the enthalpy content of a system is also favorable to spontaneity of the process.

Any reaction, then, can have its value of ΔH determined; if this is determined at 1 atm pressure and **thermodynamic** standard temperature (25°C, 298 K), the value of ΔH for the reaction is written as ΔH^0 and is referred to as the standard enthalpy change. Section 13–6 introduces the idea of a **standard molar enthalpy of formation** of a substance, which is the enthalpy change for the reaction in which *one mole* of the substance is produced from the elements, all reactants and products being at standard-state conditions. (Be sure that you understand what is meant by the **standard state** of a substance; you should also notice that the so-called standard temperature for thermodynamic studies is different than that used in gas law problems.) Therefore, the standard molar enthalpy of formation of a substance, ΔH_f^0, is just a measure of how much higher or lower the substance is in enthalpy content than are its constituent elements.

According to **Hess' Law** of heat summation, Section 13–7, we see that we can calculate what will be the ΔH (or ΔH^0) for any proposed reaction if we can either (1) think of reactions to measure that would algebraically total to the desired reaction or (2) find tabulations of the ΔH_f^0 values for all substances involved in the reaction. This is very important because we will want to use the value of ΔH^0 for a proposed reaction to help us tell whether it is spontaneous, and we can now calculate this without having to carry out the reaction. Notice that another possible use would be to tell us how much heat we will either have to supply or be able to dissipate (or use for doing work!) when the reaction occurs.

We have talked many times in earlier chapters about the stabilities of chemical bonds in covalent substances. Now we have a way of measuring these **bond energies** experimentally, Section 13–8. As you study this section, the one thing to keep in mind is that the bond energy calculation refers only to the step in which the bonds form from isolated gaseous atoms or the bonds break to form isolated gaseous atoms. Usually we cannot measure this directly, so we must deduce it from first measuring the energy (or enthalpy) associated with the formation of bonds from the elements in their standard states, and then correcting, via Hess' Law, for the conversion of elements from their stable forms (solids, diatomic molecules, and so on) to isolated atoms. Once derived, tabulations of bond energies can also be used to estimate heats of reactions and to help understand why reactions that involve the breaking of very stable bonds are so hard to carry out. A similar application to ionic compounds involves the **lattice energy,** Section 13–9. (Review the origins of this energy, Section 4–10, and its use in Chapter 10 to explain solubilities.) Again, using the **Born-Haber cycle** we can determine the crystal lattice energies of ionic substances from overall measurable heats of reduction by correcting for steps other than those involving the attraction of ions into the lattice arrangement.

So far in this chapter we have concentrated on the first factor that favors spontaneity, the exothermicity of the process. Sections 13–10 and 13–11 deal with the second favorable factor, an increase in disorder. After some general remarks about the more disordered situation being the more favorable, we introduce a thermodynamic measure of disorder called **entropy.** Thus, an increase in entropy, ΔS positive, favors a process being spontaneous. The discussion of freezing and the discussion accompanying Table 13–5 will help you to clarify this concept. The introduction of a scale of absolute entropies allows us to use a relationship analogous to Hess' Law to calculate entropy changes for any proposed process.

Now, in the final sections of the chapter, we are ready to combine the two factors that affect spontaneity into a single measure, the change in Gibbs free energy, ΔG. As seen in Section 13–12, the definition

$$\Delta G = \Delta H - T\Delta S$$

allows us to formulate simply the rules for predicting whether a reaction will be spontaneous: ΔG negative means that the reaction is **spontaneous** and *can* occur (but does not guarantee that it will at a measurable rate), whereas ΔG positive means that the reaction is **not spontaneous** and cannot occur under the conditions specified.

As for other thermodynamic quantities, we ordinarily carry out the calculation of free energy change with respect to very special conditions— most significantly, all reactants and products at 1 atm pressure or at concentrations of 1 M. We designate the free energy change at these special conditions as $\Delta G^0 = \Delta H^0 - T\Delta S^0$. The presence of T in the definition allows us to see that some reactions that are impossible at some temperatures can be made spontaneous at other temperatures. We can calculate from this relation the temperature at which the reaction will become spontaneous, if indeed, it can be spontaneous at any temperature. It is very important that you understand the discussion accompanying Table 13–6 in the text. Be sure that you can calculate ΔG^0 from either (1) known or experimentally determined values of ΔH_f^0 and S^0 or (2) known ΔG_f^0 values. In the former method, be quite careful of the units. We will see many uses of ΔG^0 in subsequent chapters including its relation to equilibrium constants (Chapter 15) and electrochemistry (Chapter 19).

There is much detail and considerable subtlety in this chapter. You must proceed slowly through the chapter, being sure that you master the terminology and the calculations of one section before proceeding. Do not be content with just seeing how to do the problems; since they involve only a little addition, subtraction, and multiplication of numbers they are easy to work. The usual difficulty with chemical thermodynamics at first encounter is in seeing what these calculations mean. Just remember that we are dealing with energy changes, calculating the predicted energy changes that will accompany reactions and trying to use these energy changes to predict whether or not a reaction can go, or to understand why it does or does not go at certain conditions. And do not memorize—think!

Study Goals

It may help you to write out a brief summary of the ideas of each study goal, summarizing the applicable portions of your class notes and text readings. Be sure to answer many of the suggested questions related to the study goals.

1. Be familiar with the calculations and units used to describe heat transfer. (Review Section 1–13)
2. State the First Law of Thermodynamics both in words and in mathematical form. Summarize its implications with respect to reaction spontaneity. Carry out calculations relating ΔE, q, and w. (Sections 13–1 and 13–3; Exercises 12 through 17 and 20)
3. Understand the basic terminology of thermodynamics as presented and used in this chapter (Be able to give examples of each.): (a) system, (b) surroundings, (c) state of a system, (d) state function, (e) standard conditions, (f) endothermic process, (g) exothermic process, (h) spontaneous process, and (i) nonspontaneous process. (Section 13–2; Exercises 1 through 4, 6 through 9, and 28)
4. Be familiar with the measurements and calculations of calorimetry. Be able to carry out the calculations, using experimental data, to determine energy changes for reactions and processes. (Section 13–4; Exercises 18 through 22)
5. Explain the relationship between energy change and enthalpy change. Explain why, in many cases, the use of ΔH is an advantage. (Section 13–5; Exercises 24 through 27)
6. Know what is meant by the standard enthalpy change of a reaction. Know what is meant by the standard molar enthalpy of formation of a substance. (Section 13–6; Exercises 29 through 32)
7. Understand the meaning of Hess' Law and why it works. Know how to carry out the calculations of Hess' Law to determine enthalpy changes for specified reactions. (Sections 13–6 and 13–7; Exercises 26 through 30 and 33 through 59)

8. Given the enthalpy changes for appropriate reactions or physical changes, be able to calculate average bond energies. Given appropriate bond energies, be able to calculate enthalpy changes for reactions. (Section 13–8; Exercises 60 through 72)

9. Be able to perform the calculations of the Born-Haber cycle. (Section 13–9; Exercises 73 through 78)

10. State the Second Law of Thermodynamics and summarize its implications with respect to reaction spontaneity. (Section 13–10; Exercises 79 through 81 and 87)

11. Understand the interpretation of entropy of a system in terms of microscopic disorder within that system. Be able to predict ΔS for many kinds of common changes, both chemical reactions and physical changes. (Section 13–11; Exercises 82 through 84 and 86)

12. Use tabulated values of absolute entropies of reactants and products to calculate the entropy change for a reaction. (Section 13–11; Exercises 83)

13. Explain how ΔH and $T\Delta S$ are related to spontaneity of a reaction. (Section 13–12; Exercises 88, 90 and 91)

14. Explain what is meant by the "Gibbs free energy change" for a reaction. Be able to relate it, both mathematically and descriptively, to enthalpy and entropy changes. (Section 13–12; Exercises 89, 92 and 94)

15. Be able to calculate the standard Gibbs free energy change for a reaction (a) from standard Gibbs free energies of formation of reactants and products and (b) from standard molar enthalpies of formation and standard entropies of reactants and products. (Section 13–12; Exercises 95 through 97)

16. Use the standard Gibbs free energy change for a reaction as an indicator of spontaneity. (Section 13–12; Exercise 97)

17. Determine the temperature range of spontaneity of a reaction from tabulated thermodynamic data. Make general statements regarding the spontaneity of a reaction at relatively low and high temperatures on the basis of the signs of ΔH^0 and ΔS^0. (Section 13–12; Exercises 98 through 104)

> *Note:* After you believe you have mastered the material of this chapter, it would be especially beneficial to try to work many of Exercises 105 through 114 in the text. This will give you valuable experience in recognizing problems of various kinds as well as applying the concept and skills you have learned in the chapter.

Some Important Terms in This Chapter

Write the meanings *in your own words.* Check the Key Terms list and the chapter reading. Then rewrite your definitions, still in your own words, to

improve them. Study other new terms and review terms from preceding chapters if necessary.

kinetic energy

potential energy

thermodynamics

thermochemistry

First Law of Thermodynamics

system

surroundings

state function

thermodynamic state of a system

enthalpy

enthalpy change

standard enthalpy change

standard molar enthalpy of formation

Hess' Law of heat summation

bond energy

Born-Haber cycle

spontaneity

entropy

standard entropy

free energy

free energy change

standard free energy change

Preliminary Test

As in other chapters, this test will check your understanding of basic concepts and types of calculations. Be sure to practice *many* of the additional textbook exercises.

True–False

Mark each statement as true (T) or false (F).

_____ 1. In order for a body to have energy it must do some work.
_____ 2. Potential energy can be changed into kinetic energy.
_____ 3. Kinetic energy can be changed into potential energy.
_____ 4. Chemical energy is a form of kinetic energy.
_____ 5. The heat capacity of a body is the same as its specific heat.
_____ 6. When we mix water at 100°C with water at 20°C the final water temperature averages out to 60°C.
_____ 7. When we put a 100-g piece of metal at 100°C into 100 g of water at 20°C the final temperature is 60°C.
_____ 8. The reverse of an exothermic process must be endothermic.
_____ 9. The term ΔH means $H_{final} - H_{initial}$.

_____ 10. The term ΔT means $T_{final} - T_{initial}$.

_____ 11. A reaction in which the system absorbs heat from its surroundings is called endothermic.

_____ 12. A reaction in which the system absorbs heat from its surroundings has a negative ΔH value.

_____ 13. The process described by the thermochemical equation

$$H_2 (g) + I_2 (g) \rightarrow 2HI (g) + heat$$

is described as exothermic.

_____ 14. The process described by the thermochemical equation

$$H_2 (g) + I_2 (g) \rightarrow 2HI (g) + heat$$

has a negative value of ΔH.

_____ 15. The thermochemical equation

$$C(graphite) + \tfrac{1}{2}O_2 (g) \rightarrow CO (g) \qquad \Delta H = -110.5 \text{ kJ}$$

refers to the reaction of one atom of C with one-half molecule of O_2 to give one molecule of CO.

_____ 16. If the temperature of a reaction mixture in a coffee-cup calorimeter increases as the reaction proceeds, the reaction is endothermic, since the mixture is absorbing heat from the surrounding air.

_____ 17. Hess' Law is true because enthalpy is a state function.

_____ 18. The standard molar enthalpy of formation of a substance is the amount of heat one mole of the substance contains at standard conditions.

_____ 19. The enthalpy change at standard conditions for the reaction

$$H_2 (g) + I_2 (s) \rightarrow 2HI (g)$$

is referred to as the standard molar enthalpy of formation of HI (g).

_____ 20. The enthalpy change at standard conditions for the reaction

$$\tfrac{1}{2}H_2 (g) + \tfrac{1}{2}I_2 (g) \rightarrow HI (g)$$

is referred to as the standard molar enthalpy of formation of HI (g).

_____ 21. The enthalpy change at standard conditions for the reaction

$$CO (g) + \tfrac{1}{2}O_2 (g) \rightarrow CO_2 (g)$$

is referred to as the standard molar enthalpy of formation of CO_2 (g).

_____ 22. According to the First Law of Thermodynamics, the only way we can increase the internal energy of a system is to heat it.

_____ 23. The advantage of a bomb calorimeter is that the volume is held constant, so that the heat change is equal to the change in internal energy of the system.

_____ 24. A reaction that is exothermic must be spontaneous.

_____ 25. A reaction that is spontaneous must be exothermic.

_____ 26. The reverse of an exothermic reaction is an endothermic reaction.

_____ 27. The reverse of a spontaneous reaction is a nonspontaneous reaction.

_____ 28. When we say that ΔE is a state function we mean that the energy change of the system does not depend on its initial or final state.

_____ 29. The enthalpy change, ΔH, of a system is a state function.

_____ 30. The heat, q, absorbed by a system is a state function.

_____ 31. The work, w, done by a system is a state function.

_____ 32. The entropy change, ΔS, of a system is a state function.

_____ 33. The Gibbs free energy change, ΔG, of a system is a state function.

_____ 34. The bond energy of any binary compound consisting of only two elements is equal to its ΔH_f^0, divided by the number of bonds formed per molecule.

_____ 35. The enthalpy change associated with the reaction in which 1 mole of H_2 at standard conditions is formed from 2 moles of H atoms is called the bond energy of the H—H bond.

_____ 36. The enthalpy change associated with the reaction in which 1 mole of HCl at standard conditions is formed from $\frac{1}{2}$ mole of H_2 and $\frac{1}{2}$ mole of Cl_2 is called the bond energy of the H—Cl bond.

_____ 37. The enthalpy change associated with the reaction in which 1 mole of HCl at standard conditions is formed from 1 mole of H atoms and 1 mole of Cl atoms is called the bond energy of the H—Cl bond.

_____ 38. For the vaporization of 1 mole of water at 1 atm at its normal boiling point, $\Delta E = \Delta H$.

_____ 39. The enthalpy change of a gas phase reaction is the energy required to break all the bonds in reactant molecules minus the energy required to break all the bonds in product molecules.

ΔH_{rxn}^0 for the reaction

$$SiH_4 \ (g) + 2O_2 \ (g) \rightarrow SiO_2 \ (s) + 2H_2O \ (\ell)$$

is -1516 kJ. The next five questions, 40 through 44, refer to this reaction.

_____ 40. The reaction is exothermic.

_____ 41. When this reaction is carried out at constant pressure with 1 mole of SiH_4 and sufficient oxygen, the reaction mixture gives off 1,516,000 joules of heat to its surroundings.

_____ 42. When this reaction is carried out at constant pressure with 2 moles of SiH_4 and sufficient oxygen, the reaction mixture gives off 1,516,000 joules of heat to its surroundings.

_____ 43. When this reaction is carried out at constant pressure, the reaction mixture does work against its surroundings.

_____ 44. When this reaction is carried out at constant volume with 1 mole of SiH_4 and sufficient oxygen, the reaction mixture gives off 1,516,000 joules of heat to its surroundings.

_____ 45. The entropy of a substance is greater as a liquid than as a solid.
_____ 46. The entropy of a substance is greater as a gas than as a liquid.
_____ 47. All reactions become more spontaneous at higher temperatures.

Short Answer

1. The sample or portion of the universe that we wish to study or describe in thermodynamics is called the _____.
2. Three examples of state functions of a gaseous sample are _____, _____, and _____.
3. In calculations with the First Law of Thermodynamics, we use the convention that heat absorbed by the system from its surroundings is given a _____ sign.
4. In calculations with the First Law of Thermodynamics, we use the convention that work done on the system by its surroundings is given a _____ sign.
5. If a gas sample absorbs 1,000 calories of heat from its surroundings and does 400 calories of work by expansion against its surroundings, its internal energy must _____ by ___ calories.
6. A reaction in which the total chemical potential energies of the products is greater than the total chemical potential energies of the reactants is said to be _____.
7. Measurements in calorimetry are based on equating heat lost by the sample to heat gained by the surroundings. This is an application of the Law of _____.
8. A pure substance is said to be in its standard state at conditions of _____ and _____.
9. For a change that takes place at constant volume, the heat gained or lost by the system is a measure of ___ for the system.
10. For a change that takes place at constant pressure, the heat gained or lost by the system is a measure of ___ for the system.
11. A statement of Hess' Law in words is that the enthalpy change for a reaction is the same whether it occurs _____ or _____.
12. The enthalpy change associated with the formation of 1 mole of any substance at standard conditions from its elements, also at standard conditions, is called the _____ of the substance.
13. The enthalpy change associated with the reaction in which 1 mole of HBr at standard conditions is formed from the appropriate numbers of moles

of hydrogen gas and bromine liquid, all at standard conditions, is called the _____ of HBr.

14. The enthalpy change associated with the reaction in which 1 mole of HBr at standard conditions is formed from the appropriate numbers of moles of hydrogen atoms and bromine atoms is called the _____ of HBr.

The following equations, referred to by letter, may be used in the next four questions, 15 through 18. Consider all reactants and products at 1 atm, 298 K.

A. C (graphite) $+ O_2$ (g) $\rightarrow CO_2$ (g)
B. C (g) $+ O_2$ (g) $\rightarrow CO_2$ (g)
C. C (graphite) $+ 2O$ (g) $\rightarrow CO_2$ (g)
D. C (g) $+ 2O$ (g) $\rightarrow CO_2$ (g)
E. CO (g) $+ \frac{1}{2}O_2$ (g) $\rightarrow CO_2$ (g)
F. C (graphite) $+ \frac{1}{2}O_2$ (g) $\rightarrow CO$ (g)
G. C (g) $+ \frac{1}{2}O_2$ (g) $\rightarrow CO$ (g)
H. C (graphite) $+ O$ (g) $\rightarrow CO$ (g)
I. C (g) $+ O$ (g) $\rightarrow CO$ (g)

15. The enthalpy change for Reaction ____ is referred to as the standard molar enthalpy of formation of carbon monoxide.
16. The enthalpy change for the reverse of Reaction ____ is referred to as the bond energy of carbon monoxide.
17. The enthalpy change for Reaction ____ is referred to as the standard molar enthalpy of formation of carbon dioxide.
18. If we subtract the ΔH^0 value for Reaction C from that for Reaction A, the result would be equal to the _____ in O_2.

19. The sequence of reactions used to determine lattice energy for an ionic substance is called a _____.
20. If we reverse a chemical equation, we must multiply its ΔH by _____.
21. The symbol for enthalpy is _____.
22. The symbol for enthalpy change for any process at any conditions is _____.
23. The symbol for enthalpy change for a process in which all substances are at standard conditions is _____.
24. The symbol for the standard molar enthalpy of formation of a substance is _____.
25. The energy holding the atoms, molecules, or ions in a crystal in their regular arrangement is called the _____.
26. A reaction in which the total heat content of the products is lower than the total heat content of the reactants is said to be _____.

27. A reaction in which the system absorbs heat from its surroundings is called _____.
28. A reaction in which the system absorbs heat from its surroundings has a _____ ΔH value.
29. The standard enthalpy change for the reaction

$$\tfrac{1}{2}H_2 \,(g) + \tfrac{1}{2}F_2 \,(g) \to HF \,(g)$$

is called the _____ of HF (g).
30. The reaction whose standard enthalpy change is the standard molar enthalpy of formation of NH_3 (g) is _____.

For each of the changes described in Questions 31–40, indicate whether the entropy of the system would increase (I), decrease (D), or remain unchanged (U). Of course, you should know which ones are described as having $\Delta S = +$, 0, or −.

31. A liquid is frozen to make a solid. _____
32. A new deck of cards is carried home from the store, its wrapper intact. _____
33. A new deck of cards is shuffled. _____
34. A shuffled deck of cards is rearranged according to suits. _____
35. Salt is dissolved in water. _____
36. 2 moles of hydrogen atoms combine to make 1 mole of hydrogen molecules: $2H \,(g) \to H_2 \,(g)$. _____
37. Calcium carbonate decomposes on heating:
    $CaCO_3 \,(s) \to CaO \,(s) + CO_2 \,(g)$. _____
38. Nitrogen gas and hydrogen gas combine to form ammonia gas:
    $N_2 \,(g) + 3H_2 \,(g) \to 2NH_3 \,(g)$. _____
39. A sample of ammonia gas, NH_3 (g), is carried from New York to Philadelphia. _____
40. Dry ice, CO_2 (s), sublimes to form CO_2 (g). _____

41. Complete the relationship: $\Delta G = \Delta H$ _____.
42. A reaction in which ΔS is positive tends to become more spontaneous as the temperature _____.

Multiple Choice

____ 1. If a system absorbs heat and also does work on its surroundings, its energy
   (a) must increase.
   (b) must decrease.

(c) must not change.

(d) may either increase or decrease, depending on the relative amounts of heat absorbed and work done.

_____ 2. A calorimeter is

(a) a dieting aid.

(b) a device used to measure transfer of heat energy.

(c) equal to the molar enthalpy of reaction.

(d) an indicator of spontaneity.

(e) only useful in measuring exothermic reactions.

_____ 3. To change 1 mole of ice to 1 mole of liquid water at 0°C 1,440 calories of heat are needed. For this process

(a) $q = 0$.   (b) $\Delta E = 0$.   (c) $\Delta H = 1,440$ cal.

(d) $\Delta H = -1,440$ cal.   (e) $w = 1,440$ cal.

_____ 4. All spontaneous reactions

(a) give off heat.   (b) are fast.   (c) have $\Delta G < 0$.   (d) have $\Delta H < 0$.   (e) have $\Delta S > 0$.

_____ 5. Given the following standard heats of reaction:

$$S\ (s) + H_2\ (g) \rightarrow H_2S\ (g) \qquad\qquad\qquad \Delta H = -65.1\ kcal$$
$$H_2\ (g) \rightarrow 2H\ (g) \qquad\qquad\qquad\qquad \Delta H = 104.1\ kcal$$
$$S\ (s) \rightarrow S\ (g) \qquad\qquad\qquad\qquad\qquad \Delta H = 5.7\ kcal$$

the bond energy for the H—S single bond is

(a) 175 kcal/mol.   (b) 164.6 kcal/mol.   (c) 87.5 kcal/mol.

(d) 82.3 kcal/mol.   (e) 33.3 kcal/mol.

_____ 6. For a reaction in which gases are neither produced nor consumed, ΔH is _____ ΔE.

(a) the same as   (b) less than   (c) greater than   (d) unrelated to

_____ 7. For a reaction in which more moles of gas are produced than are consumed, ΔH is _____ ΔE.

(a) the same as   (b) less than   (c) greater than   (d) unrelated to

_____ 8. A reaction occurring under certain conditions has an enthalpy change of $\Delta H = -50$ kJ. This means that 50 kJ of heat will be liberated

(a) if the reaction is carried out at constant volume.

(b) if the reaction is carried out at constant temperature.

(c) if the reaction is carried out at constant pressure.

(d) if the reaction involves only gases.

(e) no matter how the reaction is carried out.

_____ 9. Is an exothermic process spontaneous?

(a) Yes, always   (b) No, never   (c) Sometimes

_____ 10. Given the following reactions and their associated enthalpy changes:

$$CH_4 \text{ (g)} \rightarrow C \text{ (g)} + 4H \text{ (g)} \qquad\qquad \Delta H = 1660 \text{ kJ}$$
$$O_2 \text{ (g)} \rightarrow 2O \text{ (g)} \qquad\qquad \Delta H = \;\;490 \text{ kJ}$$
$$H_2O \text{ (g)} \rightarrow 2H \text{ (g)} + O \text{ (g)} \qquad\qquad \Delta H = \;\;929 \text{ kJ}$$
$$CO_2 \text{ (g)} \rightarrow C \text{ (g)} + 2O \text{ (g)} \qquad\qquad \Delta H = 1611 \text{ kJ}$$

Calculate ΔH for the combustion (burning) of 1 mole of CH_4 to form H_2O (g) and CO_2 (g) as described by the reaction

$$CH_4 \text{ (g)} + 2CO_2 \text{ (g)} \rightarrow 2H_2O \text{ (g)} + CO_2 \text{ (g)}$$

(a) -390 kJ   (b) 4690 kJ   (c) -829 kJ   (d) 6109 kJ
(e) -1318 kJ

_____ 11. The value of ΔH for the following reaction, as written, is -2220 kJ. How much heat is produced when 11.0 g of propane gas, C_3H_8, is burned in a constant pressure system?

$$C_3H_8 \text{ (g)} + 5O_2 \text{ (g)} \rightarrow 3CO_2 \text{ (g)} + 4H_2O \text{ (ℓ)}$$

(a) 555 kJ   (b) 2220 kJ   (c) 50.5 kJ   (d) 24420 kJ
(e) 25.96 kJ

_____ 12. When a liquid boils, which of the following must be true?
(a) $\Delta S < 0$ (b) $\Delta S > 0$ (c) $\Delta T < 0$ (d) $\Delta T > 0$

_____ 13. Which one of the following statements is correct?
(a) The standard molar enthalpy of formation of an element is usually positive.
(b) ΔH can never equal ΔE.
(c) q and w are state functions.
(d) $q - w$ is a state function.
(e) The standard entropy S^0 of an element is zero.

_____ 14. For some reaction carried out a constant atmospheric pressure and at constant temperature of 25°C, it is found that $\Delta H^0 = -38.468$ kJ and $\Delta S^0 = +51.4$ J/K. What is the value of ΔG^0 for this reaction at these conditions?
(a) -53.785 kJ   (b) -84.454 kJ   (c) 53.785 kJ
(d) 84.454 kJ

_____ 15. Is the reaction referred to in Question 14 spontaneous at the conditions given?
(a) Yes   (b) No   (c) Insufficient information is given to answer.

_____ 16. For the process H_2O (ℓ) $\rightarrow$ H_2O (g) at 1 atm and 100°C, the change in enthalpy is
(a) positive.   (b) negative.   (c) zero.

_____ 17. For the process referred to in Question 16, the change in entropy is
(a) positive.   (b) negative.   (c) zero.

_____ 18. For the process referred to in Question 17, the change in Gibbs free energy is
(a) positive.   (b) negative.   (c) zero.

_____ 19. A reaction for which $\Delta H = +$ and $\Delta S = -$
   (a) is spontaneous at all temperatures.
   (b) is not spontaneous at any temperature.
   (c) could become spontaneous at high temperature.
   (d) could become spontaneous at low temperature.
_____ 20. A reaction for which $\Delta H = -$ and $\Delta S = -$
   (a) is spontaneous at all temperatures.
   (b) is not spontaneous at any temperature.
   (c) could become spontaneous at high temperature.
   (d) could become spontaneous at low temperature.
_____ 21. A reaction for which $\Delta H = +$ and $\Delta S = +$
   (a) is spontaneous at all temperatures.
   (b) is not spontaneous at any temperature.
   (c) could become spontaneous at high temperature.
   (d) could become spontaneous at low temperature.

> *Note:* The questions in this Study Guide have not provided you
> with much practice at actual thermodynamic calculations. Be
> sure that you work many problems from the end of Chapter 13
> in the text. This is especially true for Hess' Law problems,
> Exercises 33 through 59.

Answers to Preliminary Test

Do not just look up answers. Think about the reasons for the answers.

True – False

For those that are false, it is especially important to think carefully *why* they
are false.

1. False. Energy is the *capacity* to do work or transfer heat; it is not
   necessary that work actually be done or heat actually be transferred.
2. True. Think about the rock, whose higher potential energy at the top of
   the hill can be changed (partly) into kinetic energy as it rolls down the hill.
3. True. Suppose you throw a ball into the air. As it goes up its kinetic
   energy decreases; that kinetic energy is transformed into increasing
   potential energy. Of course, after it has reached the top of its travel the
   reverse begins to happen.
4. False. It is a form of potential energy.
5. False. The heat capacity of a body is the amount of heat required to raise
   the temperature of that body (whatever its mass) by 1 degree Celsius. The
   specific heat refers specifically to one gram of the substance of which the

body is composed. In the terminology of Chapter 1, heat capacity is an extensive property whereas specific heat is an intensive property.

6. False. Common sense should tell you, for instance, that putting 1 teaspoon of 100°C water into a gallon of 40°C water cannot make the final temperature equal to 70°C! The result depends on the relative masses of water. Review the heat transfer calculations in Chapter 1.

7. False. The temperature change depends on the specific heat of each substance as well as the mass of each body. Review the heat transfer calculations in Chapter 1.

8. True

9. True

10. True

11. True

12. False. If it absorbs heat from the surroundings, its heat content (enthalpy) is increasing, so that $H_{final} > H_{initial}$. Then $\Delta H = H_{final} - H_{initial} > 0$.

13. True

14. True

15. False. Thermochemical equations always refer explicitly to the number of *moles* of substances involved. Be sure you are clear about the distinction between *molecules* and *moles* (Chapter 2).

16. False. The Styrofoam of this kind of calorimeter serves as an insulator. Any increase in temperature must come from heat liberated by the reacting substances, so the reaction is exothermic.

17. True. See the discussion in Section 13–7.

18. False. It is the heat content (enthalpy) of 1 mole of the substance at its standard state *compared to* those of the corresponding elements in their standard states. These latter values are conventionally taken to be zero, but this does not mean that they "have no heat content."

19. False. The value must refer to the formation of *1 mole* of the substance.

20. False. The reaction must involve all reactants and products at their standard states. I_2 is a solid at its standard state.

21. False. All reactants must be *elements* in their standard states. Notice that this does *not* necessarily mean that they are atoms; think about the diatomic gases, for instance.

22. False. $\Delta E = q - w$. Even if q is zero we could increase the internal energy of the system by doing work on it, such as by compressing it.

23. True

24. False. Changes in disorder of the system also affect spontaneity. Think of the example of water freezing (an exothermic process); it is certainly not spontaneous at 10°C although it is at −10°C.

25. False. For example, the melting of water is spontaneous at 10°C and this is an endothermic process (absorbs energy from the surroundings).

26. True

27. True

28. False. The change in a state function *does* depend on the initial and final states. For instance, think about (1) the heating of a substance at constant volume from the initial state of 25°C to a final state of 50°C, compared to (2) the heating of a substance at constant volume from the initial state of 25°C to a final state of 75°C. It should be apparent that ΔE is different for these two changes. You may need to review Section 13–2 where the concept of the thermodynamic state of a system is discussed.

29. True

30. False

31. False

32. True

33. True

34. False. The bond energy is ΔH for the reaction in which the *only* thing that happens is formation of 1 mole of bonds starting from isolated atoms. Very often the elements from which the compound is formed do not exist as separate atoms in their standard states. See the discussion of this important idea in the latter part of Section 13–8. Calculations illustrating this are shown in Examples 13–8 through 13–10 in the text.

35. True. This reaction *does* involve only formation of 1 mole of H—H bonds from isolated atoms.

36. False. This reaction also involves the energy necessary to break 1 mole of H—H bonds and that necessary to break 1 mole of Cl—Cl bonds. See the answer to Question 34 above.

37. True

38. False. Gas is formed, so Δn is not equal to zero. In other words, the system does work against its surroundings, so ΔE cannot be equal to ΔH.

39. True. Even though reactions do not usually proceed by first breaking all bonds in reactants and then forming products from the resultant atoms, we can calculate enthalpy changes as if they did. This is another utility of thermodynamics—the answer does not depend on the pathway used to get from initial to final states.

40. True. Negative values of ΔH^0 mean that the reaction is exothermic (enthalpy content of products is less than that of reactants).

41. True. ΔH^0 values are, among other things, a measure of the heat transferred at constant pressure.

42. False. Remember that ΔH^0 values are for the specific amount of material referred to in the equation as written. The burning of 2 moles of SiH_4 gives off twice as much heat as the 1 mole that is referred to in the reaction, or 3,032,000 joules.

43. False. The number of moles of gas decreases so at constant pressure the volume would decrease. Thus, the surroundings (atmosphere) does work on this system.

44. False. At constant volume, the amount of heat given off is equal to ΔE. Since Δn for this reaction is -3, ΔE is greater than ΔH for the reaction. Study Section 13–5 which relates ΔE to ΔH.

45. True. Remember that entropy is a measure of disorder. The particles are more ordered, thus at lower entropy, in the solid state.
46. True
47. False. This is discussed in Section 13–12, with special emphasis in connection with Table 13–6 and Examples 13–15 and 13–16.

Short Answer

1. system
2. In this chapter, we have seen many possible answers to this. Acceptable answers include pressure, volume, temperature, energy, enthalpy, entropy, and Gibbs free energy.
3. positive
4. positive
5. increase, 600
6. endothermic
7. Conservation of Energy
8. 1 atmosphere, 25°C
9. ΔE
10. ΔH
11. by one step, by a series of steps
12. standard molar enthalpy of formation
13. standard molar enthalpy of formation
14. bond energy
15. F. Notice that in thermodynamics we often write the reactions with fractional coefficients. This just means that we are dealing with some fractional numbers of moles. Do not think about a fraction of a molecule!
16. I
17. A. All substances must be in their standard states, which for carbon is solid graphite and for oxygen is the diatomic gas.
18. bond energy of the oxygen-oxygen bond
19. Born-Haber cycle
20. -1
21. H
22. ΔH
23. ΔH^0
24. ΔH_f^0
25. crystal lattice energy
26. exothermic
27. endothermic
28. positive
29. standard molar enthalpy of formation
30. $\frac{1}{2}N_2(g) + \frac{3}{2}H_2(g) \rightarrow NH_3(g)$. Be sure that you write the reaction so that 1 mole of $NH_3(g)$ is formed. You must also always include explicitly the physical state of each substance—all gases in this case.

Refer to the discussion in Section 13–11 while you think about the answers to Questions 31–40. Of course, an increase in entropy is denoted by ΔS positive, a decrease by ΔS negative, and no change by $\Delta S = 0$.

31. D
32. U
33. I
34. D
35. I
36. D
37. I
38. D
39. U
40. I

41. $-T\Delta S$
42. increases. The term in ΔG that includes ΔS is $-T\Delta S$. The more negative this term, the more likely the reaction is to be spontaneous. This term is more important at high temperatures.

Multiple Choice

1. (d)
2. (b)
3. (c). The ice must *absorb* this 1,440 calories, so $\Delta H = 1,440$ calories.
4. (c)
5. (c)
6. (a). Recall that $\Delta H = \Delta E + (\Delta n)RT$, as shown in Section 13–5. You must remember that Δn is the change in number of moles of gaseous substances, calculated as (moles of gaseous products) − (moles of gaseous reactants). In the case mentioned here, $\Delta n = 0$, so $\Delta H = \Delta E$.
7. (c). Now $\Delta n > 0$, so $\Delta H > \Delta E$.
8. (c). See Section 13–5.
9. (c). As seen in this chapter, exothermic processes *may* be spontaneous, but they are not necessarily so. The factor of change in order/disorder (entropy change) also affects spontaneity.
10. (c). Combine the reactions, as shown in Examples 13–3 and 13–4, so that they add up to the desired reaction. You need to *reverse* the last two reactions (while changing the signs of their ΔH values) and also *double* the second and third reactions (while doubling their ΔH values). If you got answer (a), you forgot to double the appropriate reactions and their ΔH values. If you got answer (d), you forgot to reverse the appropriate reactions and change the signs of ΔH. If you got answer (b), you forgot both the doubling and the reversing. If you got answer (e), you forgot to

double the H_2O reaction. If you think about it, the *positive* answers cannot be correct since this is a burning reaction. You know that burning liberates heat, so the reaction must be exothermic and have a negative ΔH value.

11. (a). The value of 2220 kJ is for the combustion of *1 mole* of propane. In the problem, we have 11.0 g, or (11.0 g)/(44.0 g/mol) = 0.25 mol.
12. (b)
13. (d)
14. (a)
15. (a)
16. (a). We must put heat into a liquid to boil it—vaporization is an endothermic process.
17. (a). A gas is in a higher state of disorder than a liquid at the same temperature.
18. (c). The boiling point of water at 1 atm is 100°C so the process is at equilibrium, which means that $\Delta G = 0$.
19. (b). This is class 4 of Table 13–6. See the discussion in Section 13–12.
20. (d). This is class 2 of Table 13–6.
21. (c). This is class 3 of Table 13–6.

14

Chemical Kinetics

Chapter Summary

In the preceding chapter, we studied the topic of chemical thermodynamics, which is concerned with the question of *whether* a reaction can go. In Chapter 14, we face another question, that of *how fast* a reaction goes. The subject of **chemical kinetics** deals with the rates of chemical reactions, the factors affecting these rates, and the information that a study of reaction rates can give regarding the detailed set of steps by which the reaction proceeds. Thus, a study of chemical kinetics will serve several purposes, from the practical one of allowing us to alter the rate of a reaction (either to increase or to decrease it, depending on whether it is a desirable reaction) to the fundamental one of learning about reactions on the molecular level.

Our approach in this chapter is first to present the modern ideas, on a molecular level, of how reactions occur. These theories will then be used to help us understand the various macroscopic factors that influence reaction rates.

The **collision theory,** Section 14–1, takes the viewpoint that in order for molecules to react they must collide (1) with sufficient energy to react—i.e., break bonds and form new ones—and (2) with the proper orientation for a reaction to occur. This idea is extended by the **transition-state theory,** Section 14–2, which says that reactants must pass through a short-lived, high-energy state known as the **transition state** in order to react. The reactants must increase their energy by an amount called the **activation energy** (E_a) to reach the transition state. Thus, the activation energy may be viewed as a barrier to the reaction. If the colliding molecules do not have this much energy, they cannot react; if they do have sufficient energy, the appropriate bonds can break, new bonds can then form, and the reaction (for those particular colliding molecules) can proceed. Some energy is then released as the new molecules are formed from the transition state. Be sure you understand, with the help of **potential energy diagrams** such as Figures 14–2 and 14–3, the relation between the activation energies for the forward and reverse reactions and the value of ΔE for the reaction.

We now turn, in the next four sections, to a consideration of the factors that affect reaction rates: **nature of the reactants, concentrations of reactants, temperature,** and **presence of a catalyst.** Section 14–3 describes the influence of the nature of the reactants—how finely divided solid reactants are, whether reactants are in a well-mixed solution, and so on.

Of course, since the presence of more substance means more can react, it is not surprising that concentration of reactants plays a very important part in determining reaction rates (Section 14–4). In this section we begin a more quantitative description of reaction rates. We could describe the rate of travel of an automobile by the expression (change in location)/(change in time). The more the location changes in a given length of time, the higher is the rate of travel. In just the same way, we describe the rate of a reaction by the expression (change in concentration of reactant or product)/(change in time). Two points of notation should be noticed here: (1) as you have already seen in an earlier chapter, the symbol Δ means "change in," and (2) the notation [X] means **molar** concentration of the substance X whose formula appears in the brackets. This latter notation will also be used throughout the next several chapters. Study very carefully the discussion in this section of the iodine chloride + hydrogen reaction—it will introduce you to several important ideas such as the **determination** of the rate from a plot of concentration vs. time, the concept of **initial rate,** and the realization that **rates change with time** (as reactants are consumed, the reaction slows). The central idea of Section 14–4 is the **rate-law** expression which relates the rate of reaction to the concentrations of reactants. Be sure that you understand that the values of the **specific rate constant *(k),*** and of the **orders** with respect to the reactants *must* be determined experimentally and cannot necessarily be related to the coefficients in the balanced overall chemical equation. The several examples in this section will clarify the deduction of rate-law expressions from experimental data. Problems 1 through 12 at the end of the text chapter will give you some necessary practice at this type of data analysis.

We find experimentally that any reaction proceeds faster if we raise the temperature. Section 14–5 relates this observation to the increase in the fraction of molecules with sufficient energy to react (remember **activation energy** and review the kinetic-molecular theory, Section 8–13). This observation may be expressed mathematically in the **Arrhenius equation.** Of course, instead of increasing the number of molecules that can "leap the energy barrier" in order to speed up the reaction, we could lower the barrier, i.e., lower E_a. This is the function of **catalysts,** discussed in Section 14–6. Some catalysts, called **inhibitory catalysts,** slow the reaction by raising E_a, but in most applications of catalysis the reaction is speeded up by the catalyst providing a lower energy pathway by which the reaction can occur. It is important to realize that catalysts cannot cause thermodynamically impossible reactions to occur; they can only alter the rates of reactions that are spontaneous. The examples, discussed in this section, of **homogeneous** and **heterogeneous** catalysis will clarify many important aspects of the action of catalysts.

One of the most important applications of the study of chemical kinetics is the information thus available about the detailed series of steps by which reactions occur, the **reaction mechanism.** Section 14–7 relates the reaction mechanism and the experimentally determined rate law, introducing the important idea of the **rate-determining step.** This interpretation of kinetics makes use of both the collision theory and the transition-state theory presented earlier.

Section 14–8 presents a mathematical reformulation of the rate-law expression, changing our viewpoint from the **rate** of the reaction to the **time** required for the reaction to proceed by a specified amount. This is often expressed in terms of the **half-life** of reactants. Again, careful attention to the examples will aid you in understanding the central idea of this mathematically somewhat complex section.

The ideas of chemical kinetics from this chapter will be the basis for our study in Chapter 15 of chemical equilibrium, which we will also find to be understandable in terms of chemical thermodynamics.

Study Goals

1. Distinguish between chemical kinetics and chemical thermodynamics. Know what each subject does and does not cover. (Chapter introduction; Exercises 2 and 4)

2. Describe simple one-step reactions in terms of (a) collision theory and (b) transition state theory. (Sections 14–1 and 14–2; Exercise 2)

3. Describe activation energy and illustrate it graphically for exothermic and endothermic reactions. Be able to relate E_a for forward and reverse reactions to ΔE_{rxn}. (Sections 14–1 and 14–2; Exercises 5 and 25)

4. Summarize the effects on reaction rates of the (a) nature of reactants, (b) concentrations of reactants, (c) temperature and (d) presence of a catalyst. (Sections 14–3 through 14–6; Exercises 1 and 6)

5. For a given reaction, express reaction rate in terms of changes of concentrations of reactants and products per unit time. (Section 14–4)

6. Describe how initial reaction rates are determined. Know what must be measured and how the data are analyzed. (Section 14–4; Exercise 3)

7. Identify all the terms in an expression such as Rate = $k[A]^x[B]^y$ and describe the significance of each. Be familiar with the terminology of order of a reaction. (Section 14–4; Exercises 3, 7, 9, 11, 12, and 16)

8. Given experimental data for a particular reaction at a specified temperature, consisting of initial rates corresponding to different combinations of initial concentrations of reactants, determine the rate law for the reaction. (Section 14–4; Exercises 3, 13 through 15, and 20 through 22)

9. Given the rate–law expression for a specific reaction at a certain temperature, calculate the initial rate of reaction at the same temperature for any set of initial concentrations of reactants. Use changes in concentrations to predict changes in initial rates. (Section 14–4; Exercises 17, 18, 23, and 24)

10. Understand, in terms of the distribution of energies of the reactant molecules, how the reaction rate depends on temperature. (Section 14-2)

11. Be able to use the Arrhenius equation to relate rate constants at two different temperatures. Know how to represent and interpret this equation graphically. (Section 14-5; Exercises 26, 27, and 33)

12. Give examples of homogeneous and heterogeneous catalysis. (Section 14-6; Exercise 10)

13. Understand, in terms of potential energy diagrams, how the reaction rate is altered by the presence of a catalyst. (Section 14-6; Exercise 6)

14. Understand how rate-law expressions are related to reaction mechanisms. (Section 14-7; Exercises 8 and 9)

15. Given the form of the rate-law expression for a reaction, (a) postulate mechanisms consistent with the data, specifying the slow step or (b) recognize whether a proposed mechanism could be the correct one. (Section 14-7; Exercises 28 through 32)

16. Perform various calculations with the integrated rate equations for first- and second-order reactions relating rate constants, half-lives, initial concentrations, and concentrations of reactants remaining at some later time. (Section 14-8; Exercises 33 through 36)

Some Important Terms in This Chapter

Write the meanings *in your own words*. Check the Key Terms list and the chapter reading. Then rewrite your definitions, still in your own words, to improve them. Study other new terms and review terms from preceding chapters if necessary.

collision theory

transition state theory

transition state

Arrhenius equation

activation energy

rate-law expression

specific rate constant

half-life

mechanism

rate-determining step

catalyst

homogeneous catalyst

heterogeneous catalyst

Preliminary Test

As in other chapters, this test will check your understanding of basic concepts and types of calculations. Be sure to practice *many* of the additional textbook exercises, including those indicated with the Study Goals.

True-False

Mark each statement as true (T) or false (F).

_____ 1. All reactions taking place at the same temperature occur at the same rate.

_____ 2. All exothermic reactions taking place at the same temperature occur at the same rate.

_____ 3. All reactions taking place at the same temperature with the same value of ΔH occur at the same rate.

_____ 4. All reactions taking place at the same temperature with the same activation energy occur at the same rate.

_____ 5. Reactions with lower (more negative) values of ΔG are more spontaneous, so they usually proceed at a higher rate.

_____ 6. The transition state is a short-lived, high-energy state, intermediate between reactants and products in the reaction.

_____ 7. According to the collision theory, all that molecules must do to react is collide with one another.

_____ 8. Once the reactants have absorbed the necessary activation energy to reach the transition state, they are stuck and cannot react further.

_____ 9. Once the reactants have absorbed the necessary activation energy to reach the transition state, they must then go ahead to form products.

_____ 10. The activation energy E_a is usually the same as ΔE for the reaction.

_____ 11. A reaction in which the activation energy of the forward reaction is greater than the activation energy of the reverse reaction is endothermic.

_____ 12. The exponents in the rate law must match the coefficients in the balanced chemical equation for the reaction.

_____ 13. The exponents in the rate law may match the coefficients in the balanced chemical equation for the reaction.

_____ 14. If the exponents in the rate law match the coefficients in the balanced chemical equation, then we know that the reaction takes place in one step.

_____ 15. The rate law for a reaction can be correctly predicted from the balanced chemical equation.

_____ 16. The value of k for a given reaction is constant at all conditions.

_____ 17. The value of k for a given reaction is constant at a given temperature.

_____ 18. If we know the mathematical form of the rate-law expression for a reaction, and we have also determined the value of the specific rate constant at some temperature, we can predict the rate at which the reaction would occur at that temperature for any specified reactant concentrations.

_____ 19. As a rule of thumb, every 10°C increase in temperature roughly doubles the rate of many reactions.

_____ 20. A catalyst works by increasing the average energy of reacting molecules.

_____ 21. A catalytic converter on an automobile is an example of a heterogeneous catalyst.

_____ 22. An effective catalyst increases the rate of the forward reaction but does not affect the rate of the reverse reaction.

_____ 23. A homogeneous catalyst is composed of a single compound, whereas a heterogeneous catalyst is a mixture of compounds.

_____ 24. A catalyst can make a thermodynamically nonspontaneous reaction spontaneous.

_____ 25. If we change the initial concentration of the reactant in a first-order reaction, the half-life changes.

_____ 26. If we change the initial concentration of the reactant in a second-order reaction, the half-life changes.

Short Answer

Answer with a word, a phrase, a formula, or a number with units as necessary.

1. The symbol [X] means _____.

2. In the rate-law expression, the quantity represented by the symbol k is called the _____.

3. For a particular reaction, the rate law is determined to be Rate =

$k[A]^2[B]$. The reaction is said to be _____ order in A, _____ order in B, and _____ order overall.

4. The rate of a reaction may be expressed either in terms of the _____ in reactant concentration with time or the _____ in product concentration with time.

5. In a reaction for which $A + B \rightarrow$ products is the rate-determining step, doubling the concentration of A and doubling the concentration of B would cause the rate to _____ by a factor of ___.

6. The amount of energy that reactants must gain above their ground states in order to react is called the _____ of the forward reaction.

7. Four factors that can influence the rate of a chemical reaction are

_____, _____, _____, and _____.

8. When heated, magnesium metal reacts with the oxygen in air to form magnesium oxide. Suppose we have a cube of magnesium metal, 1 cm on edge, and measure the initial rate at which it forms MgO. Then we cut the magnesium up into cubes 1 mm on edge. We would expect that at the same temperature the initial rate of MgO formation would _____ by a factor of _____.

9. The principal reason that a reaction speeds up at elevated temperatures is an increase in the _____.

10. A substance that alters the rate of a chemical reaction but is not itself consumed or produced in the reaction is called a _____.

11. The sequence of individual steps by which a reaction occurs is called the _____ of the reaction.

12. The slowest step in a reaction sequence is called the _____.

13. According to the collision theory, when a reaction requires the collision between two reactant molecules for the rate-determining step to proceed, that step is termed _____ and the reaction is called _____ order.

14. The time required for half of a reactant to disappear in a reaction is called the _____ of the reactant.

15. The equation $\dfrac{1}{[A]} - \dfrac{1}{[A]_0} = kt$ describes the dependence of concentration on time for a reaction that is _____ order; the rate law for this reaction would be _____.

16. For a reaction which is first order in A, the equation that relates concentration and time is _____.

The next five questions, 17 through 21, refer to the reaction

$$2A + 2B \rightarrow C + 2D$$

in which all reactants and products are gases. The reaction is observed to follow the rate law Rate $= k[A][B]^2$. The reaction is also known to be strongly exothermic. In each question, we make *only* the one change in the reaction conditions indicated. For each, predict the effect on (a) the initial rate of the forward reaction, (b) the value of the rate constant, and (c) the activation energy for the forward reaction. The possible answers are: increase (I), decrease (D), or remain unchanged (U).

Change	Initial Rate, Forward Reaction	k	E_a
17. The concentration of A is doubled.	___	___	___
18. The concentration of D is doubled.	___	___	___
19. A catalyst is introduced.	___	___	___
20. The temperature is decreased.	___	___	___
21. The volume of the container is doubled.	___	___	___

22. For a particular reaction, the rate law is determined to be Rate = $k[A]^2[B]$. We first carry out the reaction with some starting concentrations of A and B. Then we repeat it, after doubling the concentrations of A and B. The rate will change by the factor (new rate)/(old rate) = _____ (a number).

23. For a particular reaction, the rate law is determined to be Rate = $k[A]^2[B]$. We first carry out the reaction with some starting concentrations of A and B. Then we repeat it, after halving the concentration of A and doubling the concentration of B. The rate will change by the factor (new rate)/(old rate) = _____ (a number).

24. The half-life of a certain first-order reaction is 2.5 hours. After 10 hours, the fraction of initial reactant remaining is _____.

Multiple Choice

_____ 1. Which of the following reactions is expected to be the slowest?
   (a) $Ag^+ (aq) + Cl^- (aq) \rightarrow AgCl (s)$
   (b) $H^+ (aq) + OH^- (aq) \rightarrow H_2O (\ell)$
   (c) $CH_4 (g) + 2O_2 (g) \rightarrow CO_2 (g) + 2H_2O (g)$
   (d) $Pb^{2+} (aq) + CrO_4^{2-} (aq) \rightarrow PbCrO_4 (s)$
   (e) $H^+ (aq) + CN^- (aq) \rightarrow HCN (aq)$

_____ 2. One of the reactions used commercially to produce hydrogen gas is

$$H_2O (g) + CO (g) \rightarrow H_2 (g) + CO_2 (g).$$

A proper expression for the rate of this reaction could be

(a) $-\dfrac{\Delta[CO_2]}{\Delta t}$.   (b) $-\dfrac{\Delta[H_2]}{\Delta t}$.   (c) k.   (d) $\dfrac{\Delta[CO]}{\Delta t}$.

(e) $-\dfrac{\Delta[H_2O]}{\Delta t}$.

The following potential energy diagram is to be used in answering Questions 3 through 6.

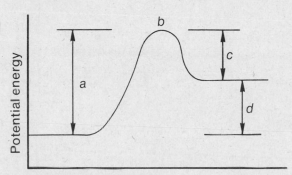

3. The reaction "reactants → products" carried out at constant volume and temperature
   (a) is exothermic.
   (b) is endothermic.
   (c) takes place without energy change.
   (d) is impossible.
   (e) may either be exothermic or endothermic.
4. The energy difference represented by arrow d is the
   (a) energy content of products.
   (b) energy content of reactants.
   (c) activation energy for the reverse reaction.
   (d) activation energy for the forward reaction.
   (e) energy change of the reaction.
5. The region designated by b in the diagram is
   (a) the energy of the mixture when half of the reactants have been converted to products.
   (b) the energy of the transition state.
   (c) the number of moles of transition state that must be formed.
   (d) the energy of the forward reaction.
   (e) the energy of the reverse reaction.
6. The energy difference represented by arrow c is the
   (a) reaction energy of the forward reaction.
   (b) activation energy of the forward reaction.
   (c) reaction energy of the reverse reaction.
   (d) activation energy of the reverse reaction.
   (e) energy content of the reactants.

_____ 7. A reaction has an activation energy of 40 kJ and an overall energy change of reaction of −100 kJ. In each of the following potential energy diagrams the horizontal axis is the reaction coordinate and the vertical axis is potential energy in kJ. Which potential energy diagram best describes this reaction?

(a)

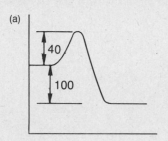

(b)

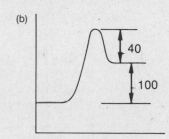

(c)

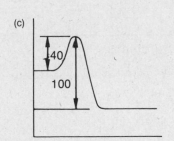

(d)

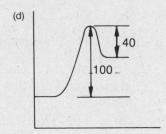

(e)

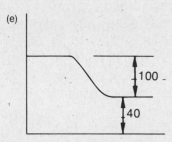

_____ 8. Four of the following factors can affect the forward rate of a chemical reaction. Which one cannot affect this rate?
(a) temperature
(b) presence of a catalyst
(c) concentration of reactants
(d) removal of some of the products
(e) state of subdivision of solid reactants

_____ 9. For a given reaction the rate law is
(a) a constant of proportionality between reaction rate and the concentrations of reactants.
(b) the sum of the powers to which reactant concentrations appear.

(c) an equation in which reaction rate is equal to a mathematical expression involving concentrations of reactants.

(d) the additional energy that the reactants must obtain in order to be able to react.

(e) 55 miles per hour.

_____ 10. A catalyst

(a) is used up in a chemical reaction.

(b) changes the value of ΔG^0 of the reaction.

(c) is always a solid.

(d) does not take part in the reaction in any way.

(e) changes the activation energy of the reaction.

_____ 11. The units of the rate constant for a second order reaction can be

(a) $M^{-1} s^{-1}$ (b) M (c) $M s^{-1}$ (d) s^{-1} (e) $M^2 s^{-1}$

In Questions 12 through 14, we refer to the gaseous reaction A + B → C whose reaction rate is experimentally observed to follow the relationship Rate = $k[A]^2[B]$.

_____ 12. The overall order of the reaction is

(a) first.   (b) second.   (c) third.   (d) zero.   (e) cannot be answered without a detailed knowledge of the reaction mechanism.

_____ 13. If the concentration of A is tripled and the concentration of B is doubled, the reaction rate would be increased by a factor of _____.

(a) 6   (b) 9   (c) 12   (d) 18   (e) 36

_____ 14. Which of the following would affect the value of the specific rate constant k?

(a) decreasing the temperature

(b) changing the concentration of A

(c) changing the concentration of B

(d) changing the concentration of C

(e) letting the reaction go on for a long time.

Rate data have been determined at a particular temperature for the overall reaction

$$2NO + 2H_2 \rightarrow N_2 + H_2O$$

in which all reactants and products are gases.

Trial Run	Initial [NO]	Initial [H$_2$]	Initial Rate ($M s^{-1}$)
1	0.10	0.20	0.0150
2	0.10	0.30	0.0225
3	0.20	0.20	0.0600

Questions 15 through 18 refer to this reaction and these data.

_____ 15. The rate law is
   (a) Rate $= k[NO]^2[H_2]^2$
   (b) Rate $= k[NO][H_2]^2$
   (c) Rate $= k[NO]^2[H_2]$
   (d) Rate $= k[NO][H_2]$
   (e) None of the preceding answers is correct.
_____ 16. The value of the specific rate constant at this temperature is
   (a) $0.75\ M^{-1}\ s^{-1}$
   (b) $7.5\ M^{-2}\ s^{-1}$
   (c) $3.0 \times 10^{-3} M^{-2}\ s^{-1}$
   (d) $3.0 \times 10^{-4} M^{-1}\ s^{-1}$
   (e) $375\ M^{-2}\ s^{-1}$
_____ 17. What would be the initial rate with the molar concentration of
   $NO = 0.30\ M$ and the molar concentration of $H_2 = 0.10\ M$?
   (a) $0.0675\ M\ s^{-1}$ (b) $0.225\ M\ s^{-1}$ (c) $0.0225\ M\ s^{-1}$
   (d) $0.0400\ M\ s^{-1}$ (e) $0.1000\ M^{-1}$
_____ 18. Does the reaction take place in one step?
   (a) Yes
   (b) No
   (c) Probably yes, but we need more information to be certain.
   (d) Probably no, but we need more information to be certain.
_____ 19. An instructor dismisses class early. Which of the following factors is
   most important in determining the rate of students exiting from the
   room (students/min)?
   (a) realizing that the instructor really meant it
   (b) gathering up books and notes
   (c) walking from the seats to the aisle
   (d) walking down the aisle to the door
   (e) crawling through a 1-ft by 2-ft hole in the locked door
_____ 20. Consider the following proposed mechanism.

$$2A \xrightarrow{k_1} C + I$$

$$I + B \xrightarrow{k_2} C + D$$

   If this mechanism for the overall reaction were correct, and if k_1
   were much less than k_2, then the observed rate law would be
   (a) Rate $= k_1 k_2[A]^2[I][B]$
   (b) Rate $= k_2[I][B]$
   (c) Rate $= k_1[A]^2$
   (d) Rate $= k_1[A]^2 - k_2[C][D]$
   (e) Rate $= k_1[A]$
_____ 21. A reaction mechanism will usually be
   (a) the only possible explanation for the reaction.
   (b) difficult to verify experimentally.
   (c) proven experimentally to be the only possible mechanism.

(d) obvious from a consideration of the balanced chemical equation.
(e) obvious from a consideration of the reaction rate data.

_____ 22. According to the Arrhenius equation for the rate constant of a chemical reaction, the higher the activation energy, the ___ at a given temperature.
(a) slower a reaction is
(b) more exothermic a reaction is
(c) more endothermic a reaction is
(d) more atoms are involved in a reaction
(c) faster a reaction is

_____ 23. The first-order rate constant for the conversion of $A \rightarrow B$ is 0.0693 min^{-1}. How many grams of A would be left after 1 hr if the reaction started with 80 g of A at $t = 0$?
(a) 1.25 g   (b) 5.0 g   (c) 10.0 g   (d) 40.0 g   (e) cannot be determined from the data given.

_____ 24. The decomposition of dimethylether at 504°C is first-order with a half-life of 1570 seconds. What fraction of an initial amount of dimethylether remains after 4710 seconds?
(a) $\frac{1}{3}$ (b) $\frac{1}{6}$ (c) $\frac{1}{8}$ (d) $\frac{1}{16}$ (e) $\frac{1}{32}$

Answers to Preliminary Test

Do not just look up answers. Think about the reasons for the answers.

True-False

1. False
2. False
3. False
4. False
5. False. One of the most important ideas of this chapter is that the rate of the reaction depends on the availability of a low-energy pathway from reactants to products. Spontaneity of a reaction does not determine its rate. Think about Study Goal 1.
6. True
7. False. According to this theory, collision is necessary but not sufficient for reaction. Be sure that you understand what is required for a collision to be effective (Section 14–1).
8. False. They either react to give products or go back to form reactants again, giving up the appropriate amount of energy.
9. False. See answer to Question 8.
10. False

11. True. Draw a potential energy diagram to help you think about this.
12. False
13. True
14. False. This important idea is discussed in Section 14 – 7. What this tells us is that it *may* take place in one step, but not necessarily. If the exponents do *not* match the coefficients in the balanced equation, then we know that the reaction definitely *does not* take place in one step.
15. False. This is an important point that can cause much confusion. Since the reaction may take place in a series of steps, some fast and some slow, the overall rate is generally impossible to predict from the balanced equation. Study Section 14 – 7.
16. False. It can be charged either by changing the temperature or by altering the activation energy by introduction of a catalyst.
17. False. It can still be changed by introduction of a catalyst.
18. True
19. True. Of course, the actual change depends on the activation energy — this is just typical of many reactions with activation energies near 50 kJ/mol. This calculation was done in Section 14 – 5.
20. False. It lowers (or, in general, alters) the activation energy, so that at a given temperature, more molecules have enough energy to react.
21. True
22. False. The action of a catalyst is to change the energy of the activated complex (transition state). Since this changes the values of E_a for both the forward and the reverse reactions, the rates of both reactions are altered.
23. False. The terms homogeneous and heterogeneous refer to the number of phases of the reaction mixture. When the catalyst is in a different physical state than the reaction mixture, it is called a heterogeneous catalyst.
24. False
25. False. For a first-order reaction, the time required for half of the initial substance to react is the same regardless of amount of starting material.
26. True. For a second-order reaction, the half-life is different depending how much material we start with. Watch out for this in calculations or reasoning involving half-lives.

Short Answer

1. the molar concentration of substance X
2. specific rate constant. Sometimes it is just referred to as the rate constant.
3. second, first, third
4. decrease, increase
5. increase, 4. *If* this is the rate-determining step, we know Rate = k[A][B].
6. activation energy
7. concentrations of reactants, temperature, nature of reactants, presence of a catalyst

8. increase, 10. The rate would depend on the surface area of magnesium exposed to air. In the 1 cm cube, the total area is 6 cm² (6 faces, 1 cm² each). After we cut it up, the total area is 60 cm²—figure it out.

9. fraction of collisions that have energy equal to or exceeding E_a. A secondary factor is the increased number of collisions, but this is less important than the increase in the fraction of high-energy molecules. Can you see this in the Arrhenius equation, Section 14–5?

10. catalyst

11. mechanism

12. rate-determining step

13. bimolecular, second

14. half-life. You may see this referred to in some books as the "half-time."

15. second, Rate $= k[A]^2$. Study Section 14–8.

16. $\log \dfrac{[A]_0}{[A]} = kt/2.303$

17. I, U, U. Changing concentration does *not* alter k. What does?

18. U, U, U

19. I, I, D. Generally, when we talk about a catalyst we are assuming that it is a catalyst that enhances the rate. If it were an inhibitory catalyst we would have specified it so.

20. D, D, U. Be sure that you know how a temperature change alters the rate.

21. D, U, U. Think about what doubling the volume does to concentrations.

22. 8. Doubling [A] would make the rate $2^2 = 4$ times as fast; doubling [B] would account for an additional factor of 2, so the total effect would be $4 \times 2 = 8$.

23. $\frac{1}{2}$. That is, it would go only $\frac{1}{2}$ as fast. Halving [A] would make the rate $(\frac{1}{2})^2 = \frac{1}{4}$ as fast; doubling [B] would account for an additional factor of 2, for a total change of $\frac{1}{2}$.

24. $\frac{1}{16}$. Since this is a first-order reaction, the half-life means that $\frac{1}{2}$ of *any* starting amount remains after 2.5 hours. Thus, after 2.5 hours, $\frac{1}{2}$ of the original remains. After the next 2.5 hours, $\frac{1}{2}$ of the amount at the beginning of *that* 2.5 hour period, or $\frac{1}{4}$ of the original, remains. Reasoning in this fashion for four half-lives, we obtain the answer.

Multiple Choice

1. (c). This reaction requires that covalent bonds be broken. The others involve only ionic reactants, either forming covalent bonds or forming ionic solids. Reactions that involve the breaking of covalent bonds are generally slower. Can you tie this in with what you know about activation energies?

2. (e)

3. (b). The energy of products is higher than that of reactants.

4. (e)

5. (b)
6. (d)
7. (a)
8. (d)
9. (c)
10. (e)
11. (a). Write down a second-order rate law and think about units.
12. (c)
13. (d)
14. (a)
15. (c). The rationale for this is like that in Example 14–1 in the text.
16. (b). Put the observed rate and the initial concentrations from any one of the three trial runs into the rate law and solve for k. Watch the units. Check to see that you get the same answer regardless of which set of data you use. This can be a check that you deduced the correct rate law as well as a check on your arithmetic.
17. (a). Put these molar concentrations into the rate law, together with the value for k that was obtained in Question 16.
18. (b). Since the exponents do not match the stoichiometric coefficients, we know that the reaction *cannot* take place in one step.
19. (e). The slow step determines the rate of overall process.
20. (c). Since k_1 is much less than k_2, the first step is much slower, so its rate determines the rate of the entie reaction. Can you write the equation for the overall reaction? Note that I is an intermediate—the reaction is $2A + B \rightarrow 2C + D$.
21. (b). Read the discussion in Section 14–7.
22. (a)
23. (a). The calculation is like that for N_2O_5 in Example 14–3, except that you cannot calculate molar concentration of A since you do not know its formula weight or the volume of the container. Proceed as follows:
$\log \dfrac{[A]_0}{[A]} = kt/2.303$, where k is given and $t = 60$ min; then $\log \dfrac{[A]_0}{[A]} = 1.80$; taking antilogarithms, $\dfrac{[A]_0}{[A]} = 63.8$. Since the volume is constant, the volumes will cancel in this ratio, so $\dfrac{m_0}{m} = 63.8$ and $m = 80/63.8 = 1.25$ g.
24. (c). 4710 seconds is $4710/1570 =$ three half-lives. Since this is a first-order reaction, each half-life period consumes $\frac{1}{2}$ of the amount present at the beginning of *that* period.

15

Chemical Equilibrium

Chapter Summary

Most chemical reactions do not go to completion, but rather they attain a state of **chemical equilibrium** consisting of some mixture of reactants and products. Some important questions regarding this equilibrium state are these: How can we describe the equilibrium condition in terms of concentrations? What factors determine the equilibrium, and how can we use these factors to enhance the occurrence of some desirable reaction? How can we predict what amounts of products will have been formed, and what amounts of reactants will remain, when equilibrium has been reached? In Chapter 15, we bring together many ideas from our earlier studies to get a general answer to these and other questions about chemical equilibrium. We will first approach the question of how chemical equilibrium is attained from the standpoint of chemical kinetics (Chapter 14). Then we will use these resulting descriptions to see how to carry out calculations of equilibrium concentrations of reactants and products and to understand the factors that influence equilibrium. Finally we shall see the relation of our equilibrium discussion to chemical thermodynamics. This general discussion of chemical equilibrium will thus both tie together many important ideas that we have been developing over the past several chapters and will serve as the basis for study of several specific types of reactions in the next three chapters.

Some basic ideas of equilibrium are presented in Section 15–1. Central to this discussion are three points you must keep in mind: (1) The first point, a conceptual one, is that equilibrium is a dynamic situation (sound familiar?) where two processes, the forward reaction and the reverse reaction, are proceeding at equal rates. (2) Since we know how rates depend on concentrations (Chapter 14), we can see that the condition $\text{rate}_{\text{forward}} = \text{rate}_{\text{reverse}}$ can be satisfied for many different combinations of concentrations. (3) The *changes* in concentrations of all reactants and products must always be in the ratio of the stoichiometric coefficients, even though the concentrations themselves may not be. The general layout of analyzing equilibrium problems presented in this section should be noted because it will also apply to any equilibrium-concentration problems in the next several chapters. For each substance, equilibrium concentration = initial concentration + change in concentration due to reaction.

Section 15–2 defines one of the most important quantities in your study of chemistry, the **equilibrium constant**. Notice that the algebraic expressions for this constant, unlike those for the rate law expressions, can *always* be written down directly from the balanced chemical equation. Always remember that the concentrations referred to in this formulation of the equilibrium constant are the concentrations of reactants and products *when the reaction has reached equilibrium.* Of course, you could put any other values of the concentrations into such an expression and carry out the arithmetic, but this would lead to the value of the equilibrium constant only if the concentrations correspond to equilibrium ones (see the discussion of reaction quotient, later in this chapter). We also see in this section how the *numerical value* of this equilibrium constant is determined for any given reaction at any temperature, from a measurement of the concentrations at equilibrium. Some further points to notice about equilibrium constants: (1) the symbol for equilibrium constant expressed in terms of molar concentrations is K_c. (2) A value of K_c for a particular reaction is only valid at a given temperature. We shall see later in the chapter how this changes with temperature. We also see in this section the variation in the form and value of K_c with the exact form of the balanced equation for a given reaction. We can use any of these forms to solve any particular problem and would always get the same answer for concentration, so long as we are careful to know which representation of the chemical equation the value of K_c corresponds to.

In Section 15–3, we get to the heart of the matter—the **calculation of concentrations from equilibrium constants.** In this crucial kind of calculation, we typically know what the concentrations of all species are at the "beginning" of the reaction, as well as the value of K_c at the relevant temperature, and we are asked to calculate the concentrations of some or all of the substances once equilibrium has been reached. It is very important that you see how this differs from the stoichiometric calculations you learned in Chapter 2. In problems such as those in Sections 2–8 through 2–12, you were finding out the maximum amount of product that could be formed if the reaction went to completion; now we are recognizing that few reactions actually go to completion. In the calculations in this section, it will not matter in setting up the problem whether the reactants are present in stoichiometric amounts. The strategy of analyzing these problems as pointed out in Section 15–1 will be very useful. Notice that you are occasionally required to solve a quadratic equation in problems of this kind. Pay close attention to the comments in the text regarding which of the two mathematically correct roots of the quadratic equation is the one to be used for the problem at hand. Do not look for a rule to tell you whether to take the + or the − sign in applying the quadratic formula, as this will depend on how you set the problem up in the first place. There is only one good rule—*think* about the physical significance of the answers. The criterion that will be most helpful is this: a concentration cannot be negative (how can you have less than none of a substance?) or, to put it another way, more of a substance cannot react than is present to begin with. (However, a change in concentration can be negative, meaning that the substance is consumed in the reaction.) While chemical equilibrium problems all use essentially the same reasoning, they can come in many different disguises and with varied wordings. You must work many of these problems to become comfortable with them. The advice you were given early in Chapter 1 of this guide to be systematic in your layout and progress through problem solutions is never more important than in learning to do equilibrium calculations!

The **reaction quotient, Q,** presented in Section 15–4, provides a useful aid to analyzing whether a reacting system is at equilibrium. You will notice that it has the same algebraic **form** in terms of concentrations as does K_c, but here the concentrations are *not necessarily* equilibrium concentrations. They may be, but only if those concentrations represent equilibrium. This means that we can use the reaction quotient with any specified combination of concentrations as a criterion (1) of whether or not the reaction is at equilibrium and (2) if not, how it must adjust to get there.

The various factors that may affect chemical equilibrium are assessed descriptively in Section 15–5. We think about the reaction at balance (equilibrium), then throw it out of balance and use LeChatelier's Principle (remember?) to tell us how it could regain equilibrium. The four "stresses" that are considered are as follows: (1) **Changes in concentration:** The reaction quotient is useful in analyzing the response to this stress. At equilibrium, Q is equal to K. Changing one or more of the concentrations, by adding or removing a reactant or product, alters the value of Q (but *not* of K!). You can then figure out whether Q must increase or decrease to get back to equilibrium value of K. Since product concentrations appear in the numerator and reactant concentrations in the denominator, this tells you which way the reaction must proceed to re-establish equilibrium. It is probably getting to be an old song by now, but in general it is safer (and surely more satisfying) to learn to analyze the situation yourself than simply to memorize the directions of shift summarized in the text. (2) **Changes in volume and pressure:** These changes can be interpreted simply in terms of the resulting changes in concentrations and then analyzed as just outlined. Since solids and liquids are nearly incompressible, pressure changes are important only if one or more reactant or product is a gas. Notice again that these changes do not change the value of K, though the value of Q may be altered. (3) **Changes in temperature:** The effects of this change can be reasoned out by thinking of heat as a product of an exothermic reaction, or as a reactant in an endothermic reaction, and then applying LeChatelier's Principle. It is important to see that this change in temperature, like *no other change,* alters the numerical value of K. The quantitative aspect of changing K by changing T will be considered later in the chapter. (4) **Introduction of a catalyst.** Dramatic as the effect of introduction of a catalyst on reaction rates can be, you must remember that it does not affect the position of an equilibrium. You should understand how this can be true in terms of the action of a catalyst in lowering the activation energies of both the forward and the reverse reactions. Of course, since not all reactions reach equilibrium quickly, the introduction of a catalyst may be helpful in causing this to occur in a useful time. Much insight into these aspects of chemical equilibrium can be gained from a thoughtful study of the discussion of the Haber process for the industrial synthesis of ammonia.

These qualitative considerations of Section 15–5 regarding stresses applied to a system at equilibrium are quantified in Section 15–6. Study the examples carefully, not just in order to learn to do these kinds of problems, but for the understanding that they can help you gain of the nature of chemical equilibrium and LeChatelier's Principle. If you have been careful to develop a facility with the approach of "equilibrium concentration = initial concentration + change in concentration due to reaction," this will be helpful to you in learning to work problems involving disturbance from equilibrium. Just think of imposing a change on the equilibrium concentrations—these altered concentrations now become the "new initial concentrations,"which are changed by the response of the reaction to the stress as discussed above, to reach the "new equilibrium concentrations." Whenever you have finished working a problem of this type, reason whether the answer is consistent with the changes expected from the approach you learned in Section 15–5.

The next three sections deal with alternative forms of representation of the equilibrium constant, which may be more useful in certain situations. In Sections 15–7 and 15–8, we see that the equilibrium condition may also be described in terms of the partial pressures of gases, an approach that may be more useful for reactions that take place in the gas phase. The relation between the **pressure equilibrium constant, K_p,** and the **concentration equilibrium constant, K_c,** is discussed in Section 15–8. Remember that Δn has the same meaning here that it had in relating ΔE to ΔH in Chapter 13, the change in number of moles of gas substances *in the balanced equation.* Section 15–9 points out how the equilibrium constant is formulated and interpreted in the case of **heterogeneous reactions,** those involving at least one phase that is a pure solid or a pure liquid.

In our study of chemical thermodynamics, we saw that ΔG could be used as a criterion for spontaneity of a reaction—a negative value of ΔG meaning that the forward reaction is spontaneous and a positive value meaning that it is spontaneous in the reverse direction. This implies that when ΔG is neither negative nor positive, but zero, the reaction is spontaneous in neither direction (or equally spontaneous in both directions), i.e., that it is at equilibrium. As developed in Section 15–10, this means that we can relate the **value of ΔG^0,** corresponding to unit concentrations of reactants and products, to the **value of the equilibrium constant, K.** Review the calculation of ΔG^0 from Chapter 13, remembering that two methods for its calculation from tabulated values are available. This relation between ΔG^0 and K has two practical uses: (1) If a value of the equilibrium constant cannot be found in tabulations, then more readily available tables of ΔG_f^0 (or ΔH_f^0 and S^0) values can be used to obtain ΔG_{rxn}^0, from which a numerical value of K can be obtained for calculation of equilibrium concentrations, and (2) experimental determination of equilibrium constant values can sometimes be used to evaluate ΔG_f^0 and other thermodynamic quantities for substances not appearing in tabulations.

The final section of the chapter, Section 15–11, returns to a quantitative consideration of the change of K with temperature, described in more general terms in Section 15–5. The key relationship of this section is the **van't Hoff equation**. This equation has two practical uses: (1) If we know the value of K at one temperature, T_1, and can evaluate the standard molar enthalpy of reaction, ΔH^0 (as from tabulated values of ΔH_f^0), we can calculate the value of K at another desired temperature, T_2, as demonstrated in Example 15–13. (2) From experimental measurements of K at different temperatures, we can calculate ΔH^0. This latter use may be handy for reactions that involve substances for which ΔH_f^0 values are not tabulated or for reactions that may be difficult to measure calorimetrically due, for instance, to scarcity of material, very low heats of reaction, or unfavorably slow reaction rates.

It is important to carry out the calculations of these last two sections using the proper form of K. For our calculations, we should remember that when the reaction takes place in the gas phase, the K referred to in Sections 15–10 and 15–11 is the *pressure* equilibrium constant, K_p; when the reaction is in liquid solution, K refers to the *concentration* equilibrium constant, K_c.

At first encounter, the topic of chemical equilibrium is often considered difficult by students. But it is one of the most important parts of a study of chemistry, and understanding it well is worth your patient, systematic, and diligent study. In the next chapters, we will see the application of these concepts of chemical equilibrium to particular types of processes such as reactions of acids and bases, hydrolysis reactions, and the dissolution and precipitation of slightly soluble ionic substances.

Study Goals

1. Describe the concept of chemical equilibrium as a dynamic equilibrium. Be able to use real or hypothetical reactions in your explanation. (Section 15–1; Exercises 1 and 2)
2. Write the equilibrium constant expression for any balanced chemical equation, describing either a homogeneous or a heterogeneous reaction. (Sections 15–2 and 15–7 through 15–9; Exercises 3 through 5, 24, and 27)
3. Be able to reason qualitatively (i.e., without calculations) from information about the magnitude of K. (Section 15–2; Exercise 6)
4. Given the equilibrium concentrations or the equilibrium partial pres-

sures, evaluate the equilibrium constant, K_c or K_p, for a reaction at a particular temperature. (Sections 15–2, 15–7, and 15–8; Exercises 10, 17, and 18)

5. Given initial concentrations of all species in a reaction and the value of K_c for this reaction, calculate equilibrium concentrations of all species. (Section 15–3; Exercises 11 through 16 and 19 through 23)

6. Distinguish between the reaction quotient, Q, and the equilibrium constant, K. Be able to use Q to assess whether or not a system is at equilibrium, and if not, how it must proceed to approach equilibrium. (Section 15–4; Exercises 7, 8, 40, and 41)

7. Carry out calculations as in Study Goals 4 and 5, but involving partial pressures and K_p. Be able to convert between K_c and K_p for gas phase reactions. (Section 15–8; Exercises 25 through 32)

8. Use LeChatelier's Principle to determine the direction in which a system at equilibrium will shift (if it does) when stresses of the following kinds are applied: (a) change in pressure, (b) change in volume, (c) change in temperature, (d) change in amounts of reactants or products present, (e) addition of a catalyst. (Section 15–5; Exercises 33 through 41)

9. Given concentrations or partial pressures of all species in a system at equilibrium, to which a stress is then applied, determine the concentrations or partial pressures of all species after equilibrium is re-established. (Section 15–6; Exercises 42 through 49)

10. Given the equilibrium constant for a reaction at a particular temperature, calculate the standard free-energy change, ΔG^0, at that temperature, and vice versa. (Section 15–10; Exercises 50, 51, 53 and 54)

11. Given the standard enthalpy change, ΔH^0, and the equilibrium constant at a particular temperature, calculate the equilibrium constant at a different temperature. (Section 15–11; Exercises 52 and 54)

Some Important Terms in This Chapter

Write the meanings *in your own words*. Check the Key Terms list and the chapter reading. Then rewrite your definitions, still in your own words, to improve them. Study other new terms and review terms from preceding chapters if necessary.

chemical equilibrium

dynamic equilibrium

equilibrium constant

reaction quotient

homogeneous equilibrium

heterogeneous equilibrium

LeChatelier's Principle

Preliminary Test

This test will check your understanding of basic concepts and types of calculations. Most students require more practice than they anticipate on the calculations and reasoning of chemical equilibrium. Be sure to practice *many* of the additional textbook exercises, including those indicated in the Study Goals.

True-False

Mark each statement as true (T) or false (F).

_____   1. In any equilibrium mixture, the amount of substances present must be in ratios given by the stoichiometric coefficients in the balanced chemical equation.

____   2. Generally the larger the numerical value of K_c, the more nearly to completion the reaction goes before reaching equilibrium.

____   3. A living organism is in a state of chemical equilibrium.

____   4. In writing the expressions for K_c, we omit species present as pure solids or pure liquids, but include all substances present in solution or as gases.

____   5. When we need to solve a quadratic equation in a chemical equilibrium problem, we always use the positive sign before the square root expression in the quadratic formula.

____   6. Since the reaction quotient has the same algebraic form of the concentrations as does the equilibrium constant, Q must always equal K_c.

____   7. For the reaction $A + B \rightleftharpoons C$, where $\Delta G^0 = -4.5$ kcal, there will be only C left after a long enough period of time if stoichiometric amounts of A and B are allowed to react.

The next eleven questions, 8 through 18, refer to the endothermic equilibrium reaction $CoCO_3$ (s) $\rightleftharpoons$ CoO (s) + CO_2 (g).

____   8. At equilibrium conditions, the forward and the reverse reactions have stopped.

____   9. The same equilibrium condition would result if we started with *only* pure $CoCO_3$ (s) in a closed container or if we started with *only* pure CoO (s) in a closed container.

____   10. Equal concentrations of CoO (s) and CO_2 (g) result from the decomposition of a given amount of $CoCO_3$ (s).

____   11. Equal numbers of moles of CoO (s) and CO_2 (g) result from the decomposition of a given amount of $CoCO_3$ (s).

____   12. Decreasing the volume of the closed system at constant temperature results in more $CoCO_3$ (s) being formed.

____   13. Introducing 1.00 atm pressure of CO_2 (g) to the system at equilibrium in a closed container results in more $CoCO_3$ (s) being formed.

____   14. Introducing 1.00 atm pressure of N_2 (g) to the system at equilibrium in a closed container results in more $CoCO_3$ (s) being formed.

____   15. Increasing the temperature of the reaction mixture, but holding the pressure constant by allowing the container to expand or contract, results in more $CoCO_3$ (s) being formed.

____   16. The equilibrium constant expression is $K_c = [CO_2]$.

____   17. The reaction is a heterogeneous reaction.

____   18. If we increase the temperature, the value of the equilibrium constant increases.

Short Answer

1. LeChatelier's Principle may be stated as follows: _____

_____.

2. If an equation for a reaction is multiplied by a number n, the original value of K_c is altered by _____.

3. Suppose we know the numerical value of K_c for a reaction (call this numercial value x). If we reverse the direction in which the equation is written, the numerical value of the equilibrium constant for this reversed equation will be ____.

4. The equilibrium constant expression, K_c, for the reaction

$$NO_2\ (g) + SO_2(g) \rightleftharpoons NO\ (g) + SO_3\ (g)$$

is _____.

5. The pressure equilibrium constant expression, K_p, for the reaction in Question 4 is _____.

6. The equilibrium constant expression, K_c, for the reaction

$$4FeS_2\ (s) + 11O_2\ (g) \rightleftharpoons 2Fe_2O_3\ (s) + 8SO_2\ (g)$$

is _____.

7. The pressure equilibrium constant expression, K_p, for the reaction in Question 6 is _____.

8. In qualitative analysis for metal ions, sulfide ions are often produced by the reaction

$$H_2S\ (aq) + 2H_2O\ (\ell) \rightleftharpoons 2H_3O^+\ (aq) + S^{2-}\ (aq).$$

The addition of ____ would effectively decrease the S^{2-} concentration in the equilibrium mixture.

9. The slightly soluble substance barium fluoride dissolves only slightly in water according to the reaction

$$BaF_2\ (s) \rightleftharpoons Ba^{2+}\ (aq) + 2F^-\ (aq).$$

The equilibrium constant expression for this reaction is _____.

In the Mond process for refining nickel, the gaseous substance nickel tetra-carbonyl, $Ni(CO)_4$, is heated to cause it to decompose into solid nickel and gaseous carbon monoxide, CO. Questions 10 through 13 refer to this reaction.

10. The expression for the equilibrium constant, K_c, for this reaction is _____.

11. The expression for the pressure equilibrium constant, K_p, for this reaction is _____.

12. The value of Δn for this reaction is ____.

13. The numerical value of K_p for this reaction at room temperature is _____ (larger than, smaller than, the same as) the numerical value for K_c.

Questions 14 through 18 refer to the reaction

$$2NO\ (g) + 2H_2\ (g) \rightleftharpoons N_2\ (g) + 2\ H_2O\ (g).$$

This reaction is strongly exothermic. In each question, we allow the reaction to attain equilibrium; then we make *only* the one change in the conditions indicated and allow the reaction to re-establish equilibrium. For each, predict the effect on (a) the amount of N_2 present compared with the original equilibrium conditions and (b) the numerical value of K. The possible answers are: increase (I), decrease (D), or remain unchanged (U).

Change	Amount of N_2	Value of K
14. More NO is added to the reaction mixture.	—	—
15. A catalyst is introduced.	—	—
16. Some H_2O (g) is removed from the reaction mixture by introducing a drying agent.	—	—
17. The temperature is decreased.	—	—
18. The volume of the reaction container is doubled.	—	—

19. The thermodynamic quantity that is most closely related to the value of the equilibrium constant is ____.
20. The thermodynamic quantity that is most closely related to the change in value of the equilibrium constant with temperature is ____.

Multiple Choice

____ 1. When a reaction reaches equilibrium,
   (a) the rate of the forward reaction and the rate of the reverse reaction are both zero.
   (b) all reaction stops.
   (c) the rate of the forward reaction is zero.
   (d) the rate of the reverse reaction is zero.
   (e) the forward and reverse reaction rates are equal.
____ 2. In which of the following cases will the least time be required to arrive at equilibrium?
   (a) K_c is a very small number.
   (b) K_c is a very large number.
   (c) K_c is approximately 1.
   (d) Cannot tell without knowing the value of K_c.
   (e) Cannot tell since the time to arrive at equilibrium does not depend on K_c.
____ 3. Which of the following statements is *not* true?
   (a) A system that is disturbed from an equilibrium condition reacts in a manner to restore equilibrium.
   (b) Equilibrium in molecular systems is static, all molecular interaction having stopped.

(c) The nature of an equilibrium mixture is the same regardless of the direction from which it was reached.

(d) A system moves spontaneously toward a state of equilibrium.

(e) The equilibrium constant usually depends on temperature.

_____ 4. In the reaction $A + B \overset{k_f}{\underset{k_r}{\rightleftharpoons}} C + D$ where k_f and k_r are the specific rate constants, which of the following is correct at equilibrium?

(a) $k_f = k_r$ (b) $k_f > k_r$ (c) $k_f < k_r$ (d) $\text{rate}_f = \text{rate}_r$

(e) $K_c = \dfrac{[A][B]}{[C][D]}$

_____ 5. For the reaction $2A + B \rightleftharpoons C + 2D$ at 35°C, the value of k_f is $3.0 \times 10^{-3}\ M^{-1}s^{-1}$ and the value of $k_r = 1.5 \times 10^{-2}\ M^{-2}\ s^{-1}$. Calculate the value of K_c for this reaction.

(a) 2.0   (b) 0.5   (c) 0.2   (d) 5.0   (e) 4.5×10^{-5}

_____ 6. Solid ammonium carbamate, $NH_4CO_2NH_2$, dissociates completely into ammonia and carbon dioxide. When pure ammonium carbamate is put into an evacuated container and allowed to come to equilibrium with the gaseous products, the total pressure at 45°C is found to be 0.6 atm. What is the value of K_p for this reaction at 45°C?

(a) 6.0×10^{-2} (b) 4.0×10^{-3} (c) 8.0×10^{-2}

(d) 3.2×10^{-2} (e) 2.16×10^{-1}

_____ 7. The equilibrium constant for the gaseous reaction $HCHO \rightleftharpoons H_2 + CO$ has the numerical value 0.50 at 600°C. A mixture of HCHO, H_2, and CO is introduced into a flask at 600°C. After a short time, analysis of a small sample of the reaction mixture shows the concentrations to be $[HCHO] = 1.5$, $[H_2] = 0.5$, $[CO] = 1.0$. (Of course these are all molar concentrations in moles/liter.) Which of the following statements about this reaction mixture is true?

(a) The reaction mixture is at equilibrium.

(b) The reaction mixture is not at equilibrium, but no further reaction will occur.

(c) The reaction mixture is not at equilibrium, but will move toward equilibrium by forming more HCHO.

(d) The reaction mixture is not at equilibrium, but will move toward equilibrium by using up more HCHO.

(e) The forward rate of this reaction is the same as the reverse rate.

_____ 8. The numerical value of the concentration equilibrium constant for the gaseous reaction $2SO_2 + O_2 \rightleftharpoons 2SO_3$ is 0.5 at some temperature. When a reaction mixture is brought to equilibrium, $[O_2]$ is found to be 2.0 M, and $[SO_3]$ is found to be 10 M. What is the equilibrium concentration of SO_2 in this mixture?

(a) 0.5 M (b) 10 M (c) 2.0 M (d) 5.0 M (e) 1.0 M

_____ 9. The equilibrium constant for the gaseous reaction $CO + H_2O \rightleftharpoons CO_2 + H_2$ is 4.0 at a certain temperature. A reaction is carried out at this temperature starting with 2.0 mol/L of CO and 2.0 mol/L of H_2O. What will be the equilibrium concentration of H_2?

(a) 2.0 M (b) 0.75 M (c) 1.33 M (d) 0.67 M

(e) 1.5 M

_____ 10. The introduction of a catalyst into a reaction mixture at equilibrium would

(a) cause a change in the amount of heat absorbed or evolved.

(b) change the value of ΔG^0 for the reaction.

(c) change the value of the equilibrium constant.

(d) change the relative amounts of reactants and products present at equilibrium.

(e) cause none of the changes listed above.

_____ 11. Suppose the reaction mixture N_2 (g) + $3H_2$ (g) $\rightleftharpoons$ $2NH_3$ (g) is at equilibrium at a given temperature and pressure. The pressure is then increased at constant temperature by compressing the reaction mixture, and the mixture is allowed to re-establish equilibrium. At the new equilibrium

(a) there is more ammonia present than there was originally.

(b) there is less ammonia present than there was originally.

(c) there is the same amount of ammonia present as there was originally.

(d) the nitrogen is used up completely.

(e) the amount of ammonia present may be either greater or smaller than it was originally, depending on the value of K.

_____ 12. Suppose the reaction mixture H_2 (g) + Cl_2 (g) $\rightleftharpoons$ $2HCl$ (g) is at equilibrium at a given temperature and pressure. The pressure is then increased at constant temperature, by compressing the reaction mixture and the mixture is allowed to re-establish equilibrium. At the new equilibrium

(a) there is more hydrogen chloride present than there was originally.

(b) there is less hydrogen chloride present than there was originally.

(c) there is the same amount of hydrogen chloride as there was originally.

(d) the hydrogen and chlorine are completely used up.

(e) the amount of hydrogen chloride present may be either greater or smaller than it was originally, depending on the value of K.

_____ 13. An acetic acid solution is allowed to come to equilibrium:

$$CH_3COOH + H_2O \rightleftharpoons H_3O^+ + CH_3COO^-$$

If some silver ion, Ag^+, is then added to the solution, solid silver acetate, $AgCH_3COO$, is formed. The resulting amount of undissociated acetic acid, CH_3COOH, in solution would be

(a) unchanged from that in the original solution.
(b) higher than that in the original solution.
(c) lower than that in the original solution.
(d) zero.

_____ 14. The reaction

$$CaCO_3 \text{ (s)} + 2H_3O^+ \text{ (aq)} \rightleftharpoons Ca^{2+} \text{ (aq)} + 2H_2O \text{ (}\ell\text{)} + CO_2 \text{ (g)}$$

may be forced to completion (that is forced to consume more $CaCO_3$) by which of the following methods?
(a) removing some H_3O^+ from the reaction mixture by neutralizing it with base
(b) adding more Ca^{2+} to the solution
(c) removing CO_2 gas as it is formed
(d) adding CO_2 gas to the reaction mixture
(e) none of the preceding would have any effect on the amount of $CaCO_3$ consumed.

_____ 15. For the heterogeneous reaction $2MnO_2 \text{ (s)} \rightleftharpoons 2MnO \text{ (s)} + O_2 \text{ (g)}$, the equilibrium constant expression for K_c is which of the following?

(a) $K = \dfrac{[MnO]^2[O_2]}{[MnO_2]^2}$ (b) $K = [O_2]$ (c) $K = 1/[O_2]$

(d) $K = k[MnO_2]^2$ (e) $K = \dfrac{[MnO_2]^2}{[MnO]^2[O_2]}$

_____ 16. Given the equilibrium reaction $MgSO_4 \text{ (s)} \rightleftharpoons MgO \text{ (s)} + SO_3 \text{ (g)}$, which of the following statements is true?
(a) If the container were opened to the atmosphere, eventually only $MgSO_4$ (s) would remain.
(b) Decreasing the volume of the closed container at constant temperature results in more MgO (s) being formed.
(c) The same equilibrium condition would result if we started with *only* pure $MgSO_4$ (s) in a closed container as if we started with *only* pure MgO (s) in a closed container.
(d) At equilibrium the forward and reverse reactions have stopped.
(e) If *pure* $MgSO_4$ (s) were placed in a closed container filled with N_2 (g) at 1 atm, the total pressure would increase due to SO_3 (g) being formed.

The following three questions, 17 through 19, refer to the endothermic reaction

$$2SO_2 \text{ (g)} + O_2 \text{ (g)} \rightleftharpoons 2SO_3 \text{ (g)}.$$

_____ 17. Suppose we let the reaction come to equilibrium. Then we increase the temperature of the reaction mixture. What will be the effect on the net amount of SO_3 (g) present?

(a) It increases.
(b) It decreases.
(c) It does not change.
(d) The question cannot be answered without some knowledge of the value of K_c or K_p.
(e) The question cannot be answered without some knowledge of the value of ΔH^0.

_____ 18. Suppose we let the reaction come to equilibrium. Then we decrease the total pressure by increasing the volume of the container. What will be the effect on the net amount of SO_3 (g) present?
(a) It increases.
(b) It decreases.
(c) It does not change.
(d) The question cannot be answered without some knowledge of the value of K_c or K_p.
(e) The question cannot be answered without some knowledge of the value of ΔH^0.

_____ 19. Suppose we let the reaction come to equilibrium. Then we increase the temperature and decrease the total pressure simultaneously. What will be the effect on the net amount of SO_3 (g) present?
(a) It increases.
(b) It decreases.
(c) It does not change.
(d) It may either increase, decrease, or remain the same, depending on the sizes of the temperature and pressure changes.
(e) It may either increase, decrease, or remain the same, depending on the numerical value of the equilibrium constant.

_____ 20. At 25°C, the value of K_c for a particular reaction is 30. At 75°C, the value of K_c for this same reaction is 40. Which one of the following statements about this reaction is true?
(a) The reaction is at equilibrium
(b) LeChatelier's Principle does not apply to this reaction.
(c) The reaction is endothermic.
(d) The reaction is exothermic.
(e) Increasing the pressure would decrease the value of K_c.

Answers to Preliminary Test

Do not just look up answers. Think about the reasons for the answers.

True-False

1. False

2. True
3. False. Obviously not all (and perhaps not any) reactions in a living organism are at equilibrium at any given time.
4. True
5. False. The only way we know is to find out which leads to physically reasonable results.
6. False. This is true only at equilibrium. Study Section 15–4 and the uses of the reaction quotient outlined in Section 15–5.
7. False
8. False
9. False. Starting with only pure CoO (s), equilibrium could never be reached. Some CO_2 (g) is necessary to allow the reaction (reverse) to proceed at all.
10. False. We do not refer to "concentrations" of pure solvents.
11. True
12. True
13. True
14. False. Since N_2 (g) is neither a reactant nor a product, its presence does nothing to disturb the equilibrium.
15. False
16. True. Remember that solids do not appear in the equilibrium constant expression.
17. True
18. True. Since the reaction is endothermic (consumes heat), the forward reaction would be favored at higher temperatures. This would form more products, consuming reactants, so the value of K, which is equal to $[CO_2]$ for this reaction, would increase.

Short Answer

1. if a change of conditions is applied to a system at equilibrium, the system will respond so as to reduce the disturbance to reach a new equilibrium state. Of course, it is much better for you to know this and be able to state it in your own words than just to memorize a set statement.
2. raising it to the nth power. You do not need to remember this rule — if you understand how to write an equilibrium constant from the chemical equation, you can easily figure it out.
3. $1/x$. Same comments as for Question 2.
4. $\dfrac{[NO][SO_3]}{[NO_2][SO_2]}$
5. $\dfrac{P_{NO}P_{SO_3}}{P_{NO_2}P_{SO_2}}$
6. $\dfrac{[SO_2]^8}{[O_2]^{11}}$

7. $\dfrac{P_{SO_2}{}^8}{P_{O_2}{}^{11}}$

8. H_3O^+. This is an example of a weak acid equilibrium, which will be covered in more detail in Chapter 16, but you can answer this with what you know in general about equilibrium from Chapter 15.

9. $[Ba^{2+}][F^-]^2$. Equilibria involving slightly soluble salts will be covered in more detail in Chapter 18. This is clearly just a case of heterogeneous equilibrium, which you have learned about in Chapter 15.

10. $K = \dfrac{[CO]^4}{[Ni(CO)_4]}$. From the description given in the question, you should be able to write the chemical equation as $Ni(CO)_4 (g) \rightleftharpoons Ni (s) + 4CO (g)$.

11. $K_p = P_{CO}{}^4 / P_{Ni(CO)_4}$

12. 3. Remember that this is the number of moles of gas products minus the number of moles of gas reactants in the balanced equation.

13. larger than. Remember (Section 15–8) that $K_p = K_c (RT)^{\Delta n}$; from the preceding question, Δn is positive.

14. I, U

15. U, U

16. I, U

17. I, I. Notice that only a temperature change alters the value of K.

18. D, U. The only way to change the value of K is to change the temperature, so K does not change. Doubling the volume of the container has the effect of multiplying all gas concentrations by a factor of $\frac{1}{2}$ (or all gas pressures by a factor of $\frac{1}{2}$). Since there are more moles of gas on the left (denominator) than on the right (numerator), Q is now greater than K. The reaction shifts to re-establish equilibrium by proceeding to the left (making more moles of gas), decreasing the amount of N_2 present.

19. ΔG^0

20. ΔH^0

Multiple Choice

1. (e)

2. (e)

3. (b)

4. (d). As equilibrium is reached, the rates change, but the values of k_f and k_r do not. Do not get the idea that $k_f = k_r$ at equilibrium; rather, the concentrations are such that (d) is true. Answer (e) is inverted.

5. (c). From Section 15–2, $K_c = k_f / k_r$.

6. (d). You should be able to figure out that the reaction is

$$NH_4CO_2NH_2 (s) \rightleftharpoons 2NH_3 (g) + CO_2 (g)$$

Thus the expression for $K_p = P_{NH_3}{}^2 P_{CO_2}$. If the total pressure is 0.6 atm, the partial pressure of NH_3 is 0.4 atm and that of CO_2 is 0.2 atm, as you should be able to reason from the stoichiometry.

7. (d). Putting the given values of concentrations into the expression for Q, you find that $Q = 0.333$. This is less than K, so the reaction must proceed to make more products, raising the value of the numerator and lowering the denominator. This uses up HCHO.

8. (b). Put the known values of concentrations into the expression for K_c and then solve for $[SO_2]$.

9. (c)

10. (e)

11. (a). There are more moles of gas on the left than on the right of the balanced equation, so an increase in pressure, which would disturb the equilibrium, could be relieved by the reaction proceeding more to the right.

12. (c). In this case, there are equal numbers of moles of gas on the two sides of the balanced equation. Thus, an increase in pressure would not disturb the equilibrium.

13. (c). This combines the ideas which will be covered quantitatively in Chapter 16 (weak acid equilibrium) and in Chapter 18 (slightly soluble salt equilibrium). It can easily be answered from the general principles of equilibrium in Chapter 15.

14. (c)

15. (b)

16. (e)

17. (a)

18. (b)

19. (d)

20. (c). You should be able to figure this out by the ideas of Section 15–5. You should also be able to reason it out, without calculation, from the van't Hoff equation, Section 15–11.

16

Equilibrium in Aqueous Solutions—I

Chapter Summary

Many important reactions take place in water solutions—in the laboratory, in living organisms, and in industrial chemistry. In Chapter 16, we focus what we have learned about chemical equilibrium in Chapter 15 and about strong and weak electrolytes (Section 7–1) into a study of equilibria in aqueous solutions, with special emphasis on weak acids and bases (Chapter 11). Perhaps some review of the appropriate sections of the chapters just mentioned would be helpful prior to beginning your detailed study of Chapter 16.

Section 16–1 opens the chapter with a review of the terminology of **strong** and **weak** electrolytes. This topic, which until now you have seen only in a descriptive way, is extended quantitatively here to calculate concentrations of each ionic species present in solution when a **strong electrolyte** (a strong acid, a strong soluble base, or a soluble ionic salt) dissolves in water. The key point here is that each reaction is considered to go *virtually to completion,* so that calculation of concentrations depends only on a proper interpretation of the stoichiometric coefficients in the balanced chemical equation. Thus, we do not apply the ideas of chemical equilibrium to solutions of strong electrolytes. (But we will see in Chapter 17 that some extension must be made to this interpretation when one of the ions is a conjugate acid of a weak base or a conjugate base of a weak acid.)

Application of chemical equilibrium does become important, however, when we consider the **ionization of water** to form H_3O^+ and OH^- (Section 16–2). Since this reaction proceeds only slightly, it is appropriate to describe it in terms of an equilibrium constant, $K_w = [H_3O^+][OH^-] = 1.0 \times 10^{-14}$ at 25°C. A very important point to be grasped here is that this equilibrium constant expression *must be satisfied in all aqueous solutions,* no matter what the source of H_3O^+ or OH^- and no matter what other ions may be present. This allows us to relate $[H_3O^+]$ and $[OH^-]$ in any aqueous solution, since their product must be equal to 10^{-14}. Be sure that you are comfortable with the terminology at the end of Section 16–2, by which we refer to a solution as acidic, basic, or neutral, depending on the relative values of

[H$_3$O$^+$] and OH$^-$]. Notice that such solutions can contain Brønsted-Lowry or Lewis acids and bases, but it is an overall characteristic of the solution that we are describing here.

Because of the inconvenience of the great range of numbers necessary to describe [H$_3$O$^+$], chemists use the **pH scale** (Section 16–3). The nature of this scale is such that (1) a ten-fold change in [H$_3$O$^+$] is described by a change of 1 pH unit and (2) increasing [H$_3$O$^+$] corresponds to decreasing pH. Study this section carefully as the terminology of pH is widespread in chemistry.

There are only a few common strong acids and bases, so many solutions involve **weak acids and bases.** Since these, by definition, are involved in dissociation or ionization reactions that reach equilibrium without going to completion, we describe the ionization reactions of these substances in terms of equilibrium constants (Section 16–4). This is the most important section of this chapter—do not hurry your study of it. These equilibrium constants are known as **ionization constants** and are denoted as K_a for weak acids and K_b for weak bases. In fact, we are really just applying here the same kind of equilibrium-constant calculations that you learned in Chapter 15. However, the frequently *very small* values of K_a and K_b lead us to some conveniences in solving problems, such as the neglect of predictably very small values when added to or subtracted from larger numbers. This is discussed in the section entitled "Simplifying Quadratic Equations" in Section 16–4; be sure that you understand how and when this approximation is appropriate. In addition to learning to work problems to solve for concentrations, you should (1) have a feel for relative strengths of acids or bases from looking at K_a and K_b values, (2) be familiar with the **percentage ionization** representation, and (3) recall the weak acid–strong conjugate base relationships from Chapter 11 and see how they apply here. Of course the pH description is used throughout these calculations.

The action of very useful substances called **acid-base indicators** is discussed in Section 16–5. As you see, these are either weak acids or weak bases that undergo a marked color change when converted to their conjugate bases or conjugate acids, respectively. As we gradually add a solution of a strong base to a solution of a strong acid **(titration)** we are gradually neutralizing the acid. Before a stoichiometric amount of base has been added, the solution is still acidic; at the **equivalence point,** the acid and base have just neutralized each other; and beyond this point the solution is basic. Section 16–6 shows how this information may be quantitatively represented in a graph known as a **titration curve.** We also see in this section how an indicator may be used to provide a visual signal when the equivalence point of a titration has been reached. Of course, an analogous discussion would apply to the titration of a strong base by a strong acid solution. The calculations in this section provide useful practice in stoichiometry.

We remember from Chapter 15 that LeChatelier's Principle tells us that the addition from an outside source of one of the products to a reaction at equilibrium results in "shifting the equilibrium to the left," i.e., tending to suppress the reaction. When the reaction is the ionization of a weak acid (or base) and the product added is the conjugate base (or acid) from an appropriate soluble salt, this is referred to as the **common ion effect** (Section 16–7).

The resulting solution, which is able to absorb modest amounts of acid or base and thus to resist changes in pH, is called a **buffer solution.** The buffering action (Section 16–8) of such a solution may be understood as follows.

Suppose we had a solution of an acid, either weak or strong, and then added to it some additional acid from an external source. If the original solution contained only a strong acid, its conjugate base would be far too weak to react with the added acid, so the pH would change greatly. If the original solution contained a weak acid, its conjugate base would be strong, but there would be only a tiny bit of that strong base present to react with the added acid, so the pH still would change markedly. However, if the original solution had been made by including *both* the weak acid HA *and* a separate source of its conjugate base A^- (Section 16–8.1), there would then be high concentrations of both the undissociated acid and its conjugate base. This solution would be able to absorb added acid by reaction with the base A^-; on the other hand, the weak acid HA could ionize additionally to provide more H_3O^+ if we introduced a little OH^-. Thus, the solution is far more resistant than most others to large pH changes. A solution made by dissolving a weak base and a separate source of its conjugate acid shows similar buffering action (Section 16–8.2). Buffer solutions of desired pH are made either by mixing appropriate solutions or by dissolving the appropriate salt in an acidic or in a basic solution (Section 16–9).

The calculations of Sections 16–7 through 16–9 will help you to see more clearly how such a buffer solution works. The key relationship for use in buffer calculations is the **Henderson-Hasselbalch equation** for acid/salt buffers (and the analogous equation for base/salt buffers later in the section). Be sure you see that in application of this equation and related ones, the concentrations to be used are, for all practical purposes, the total added concentration of weak acid, weak base, or salt. But do not be content with plugging into equations. An understanding of the mode of action of buffer solutions and of the chemical reactions and equilibrium calculations associated with them will lead to a better understanding of the nature of acid-base equilibria in aqueous solution.

This chapter closes with a discussion of the equilibrium constants and expressions that we use to describe **polyprotic weak acids** (Section 16–10), those that ionize stepwise (with varying strengths), each step yielding H_3O^+. Notice that successive steps are always less complete, so that $K_2 < K_1$, and so on. There are no *common* examples of weak bases that ionize in a stepwise fashion, although a few inorganic bases and many weak organic bases do.

Study Goals

There is a large amount of apparently diverse material in this chapter, but it is all tied together in terms of (a) acid-base behavior and (b) equilibrium considerations. The following study goals will help you to organize this material. Be systematic in your study. Write your own summary of each section, with these goals in mind. Also be systematic in answering questions and working problems from the text.

1. Review the fundamental ideas of acids and bases from earlier chapters. Memorize the lists of the common strong acids (Table 9–2) and the common strong soluble bases (Table 9–4). Classify common acids as strong or weak; classify common bases as strong soluble, insoluble, or weak. (Review Sections 7–1, 11–3, 11–5, and 11–8; Exercise 1)

2. Understand the Brønsted-Lowry acid-base theory. Be able to identify the Brønsted-Lowry acids and Brønsted-Lowry bases in reactions. Understand and apply the Brønsted-Lowry terminology of conjugate acid-base pairs and their relative strengths. (Review Section 11–3)

3. Be able to calculate the concentrations of constituent ions in solutions of strong electrolytes (whether they are strong acids, strong bases, or soluble salts). (Section 16–1; Exercises 2 and 3)

4. Be familiar with the autoionization of water, including the chemical equation and the significance and uses of its equilibrium constant, K_w. (Section 16–2; Exercises 4 through 8)

5. Be familiar with the pH scale. Given any one of the following for any aqueous solution, calculate the other three: hydronium ion concentration, hydroxide concentration, pH, or pOH. (Section 16–3; Exercises 9 through 21)

6. Know how to write the equations for the ionization of any weak acid or weak base. Be able to write and interpret the expression for the corresponding equilibrium constant. (Section 16–4)

7. Be able to perform equilibrium calculations for solutions of weak acids and weak bases, relating initial concentrations, value of ionization constants, and equilibrium concentrations of all species present. Given any one of these quantities, be able to calculate the others. (Section 16–4; Exercises 22 through 37)

8. Describe why acid-base indicators change color over a definite pH range and why this range differs for different indicators. (Section 16–5; Exercises 38 through 41)

9. Calculate concentrations and pH values of solutions resulting from the mixture of any volumes of any concentrations of acids and bases. Either the acid or the base may be added as a pure substance. (Section 16–6; Exercises 42 through 44 and 57)

10. Use the results of calculations related to Study Goal 9 to plot titration

curves for titrations involving strong acids and bases. (Section 16–6; Exercises 42 through 44)

11. Describe the common ion effect in terms of LeChatelier's Principle; use this effect to understand and explain buffering action. (Sections 16–7; Exercises 45 and 47)

12. Know how buffer solutions are prepared. Be able to calculate $[H_3O^+]$, $[OH^-]$, pH, and pOH in buffer solutions of the acid/salt type and the base/salt type. (Sections 16–8 and 16–9; Exercises 46, 48 through 53, and 58 through 63)

13. Be able to calculate the changes in the quantities of Study Goal 12 when specified amounts of acid or base are added to the buffer solution. (Section 16–8; Exercises 54 through 56)

14. Be able to apply Study Goal 7 to polyprotic weak acids. (Section 16–10; Exercises 64 through 67)

Some Important Terms in This Chapter

Many of the important terms in this chapter have been encountered before, especially in Chapters 7 and 11. Write the meanings of the following terms *in your own words*. Check the Key Terms list and the chapter reading. Then rewrite your definitions, still in your own words, to improve them. Study other new terms and review terms from preceding chapters if necessary.

Brønsted-Lowry acid

Brønsted-Lowry base

conjugate acid-base pair

ionization

autoionization

ionization constant

ion product for water

pH

pOH

p[ ]

monoprotic acid

polyprotic acid

common ion effect

buffer solution

indicator

titration

titration curve

equivalence point

end point

Preliminary Test

This test will check your understanding of basic concepts and types of calculations. Be sure to practice *many* of the additional textbook exercises, including those indicated with the Study Goals.

Short Answer

1. Strong electrolytes _____ electricity better than weak electrolytes in aqueous solution, because they are more completely _____.

2. The seven common strong acids are _____, _____, _____, _____, _____, _____, and _____.

3. The eight strong soluble bases are the hydroxides of _____,

_____, _____, _____, _____, _____,
_____, and _____.

4. The five acids listed in Table 16–2 of the text, arranged according to increasing acid strength, are _____.

5. In Table 16–2 of the text, there are five bases listed (excluding water). Arranged according to increasing strength, these bases are _____ _____.

6. The common weak bases discussed in this chapter are the compound _____ and several of its organic derivatives, called _____.

7. The ionization constant for a weak base is represented by the symbol ___.

8. The symbol for the ionization constant of a weak acid is ___.

9. The weaker the acid, the _____ the percentage ionization of the acid in solution.

10. The definition of pH is _____.

11. In a solution of pH 9.0, $[H_3O^+] =$ ___.

12. In a solution of pH 9.3, $[H_3O^+] =$ _____.

13. In any aqueous solution, as $[H_3O^+]$ increases, $[OH^-]$ _____.

14. In any aqueous solution at 25°C, _____ $= 10^{-14}$ and _____ $= 14$.

15. In 0.1 M HCl, $[H_3O^+] =$ ___.

16. In 0.1 M HCl, $[OH^-] =$ ___.

17. The pH of a solution in which $[H_3O^+] = 1.0 \times 10^{-5}$ is ___.

18. The pH of a solution in which $[H_3O^+] = 2.0 \times 10^{-5}$ is ___.

19. In a solution with pH $= 3.0$, pOH $=$ ___.

20. In the solution of Question 19, $[H_3O^+] =$ ___ M and $[OH^-] =$ ___ M.

21. The solution of Question 19 would be described as _____ (acidic, basic, neutral).

22. By definition, an acidic solution is one in which $[H_3O^+]$ ___ $[OH^-]$, a basic solution is one in which $[H_3O^+]$ ___ $[OH^-]$, and a neutral solution is one in which $[H_3O^+]$ ___ $[OH^-]$.

23. If the concentration of monoprotic strong acid is x molar, then the concentration of hydronium ions, $[H_3O^+]$, will be equal to ___ M.

24. In a solution of RbOH that is x molar, $[Rb^+] =$ ___ M and $[OH^-] =$ ___ M.

25. In a solution of $Ba(OH)_2$ that is x molar, $[Ba^{2+}] =$ ___ M and $[OH^-] =$ ___ M.

26. In a 0.10 M solution of any monoprotic strong acid, pH $= 1.0$; in a 0.1 M solution of any weak acid, pH is _____ (greater than, less than, equal to) 1.0.

27. In a solution containing only a weak monoprotic acid HA, $[H_3O^+]$ is _____ (greater than, less than, equal to) $[A^-]$; if the solution is not very dilute, the concentration of nonionized HA is approximately equal to the _____ of the solution.

28. An acid-base indicator changes color when the ____ changes sufficiently.
29. For most indicators, one color is distinct if the ratio of $[In^-]/[HIn]$ is greater than about ____ and the other color is seen distinctly if this ratio is less than about ____; thus, most indicators change color over a range of about ____ pH units.
30. A procedure in which a solution containing one reactant is slowly added to a solution of unknown concentration of another reactant until the reaction is complete is called _____.
31. The point in a titration at which chemically equivalent amounts of acid and base have reacted is called the _____; the point at which the indicator changes color is known as the _____.
32. We can describe the titration curve for the reaction in which a strong acid solution is titrated by a strong base as follows: first there is a region in which the pH is relatively constant at a _____ value, followed by a region where the pH _____.
33. In a solution that is 0.1 M in acetic acid and 0.1 M in sodium acetate, the $[H_3O^+]$ is _____ (greater than, less than, equal to) the $[H_3O^+]$ in a solution of 0.1 M acetic acid.
34. Two of the most common kinds of buffer solutions are _____ _____ and _____.
35. The utility of a buffer solution is that it _____ when moderate amounts of acid or base are added to the solution.
36. The Henderson-Hasselbalch equation for pH in a weak acid buffer is _____.
37. H_2SO_4 is a _____ acid than HSO_4^-, and HSO_4^- is a _____ acid than SO_4^{2-}.
38. For all diprotic weak acids, K_1 ___ K_2.

Multiple Choice

____   1. Which of the following is a weak electrolyte in aqueous solution?
(a) $HClO_4$ (b) NaOH   (c) NaCl   (d) HNO_2
(e) $Ca(NO_3)_2$

____   2. Ammonia dissolves in water by the reaction

$$NH_3 (g) + H_2O (\ell) \rightleftharpoons NH_4^+ (aq) + OH^- (aq).$$

We would expect the resulting solution to be
(a) acidic.   (b) neutral.   (c) basic.

____   3. A solution in which the pH was 12.5 would be described as
(a) very basic.   (b) slightly basic.   (c) neutral.   (d) slightly acidic.   (e) very acidic.

____   4. We add enough base to a solution to cause the pH to increase from 7.5 to 8.5. This means that
(a) $[OH^-]$ increases by a factor of 10.

    (b) $[H_3O^+]$ increases by a factor of 10.
    (c) $[OH^-]$ increases by 1 M.
    (d) $[H_3O^+]$ increases by 1 M.
    (e) $[OH^-]$ increases by a factor of 8.5/7.5.

_____ 5. Calculate the pH of a 0.04 M HNO_3 solution.
    (a) 2.4   (b) 12.5   (c) 4.0×10^{-2} (d) 1.4   (e) 1.6

_____ 6. What would be the $[OH^-]$ concentration in the 0.04 M HNO_3 solution of Question 5?
    (a) 2.5×10^{-10} M (b) 12.6 M (c) 1.4 M
    (d) 2.5×10^{-13} M (e) 0 M

_____ 7. For a given acid HA, the value of K_a
    (a) will change with pH.
    (b) cannot be less than 10^{-7}.
    (c) cannot be greater than 10^{-7}.
    (d) does not change with temperature.
    (e) None of the preceding answers is correct.

Hypobromous acid, HBrO, is a weak acid with an acid dissociation constant of 2.5×10^{-9}. The next three questions, 8 through 10, refer to a 0.01 M HBrO solution.

_____ 8. Calculate the value of $[H_3O^+]$ in this solution.
    (a) 5.0×10^{-6} M (b) 5.0×10^{-5} M (c) 2.5×10^{-7} M
    (d) 2.5×10^{-11} M (e) 5.0×10^{-7} M

_____ 9. What is the pH of this solution?
    (a) 3.50   (b) 4.70   (c) 5.30   (d) 5.70   (e) 6.30

_____ 10. What is the value of $[OH^-]$ in this solution?
    (a) 2.0×10^{-9} M (b) 2.0×10^{-8} M (c) 1.0×10^{-7} M
    (d) 5.0×10^{-6} M (e) 5.0×10^{-5} M

_____ 11. In a sample of pure water, only one of the following statements is _always_ true at all conditions of temperature and pressure. Which one is _always_ true?
    (a) $[H_3O^+] = 1.0 \times 10^{-7}$ M
    (b) $[OH^-] = 1.0 \times 10^{-7}$ M
    (c) pH = 7.0
    (d) pOH = 7.0
    (e) $[H_3O^+] = [OH^-]$

_____ 12. Which of the following expressions correctly describes the relationship between pH and pOH in any aqueous solution at 25°C?
    (a) $(pH)(pOH) = 10^{-14}$
    (b) $pH/pOH = 10^{-14}$
    (c) $pOH/pH = 10^{-14}$
    (d) $pH + pOH = 14$
    (e) $pH - pOH = 14$

_____ 13. Which of the following expressions correctly describes the relationship between $[H_3O^+]$ and $[OH^-]$ in any aqueous solution at 25°C?
  (a) $[H_3O^+][OH^-] = 10^{-14}$
  (b) $[H_3O^+]/[OH^-] = 10^{-14}$
  (c) $[OH^-]/[H_3O^+] = 10^{-14}$
  (d) $[H_3O^+] + [OH^-] = 14$
  (e) $[H_3O^+] - [OH^-] = 14$

_____ 14. The acid form of an indicator is yellow and its anion is blue. The K_a of this indicator is 10^{-5}. What will be the approximate pH range over which this indicator changes color?
  (a) 3–5   (b) 4–6   (c) 5–7   (d) 8–10   (e) 9–11

_____ 15. What will be the color of the indicator in Question 14 in a solution of pH 3?
  (a) red   (b) orange   (c) yellow   (d) green   (e) blue

_____ 16. A buffer solution contains 0.56 M acetic acid and 1.00 M sodium acetate. K_a for acetic acid is 1.8×10^{-5}. The $[H_3O^+]$ in this buffer solution would be nearest
  (a) $10^{-3}\ M$ (b) $10^{-4}\ M$ (c) $10^{-5}\ M$
  (d) $10^{-6}\ M$ (e) $10^{-7}\ M$

Be sure that you work many of the text exercises involving weak acid equilibria, titrations, and buffer solutions.

Answers to Preliminary Test

Do not just look up answers. Think about the reasons for the answers.

Short Answer

1. conduct, ionized (dissociated)
2. hydrochloric (HCl), hydrobromic (HBr), hydroiodic (HI), nitric (HNO_3), perchloric ($HClO_4$), chloric ($HClO_3$), sulfuric (H_2SO_4). Will it help to remember that three of these are binary acids of halogens? HF is a weak acid.
3. lithium, sodium, potassium, rubidium, cesium, calcium, strontium, barium. Notice that these are the alkali metals (Group IA) and the heavier alkaline earth metals (Group IIA).
4. $HCN < HClO < CH_3COOH < HNO_2 < HF$. Smaller values of K_a mean weaker acids.
5. $F^- < NO_2^- < CH_3COO^- < ClO^- < CN^-$. Remember that the stronger the acid, the weaker its conjugate base.
6. ammonia, amines
7. K_b

8. K_a
9. smaller
10. $-\log[H_3O^+]$
11. 10^{-9}
12. 5.0×10^{-10}
13. decreases
14. $[H_3O^+][OH^-]$, pH + pOH
15. 0.1. Remember that HCl is a strong acid and is completely dissociated.
16. 10^{-13}. $[H_3O^+] = 0.1$ (from preceding problem) and $[OH^-] = K_w/[H_3O^+]$.
17. 5.00
18. 4.70
19. 11.0
20. 10^{-3}, 10^{-11}
21. acidic
22. $>, <, =$
23. x. Strong acids are completely dissociated, so x moles of a monoprotic strong acid would yield x moles of H_3O^+ on dissociation.
24. x, x. RbOH is a strong soluble base.
25. $x, 2x$. $Ba(OH)_2$ is a strong soluble base that gives 2 moles OH^- for each mole dissolved.
26. greater than. In weak acid solutions, $[H_3O^+]$ would be less than 0.10, so pH would be greater than 1.00.
27. equal to, molarity
28. pH (or $[H_3O^+]$)
29. 10, 0.1, 2.0
30. titration
31. equivalence point, end point
32. low, increases rapidly over a very small volume of base added.
33. less than. No calculations are needed; think about the common ion effect. Of course, you could do these two calculations if you wish. (Sections 16–4 and 16–7)
34. a solution of a weak acid plus a soluble salt of this weak acid, a solution of a weak base plus a soluble salt of this weak base
35. resists changes in pH
36. $pH = pK_a + \log \dfrac{[salt]}{[acid]}$
37. stronger, stronger
38. $>$

Multiple Choice

1. (d). Remember the list of strong acids and strong bases. Also review the solubility rules. HNO_2 is a weak acid, so it is only slightly dissociated into ions in water solution.

2. (c)

3. (a)

4. (a)

5. (d). Since HNO_3 is a strong acid $[H_3O^+] = 0.04 = 4 \times 10^{-2}$; pH $=$ $-\log(4 \times 10^{-2}) = 1.4$.

6. (d)

7. (e)

8. (a). This must be solved by the methods in Section 16–4.

9. (c)

10. (a)

11. (e). The others all depend on $K_w = 10^{-14}$, which is only true at 25°C. K_w, like all equilibrium constants, changes with temperature.

12. (d)

13. (a)

14. (b). For an indicator (Section 16–5), the color change occurs when $[In^-]/[HIn] = 1$; this occurs when $[H_3O^+] = K_a$. For this indicator, this is at $[H_3O^+] = 10^{-5}$ M, or pH $= 5$. The color change becomes discernible from about 1 pH unit above this to about 1 pH unit below it, or from pH 4 to pH 6.

15. (c). At pH $= 3$, there is considerable excess H_3O^+. In this excess H_3O^+ the indicator equilibrium is shifted to less dissociation or predominantly to the form HIn. This form is yellow.

16. (c). This calculation is done as in Section 16–7.

17

Equilibrium in Aqueous Solutions — II

Chapter Summary

In Chapter 17 we continue our study of chemical equilibrium, now applied to the description of **hydrolysis reactions,** in which water or one of its ions is a reactant. Much of the chapter deals with hydrolysis reactions involving salts of Brønsted-Lowry acids or bases, which may be weak or strong. At the end of the chapter, reactions in which water interacts with metal ions will be considered. As background to the discussion of this chapter, you must be certain you are familiar with the Brønsted-Lowry terminology, especially with regard to **conjugate acid-base pairs** and their **relative strengths,** Section 11-2.

In Chapter 16, the principal consideration was of solutions to which an acid or base, either strong or weak, had been added. In the first four numbered sections of Chapter 17, we are concerned with solutions to which no free acid or base has been added, but rather only a salt. Remember that in pure water $[H_3O^+] = [OH^-]$. In aqueous solutions, reactions *may* occur in which the H_3O^+/OH^- balance is upset; thus, the resulting solutions could be acidic (excess H_3O^+), basic (excess OH^-), or neutral. Recall (Chapter 11) that salts may be viewed as composed of the cation of a base and the anion of an acid. Since acids and bases may each be classified as either strong or weak, four classes of salts can be identified; the hydrolysis reactions of these four classes of salts are the subject of the first four sections of Chapter 17. These four classes of salts and the nature of the resulting solution are as summarized in the following table.

Salt of				
Base	*Acid*	**Section**	**Nature of Solution**	**Comments**
strong	strong	17-1	neutral	Conjugate base of strong acid is too weak to react with H_3O^+; conjugate acid of strong base is too weak to react with OH^-. H_3O^+/OH^- balance is undisturbed.

cont.

Salt of

Base	Acid	Section	Nature of Solution	Comments
strong	weak	17–2	basic	Anion of weak acid is strong base so it reacts with H_3O^+, leaving excess OH^-; water equilibrium shifts, making more H_3O^+ and OH^- in equal amounts but H_3O^+/OH^- balance is still disturbed, with OH^- in excess. The equilibrium constant for this hydrolysis reaction is $K_b = K_w/K_a$, where K_a is the ionization constant for the parent weak acid.
weak	strong	17–3	acidic	Conjugate acid of weak base is strong so it reacts with OH^-, leaving excess H_3O^+; water equilibrium shifts, making more H_3O^+ and OH^- in equal amounts but H_3O^+/OH^- balance is still disturbed, with H_3O^+ in excess. The equilibrium constant for this hydrolysis reaction is $K_a = K_w/K_b$, where K_b is the ionization constant for the parent weak base.
weak	weak	17–4	acidic, basic, or neutral	Both ions hydrolyze; result depends on relative strengths of acid and base. The three types are discussed in Section 17–4.

You should be able to calculate the result of hydrolysis of salts of strong base–weak acid or weak base–strong acid. Note that these results can be expressed either in terms of $[H_3O^+]$, $[OH^-]$, pH, pOH, or % hydrolysis. The relation $K_a K_b = K_w$ is of general utility in equilibrium constant calculations involving conjugate acid-base pairs.

After we understand hydrolysis reactions, we can consider the titration curves which describe the **neutralization of weak acids with strong bases** (Section 17–5). We see that (1) before the equivalence point, a buffer is formed so we can calculate pH as in Section 16–7, and (2) at the equivalence point, the solution is that of a strong base–weak acid salt, so the calculations can be done as in Section 17–2. Analogous considerations apply to **titration of a weak base with a strong acid**.

Another type of hydrolysis reaction occurs in solutions containing **small, highly charged metal ions.** As is described in Section 17–6, water molecules coordinate with these ions. The resulting strong interaction of the metal ion with the oxygen atom of water weakens the O—H bond. This causes the complex hydrated ion to readily lose H^+—that is, to act as a Brønsted-Lowry acid—to a solvent water molecule. Thus, the solution contains an excess of H_3O^+ over OH^-, and is acidic. As with other reactions that occur only to a limited extent, the principles of chemical equilibrium can be applied. The equilibrium constant that is used for this type of hydrolysis reaction is given the symbol K_a, but is called a **hydrolysis constant.** Do not get so involved with the calculation of concentrations that you forget to see which metal ions hydrolyze readily. Pay attention to the correlations of ease of hydrolysis of metal ions with position in the periodic table, with charge density, and with oxidation state of the metal.

Study Goals

1. Classify salts into one of the following categories: (a) salts of strong soluble bases and strong acids, (b) salts of strong soluble bases and weak acids, (c) salts of weak bases and strong acids, or (d) salts of weak acids and weak bases. (Sections 17–1 through 17–4; Exercises 3, 7, and 12)
2. Write the chemical equation and the equilibrium constant expression describing any possible hydrolysis of salts listed in Study Goal 1, and evaluate the hydrolysis constant in terms of the parent weak acid or base to which the salt is related. (Sections 17–1 through 17–4; Exercises 4 through 6, 8, 11, 13, 17, 18, and 22)
3. Given the initial concentration of a salt and the ionization constant for the weak acid or base to which it is related, calculate the concentrations of all species in the solution and the solution's pH, pOH, and % hydrolysis. (Sections 17–1 through 17–4; Exercises 9, 10, and 14 through 16)
4. Calculate concentrations and pH values of solutions resulting from the mixing of any volumes of any concentrations of acids and bases when one of these may be weak. (Review Section 16–6; Section 17–5; Exercises 23 through 26)
5. Write equations for and describe the hydrolysis of small, highly charged metal ions. (Section 17–6; Exercise 19)
6. Given the hydrolysis constant of a small, highly charged metal ion, calculate the concentrations of all species in a solution of a given concentration of a salt of the cation. (Section 17–6; Exercises 20, 21)

Some Important Terms in This Chapter

Write the meanings *in your own words.* Check the Key Terms list and the chapter reading. Then rewrite your definitions, still in your own words, to

improve them. Study other new terms and review terms from preceding chapters if necessary.

solvolysis

hydrolysis

hydrolysis constant

Preliminary Test

This test will check your understanding of basic concepts and types of calculations. Be sure to practice *many* of the additional textbook exercises, including those indicated with the Study Goals.

Short Answer

1. The reaction of a substance with the solvent in which it is dissolved is called _____; when the solvent is water, these are called _____ reactions.
2. The stronger an acid, the _____ is its conjugate base.
3. There are two types of salts that lead to neutral solutions when dissolved in water. These are (1) salts of _____ acids and strong bases and (2) salts of _____ acids and _____ bases, but only (in the latter case) if _____ are the same.
4. One reaction whose equilibrium is always disturbed when a hydrolyzable salt is dissolved in water is _____.
5. The hydrolysis reaction that occurs when ammonium chloride is dissolved in water is _____.
6. The hydrolysis reaction that occurs when potassium fluoride is dissolved in water is _____.
7. HX is a weak acid. When a salt such as NaX is dissolved in water, the net hydrolysis reaction that occurs can be represented as _____.
8. When the salt of a strong base and a strong acid is dissolved in water, the resulting solution is _____. An example would be _____.
9. When the salt of a strong base and a weak acid is dissolved in water, the resulting solution is _____. An example would be _____.

10. When the salt of a weak base and a strong acid is dissolved in water, the resulting solution is _____. An example would be _____.
11. An example of a salt of a weak base and a weak acid is _____.
12. Whether the solution of a salt of a weak acid and a weak base is acidic, basic, or neutral depends on the value of _____ and on the value of _____.
13. The value of K_a for benzoic acid, C_6H_5COOH, is 6.3×10^{-5}. When a salt such as sodium benzoate is dissolved in water, the reaction that occurs is _____, leading to a solution that is _____. The value of the equilibrium constant for this reaction is _____.
14. The value of K_b for methylamine, $(CH_3)NH_2$, is 5.0×10^{-4}. When a salt such as methylammonium chloride is dissolved in water, the reaction that occurs is _____, leading to a solution that is _____. The value of the equilibrium constant for this reaction is _____.
15. When a salt such as methylammonium benzoate is dissolved in water, the two hydrolysis reactions that occur are _____ and _____. The resulting solution would be _____ because _____.
16. The _____ of the ionization constant for an acid and the hydrolysis constant for its conjugate base is equal to K_w.
17. After the start of titration of a weak acid with a strong base, but before the equivalence point is reached, the solution acts as a _____.
18. When a salt of a small, highly charged metal ion such as Al^{3+} is dissolved in water, the resulting solution is _____.
19. Comparing isoelectronic cations in the same period of the periodic table, the ease or extent of hydrolysis increases as the _____ increases.
20. Classify each of the following as a salt of a *strong, weak,* or *insoluble* base and a *strong* or *weak* acid. Tell whether an aqueous solution of each would be *acidic, basic,* or *neutral.* It should usually not be necessary to refer to tables of ionization constants, but you may find them helpful in a few cases. Write the equation for any hydrolysis reaction.

Salt	Salt of Base	Acid	Nature of Solution	Hydrolysis Reaction
a. KCH_3COO	____	____	____	_____
b. RbI	____	____	____	_____
c. $CaBr_2$	____	____	____	_____
d. NH_4Cl	____	____	____	_____

| Salt | Salt of | | Nature of Solution | Hydrolysis Reaction |
	Base	Acid		
e. $(CH_3)_2NH_2Cl$	_____	_____	_____	_____
f. K_3AsO_4	_____	_____	_____	_____
g. $Ba(NO_2)_2$	_____	_____	_____	_____
h. $Ba(NO_3)_2$	_____	_____	_____	_____
i. NaF	_____	_____	_____	_____
j. $NaCl$	_____	_____	_____	_____
k. $NaBr$	_____	_____	_____	_____
l. $NaClO_4$	_____	_____	_____	_____
m. Na_2CO_3	_____	_____	_____	_____
n. NH_4ClO_4	_____	_____	_____	_____
o. KCN	_____	_____	_____	_____
p. NH_4Br	_____	_____	_____	_____
q. $AlCl_3$	_____	_____	_____	_____
r. $Fe(NO_3)_3$	_____	_____	_____	_____
s. $BiCl_3$	_____	_____	_____	_____
t. K_2S	_____	_____	_____	_____
u. $BeCl_2$	_____	_____	_____	_____
v. NH_4CN	_____	_____	_____	_____
w. NH_4OCN	_____	_____	_____	_____

Multiple Choice

_____ 1. In water solution, HCN is only very slightly ionized according to

$$HCN + H_2O \rightleftharpoons H_3O^+ + CN^-.$$

This observation shows that CN^- is a _____ than H_2O.
(a) stronger acid   (b) stronger base   (c) weaker acid
(d) weaker base

_____ 2. When solid NaCN is added to water,
(a) the pH remains at 7.
(b) the pH becomes greater than 7 because of hydrolysis of Na^+.
(c) the pH becomes less than 7 because of hydrolysis of Na^+.
(d) the pH becomes greater than 7 because of hydrolysis of CN^-.
(e) the pH becomes less than 7 because of hydrolysis of CN^-.

_____ 3. When the salt NH_4CH_3COO is dissolved in water, the resulting solution is
(a) acidic.   (b) basic.   (c) neutral.

_____ 4. When the salt NH_4NO_2 is dissolved in water, the resulting solution is
(a) acidic.   (b) basic.   (c) neutral.

_____ 5. Each of the following salts is completely ionized when dissolved in water. Which of these salts will produce a basic solution when dissolved in water?
(a) sodium chloride   (b) sodium acetate   (c) ammonium chloride   (d) calcium nitrate   (e) rubidium perchlorate

_____ 6. Which of the following salts will produce an acidic solution when dissolved in water?
(a) sodium chloride   (b) sodium acetate   (c) ammonium chloride   (d) calcium nitrate   (e) rubidium perchlorate

_____ 7. The value of K_a for acetic acid is 1.8×10^{-5}. What is the value for the equilibrium constant for the following reaction?

$$CH_3COO^- + H_2O \rightleftharpoons CH_3COOH + OH^-$$

(a) 1.8×10^{-5} (b) 1.8×10^{-10} (c) 1.0×10^{-14}
(d) 5.6×10^{-10} (e) 5.6×10^{-5}

_____ 8. Which of the following indicators would be most appropriate to use for the detection of the equivalence point of the titration of a weak base, such as ammonia, with a strong acid, such as HCl?
(a) methyl red   (b) neutral red   (c) phenolphthalein
(d) Any of the preceding would be equally useful.

_____ 9. At the equivalence point in the titration of $0.1\ M$ acetic acid with $0.2\ M$ sodium hydroxide, which of the following will be true?
(a) $pH = 7$.
(b) For every mL of acid used, 2 mL of base will have been used.

(c) For every 2 mL of acid used, 1 mL of base will have been used.

(d) For every mL of acid used, 1 mL of base will have been used.

(e) For every 1 g of acid used, 2 g of base will have been used.

___ 10. When we titrate a strong acid with a strong base, the pH at the equivalence point is

(a) 7.   (b) less than 7.   (c) greater than 7.

___ 11. When we titrate a weak base with a strong acid, the pH at the equivalence point is

(a) 7.

(b) less than 7.

(c) greater than 7.

(d) Any of the preceding answers may be correct, depending on the K_b value for the base.

___ 12. When we titrate a weak acid with a strong base, the pH at the equivalence point is

(a) 7.

(b) less than 7.

(c) greater than 7.

(d) Any of the preceding answers may be correct, depending on the K_a value for the acid.

___ 13. When we titrate a weak base with a weak acid, the pH at the equivalence point is

(a) 7.

(b) less than 7.

(c) greater than 7.

(d) Any of the preceding answers may be correct, depending on the K_a value for the acid and the K_b value for the base.

Answers to Preliminary Test

Short Answer

1. solvolysis, hydrolysis
2. weaker
3. (1) strong, (2) weak, weak, the strengths of the parent acid and base
4. $2H_2O \rightleftharpoons H_3O^+ + OH^-$
5. $NH_4^+ + H_2O \rightleftharpoons NH_3 + H_3O^+$. NH_4^+ is the conjugate acid of the weak base NH_3.
6. $F^- + H_2O \rightleftharpoons HF + OH^-$. F^- is the conjugate base of the weak acid HF.
7. $X^- + H_2O \rightleftharpoons HX + OH^-$.
8. neutral. The example discussed in the chapter is NaCl. There are many other correct answers, such as $NaNO_3$, KBr, $RbClO_4$, and CaI_2.
9. basic. Examples discussed in the chapter include $NaCH_3COO$ and NaCN. There are many others.

10. acidic. Among the examples in this chapter are NH_4NO_3 and NH_4Cl.
11. Several examples are listed in the chapter: NH_4CH_3COO, NH_4CN, NH_4F.
12. K_a for the acid, K_b for the base from which the salt is derived.
13. $C_6H_5COO^- + H_2O \rightleftharpoons C_6H_5COOH + OH^-$, basic, 1.6×10^{-10}. Remember that the hydrolysis constant (K_b) for the conjugate base of a weak acid with ionization constant K_a is given by $K_a K_b = K_w$.
14. $(CH_3)NH_3^+ + H_2O \rightleftharpoons (CH_3)NH_2 + H_3O^+$, acidic, 2.0×10^{-11}. The hydrolysis constant (K_a) for the conjugate acid of a weak base with ionization constant K_b is given by $K_a K_b = K_w$.
15. $C_6H_5COO^- + H_2O \rightleftharpoons C_6H_5COOH + OH^-$, $(CH_3)NH_3^+ + H_2O \rightleftharpoons (CH_3)NH_2 + H_3O^+$, basic, $K_{base} > K_{acid}$. Be sure (Section 17–4, parts 2 and 3) that you understand how to reason this out. Compare K values for the hydrolyses, which you calculated in the preceding two questions. From these you can see that the hydrolysis of benzoate occurs (slightly) more readily than the hydrolysis of methylammonium ion, so the solution is basic, though only slightly so.
16. product
17. buffer
18. acidic. Section 17–6 discusses the hydrolyses of such ions. Note that this type of reaction can only cause the solution to become acidic, never basic.
19. charge
20. a. strong, weak, basic, $CH_3COO^- + H_2O \rightleftharpoons CH_3COOH + OH^-$
    b. strong, strong, neutral, none
    c. strong, strong, neutral, none
    d. weak, strong, acidic, $NH_4^+ + H_2O \rightleftharpoons NH_3 + H_3O^+$
    e. weak, strong, acidic, $(CH_3)_2NH_2^+ + H_2O \rightleftharpoons (CH_3)_2NH + H_3O^+$
    f. strong, weak, basic, $AsO_4^{3-} + H_2O \rightleftharpoons HAsO_4^{2-} + OH^-$. Probably $HAsO_4^{2-}$ further hydrolyzes, but the reaction shown is the predominant one.
    g. strong, weak, basic, $NO_2^- + H_2O \rightleftharpoons HNO_2 + OH^-$
    h. strong, strong, neutral, none
    i. strong, weak, basic, $F^- + H_2O \rightleftharpoons HF + OH^-$
    j. strong, strong, neutral, none
    k. strong, strong, neutral, none
    l. strong, strong, neutral, none
    m. strong, weak, basic, $CO_3^{2-} + H_2O \rightleftharpoons HCO_3^- + OH^-$. This reaction is probably accompanied by some hydrolysis of HCO_3^-.
    n. weak, strong, acidic, $NH_4^+ + H_2O \rightleftharpoons NH_3 + H_3O^+$
    o. strong, weak, basic, $CN^- + H_2O \rightleftharpoons HCN + OH^-$
    p. weak, strong, acidic, $NH_4^+ + H_2O \rightleftharpoons NH_3 + H_3O^+$
    q. insoluble, strong, acidic, $Al^{3+} + 2H_2O \rightleftharpoons Al(OH)^{2+} + H_3O^+$
    r. insoluble, strong, acidic, $Fe^{3+} + 2H_2O \rightleftharpoons Fe(OH)^{2+} + H_3O^+$
    s. insoluble, strong, acidic, $Bi^{3+} + 2H_2O \rightleftharpoons Bi(OH)^{2+} + H_3O^+$

- t. strong, weak, basic, $S^{2-} + H_2O \rightleftharpoons HS^- + OH^-$
- u. insoluble, strong, acidic, $Be^{2+} + 2H_2O \rightleftharpoons Be(OH)^+ + H_3O^+$
- v. weak, weak, basic, $NH_4^+ + H_2O \rightleftharpoons NH_3 + H_3O^+$ *and* $CN^- + H_2O \rightleftharpoons HCN + OH^-$. K_b for NH_3 is greater than K_a for HCN, so the second hydrolysis reaction occurs to a greater extent, making the solution *basic*. See the discussion in Section 17–5.2.
- w. weak, weak, acidic, $NH_4^+ + H_2O \rightleftharpoons NH_3 + H_3O^+$ *and* $OCN^- + H_2O \rightleftharpoons HOCN + OH^-$. Now K_b for NH_3 is less than K_a for HOCN, so the solution is *acidic*. See Section 17–5.3.

Multiple Choice

1. (b)
2. (d). The hydrolysis reaction $CN^- + H_2O \rightleftharpoons HCN + OH^-$ occurs. This raises $[OH^-]$, lowers $[H_3O^+]$, and thus raises pH.
3. (c). Remember that this is the only common case of a weak base–weak acid salt where the acid and base strengths are essentially equal. See the first part of Section 17–4.
4. (a). K_{acid} for HNO_2 (4.5×10^{-4}) is greater than K_{base} for NH_3 (1.8×10^{-5}). Thus NH_4^+ would hydrolyze to a greater extent than NO_2^-, and the resulting solution would be acidic. See the third part of Section 17–4.
5. (b)
6. (c)
7. (d). This is the hydrolysis reaction of the base CH_3COO^-. For such a conjugate acid-base pair (CH_3COOH and CH_3COO^-), $K_a K_b = K_w = 1.0 \times 10^{-14}$.
8. (a). From Figure 17.2 we see that the equivalence point occurs at about pH 5. Of the indicators listed above, methyl red has a color change at a pH nearest this. See Table 16–5.
9. (c). If you thought the answer was (a), study Section 17–5. If you picked one of the other incorrect answers, think more carefully about the stoichiometry and about the relation between number of moles and volume of solution.
10. (a). See Chapter 16.
11. (b). See Figure 17–2 and the associated discussion in Section 17–5.
12. (c). See Figure 17–1 and the associated discussion in Section 17–5.
13. (d)

18

Equilibrium in Aqueous Solutions — III

Chapter Summary

This, the final chapter dealing with equilibria in aqueous solutions, is devoted to a consideration of equilibria involving *slightly soluble ionic compounds*. This is, in many ways, the simplest of the types of ionic equilibria. It is the basis for many useful laboratory techniques, such as separation by fractional precipitation and the dissolving of precipitates. You will recall from your study of acid-base equilibria that some acids are so strong (completely ionized) that equilibrium considerations do not apply. In similar fashion, the equilibrium studies of this chapter do not apply to the dissolving of quite soluble substances (It will be important though to know the concentrations of ions contained in such solutions). Before you begin your study of this material, be sure you *know* the solubility rules, Section 7-1.5. Be aware, however, that the substances classified in those rules as "insoluble" are actually very slightly soluble, and it is these types of compounds that we are considering in Chapter 18.

As you shall see, the reactions studied here can be viewed in either of two ways: as the dissolving of slightly soluble substances to form ions in solution (**dissolution**) or as the ions in solution coming together to form ionic solids (**precipitation**). From either point of view, the equation for the reaction may be written as **solid $\rightleftharpoons$ dissolved ions.** As you see in Section 18-1, we can define an equilibrium constant for this equilibrium process. You will notice that, consistent with our treatment of heterogeneous equilibria in Chapter 16, the solid does not appear in the expression for the equilibrium constant. This type of equilibrium constant is given the symbol K_{sp} and is referred to as the **solubility product constant,** or sometimes simply the **solubility product.** The remainder of the chapter consists of applications of the **solubility product principle.**

In Section 18-2, we see how the value of K_{sp} is determined for any slightly soluble substance from an experimental measurement of its solubility. In carrying out these calculations, remember (1) that the measured solubility, which is usually stated in terms of grams of substance dissolving to make a specified volume of **saturated** solution, must be converted to a molar basis and (2) that you must use the stoichiometry of the dissolution process to find out the concentration in moles/liter of each ion present. Since solubilities of solids in liquid are usually quite dependent on temperature, you should remember that values of K_{sp} can vary considerably as temperature changes.

Several uses of K_{sp} are detailed in Section 18–3. Pay close attention to the reasoning in the examples in this section. All subsequent sections of this chapter will involve application of the type of calculations you learn about in Section 18–3. The major uses of the solubility product principle are these: (1) *To calculate the solubility,* either in terms of moles or grams of a substance that will dissolve to make a specified amount of saturated solution. This calculation can, of course, be extended to find the concentration of each ionic species in the saturated solution. Be sure you understand that when we refer to the solubility of a substance we are talking about the amount that dissolves to make a saturated solution. (2) *To calculate the concentrations of ions that can exist together in solution.* A very useful extension of this is deciding whether or not a precipitate will form at specified concentrations. Note the utility of the reaction quotient (Section 15–4), here denoted as Q_{sp}, in arriving at this decision. (3) *To calculate the concentration of an ion necessary to initiate precipitation* of a substance from a solution containing other ions. (4) *To calculate the concentrations of ions remaining in solution* after precipitation has occurred. This last type of calculation is useful in predicting the efficiency of precipitation methods for recovering valuable metals and removing objectionable ions from solution.

One application of the calculations from Section 18–3 is in designing methods for separating the ions in a mixture in solution. This technique, called **fractional precipitation** (Section 18–4) makes use of K_{sp} differences among salts having an ion in common. Examples 18–8 and 18–9 illustrate this with the silver halides. Did you notice which types of calculations from Section 18–3 we are using here?

An important principle of chemical equilibrium, easily overlooked at first by students, is that in a solution, *all species must be at equilibrium with respect to all relevant reactions.* For example, this principle was used, though often without stating it, throughout the discussions of Chapters 16 and 17, where the equilibrium involving the dissociation of water and the resulting $[H_3O^+]/[OH^-]$ ratio was affected by other reactions taking place in the same solution. This principle is emphasized again in Section 18–5 for simultaneous equilibria involving slightly soluble compounds. Such calculations usually involve one species that is involved in more than one reaction and which therefore affects the equilibria of several processes. In Examples 18–10 through 18–12, OH^- is involved both in the equilibrium for the dissolution or precipitation of $Mg(OH)_2$ and also in that for the ionization of NH_3 as a weak base in aqueous solution. Thus, both equilibrium constant expressions must be satisfied. Of course, OH^- is also involved in a third reaction, that with H_3O^+ to form water (and the reverse of this reaction), so that the equilibrium condition for this third reaction may also be used, for example, to calculate $[H_3O^+]$ or pH of the solution.

Section 18–6, which discusses methods for **dissolving precipitates,** is merely an application of the ideas presented in Section 18–5. In each of the three methods presented, (1) *converting an ion into a weak electrolyte,* (2) *converting an ion to another species* (usually by oxidation or reduction), and (3) *forming complex ions,* the essential strategy is to lower the concentration of one of the products (ions) of the dissolution process. In the first and third of these methods, other equilibria are used to help remove one of the ions from solution; in the second, a less reversible reaction is used, for example, the oxidation of S^{2-} to elemental sulfur. You should think about each of these methods from the viewpoint of LeChatelier's Principle. The latter part of Section 18–6 also includes the application of equilibrium principles to still another type of reaction, the **formation/dissociation of complex ions,** for which we usually express the equilibrium constant as K_d, referring to the reaction written as a dissociation.

This chapter brings us to the end of four chapters dealing with chemical equilibrium and its applications. Even though many different types of reactions have been studied, each with perhaps its own characteristic terminology and notation, you should be able to see that it is really the same set of principles that we have been applying—(1) the general formulation of the concentration relationships in the equilibrium-constant expression and (2) LeChatelier's Principle. Perhaps you can examine your understanding of these chapters by summarizing the different types of reactions or processes that have been studied and comparing the differing terminologies by which these two principles are discussed for the various reaction types.

Study Goals

1. Know the solubility rules. By application of these rules, be able to determine which ionic solids are soluble and which are slightly soluble ("insoluble"). (Review Section 7–1.5; review Exercises 9 through 15 of Chapter 7; Exercise 1 of Chapter 18)
2. Write the solubility product expression for any slightly soluble compound that ionizes upon dissolution in water. (Section 18–1; Exercises 2 through 4)
3. Calculate the solubility product constant for a compound, given its molar solubility or the amount of the substance that dissolves to give a specified volume of saturated solution. (Section 18–2; Exercises 5 and 6)
4. Given its solubility product constant, calculate the solubility of a com-

pound. Given solubility product constants for a series of slightly soluble compounds, determine which is most and which is least soluble by comparing molar solubilities. (Section 18–3; Exercises 7 and 8)

5. Describe the common ion effect as it applies to solid-dissolved ion equilibria. (Section 18–3; Exercise 9)

6. Given appropriate solubility product constants, determine whether precipitation will occur (1) when two solutions of given concentrations of specified solutes are mixed, or (2) when a specified amount of a solute is added to a solution of specified concentration of another solute. (Section 18–3; Exercise 10)

7. Given appropriate solubility product constants, determine how much or what concentration of a given solute must be added to a solution of known concentration of another solute (1) to cause precipitation of a compound to begin and (2) to remove all but a desired amount, concentration, or percentage of a particular dissolved ion. (Section 18–3; Exercises 11 through 15)

8. Describe the process of fractional precipitation and perform related calculations given appropriate solubility product constants. (Section 18–4; Exercises 16 through 19)

9. Given appropriate equilibrium constants, perform calculations involving determinations like those listed above for systems that simultaneously involve solid-dissolved ion equilibria *and* one or more kinds of other previously studied equilibria. (Section 18–5; Exercises 20 through 25)

10. Describe and give specific examples of three general methods of dissolving precipitates. Discuss each in terms of LeChatelier's Principle. Explain why the processes work. (Section 18–6; Exercises 26 through 30)

11. Given appropriate constants, perform calculations involving the formation and dissociation of complex ions to determine concentrations of various species present in solution. Be able to include in these calculations the effects of other equilibria that may be simultaneously involved. (Section 18–6.3; Exercise 31)

Some Important Terms in This Chapter

Write the meanings *in your own words*. Check the Key Terms list and the chapter reading. Then rewrite your definitions, still in your own words, to improve them. Study other new terms and review terms from preceding chapters (especially Chapters 15 through 17) if necessary.

solubility product principle

solubility product constant

molar solubility

precipitate

fractional precipitation

complex ion

dissociation constant

Preliminary Test

This test will only check your understanding of basic concepts and types of calculations. It is very important to get much additional practice by working problems, so be sure to do *many* of the additional textbook exercises. This is especially true for fractional precipitation and dissolution of precipitates.

Short Answer

1. The number of moles of a substance that will dissolve to give 1 liter of saturated solution is called the _____ of the substance.
2. The symbol for the solubility product constant is ____.
3. The expression for the solubility product of $CuCO_3$ is _____.
4. The expression for the solubility product of $Mn(OH)_2$ is _____.

5. The expression for the solubility product of $Mg_3(PO_4)_2$ is _____ .

6. When we mix together, from separate sources, the ions of a slightly soluble ionic substance, the salt will begin to precipitate if Q_{sp} ____ K_{sp}, and will continue to precipitate until Q_{sp} ____ K_{sp}.

7. Insoluble metal hydroxides are ____ (more, less) readily soluble in acidic solution than in basic solution.

8. Lead chloride, $PbCl_2$, is much more soluble in warm water than in cold water. This tells us that the dissolution reaction of lead chloride is _____ .

9. The dissociation constant for a complex ion in solution is represented by the symbol ____ .

10. Three methods for dissolving a precipitate of a slightly soluble ionic substance are _____ , _____ , and _____ .

11. Given the following values of equilibrium constants:

$$K_{sp}(FeS) = 4.9 \times 10^{-18} \text{ and } K_d(Fe(CN)_6{}^{4-}) = 1.3 \times 10^{-37},$$

complete the following: The equation for the dissolution of FeS (s) in a solution that contains cyanide ions, CN^-, is _____ .
The value of K for this reaction is _____ , which tells us that it would be _____ to dissolve FeS by addition of a soluble compound such as NaCN that dissociates completely into Na^+ and CN^-.

12. Given the following values of equilibrium constants:

$$K_{sp}(CdS) = 3.6 \times 10^{-29} \text{ and } K_d(Cd(CN)_4{}^{2-}) = 7.8 \times 10^{-18},$$

complete the following: The equation for the dissolution of CdS (s) in a solution that contains cyanide ions, CN^-, is _____ .
The value of K for this reaction is _____ , which tells us that it would be _____ to dissolve CdS by addition of a soluble compound such as NaCN that dissociates completely into Na^+ and CN^-.

13. In order to dissolve a precipitate we must adjust concentrations of the constituent ions in the solution until Q_{sp} is _____ (less than, greater than, equal to) K_{sp}; this is usually done by _____ from the solution.

14. In order to prevent precipitation of $Cu(OH)_2$ from a solution that is 0.10 M in $Cu(NO_3)_2$, the $[OH^-]$ must be kept lower than _____ .

15. Another way of expressing the result of Question 14 is that the pH must be kept _____ .

Multiple Choice

____ 1. Which of the following ionic chlorides is least soluble in water?
(a) NH_4Cl (b) AgCl (c) $BaCl_2$ (d) KCl (e) NaCl

____ 2. In a solution obtained by dissolving only silver sulfate, Ag_2SO_4, the

concentration of silver ion is observed to be 2×10^{-5} M. What would be the molar concentration of sulfate ion in this solution?
(a) 1×10^{-5} M (b) 2×10^{-5} M (c) 3×10^{-5} M
(d) 4×10^{-5} M (e) Cannot be answered without knowing the solubility product constant, K_{sp}, for Ag_2SO_4.

_____ 3. The molar solubility of $PbSO_4$ is 1.34×10^{-4} mol/L. What is the value of K_{sp} for $PbSO_4$?
(a) 1.16×10^{-14} (b) 8.8×10^{-11} (c) 3.45×10^{-2}
(d) 3.75×10^{-7} (e) 1.3×10^{-8}

_____ 4. The solubility of PbF_2 in water is 0.0021 mol/L. K_{sp} for PbF_2 is closest to which of the following values?
(a) 2.1×10^{-3} (b) 2.0×10^{-4} (c) 4.4×10^{-6}
(d) 9.2×10^{-9} (e) 3.7×10^{-8}

_____ 5. AgCl would be least soluble in
(a) pure water.   (b) 0.1 M $CaCl_2$.   (c) 0.1 M HCl.
(d) 0.1 M HNO_3.   (e) AgCl would be equally soluble in all.

_____ 6. The value of K_{sp} for $SrSO_4$ is 2.8×10^{-7}. What is the solubility of $SrSO_4$ in mol/L?
(a) 7.6×10^{-7} M (b) 1.4×10^{-7} M (c) 5.3×10^{-4} M
(d) 5.7×10^{-3} M (e) 1.3×10^{-8} M

_____ 7. The value of K_{sp} for CuI is 1×10^{-12}. What is the solubility of CuI expressed in grams per liter?
(a) 9.0×10^{-6} g/L   (b) 1.0×10^{-12} g/L   (c) 1.9×10^{-4} g/L
(d) 1.0×10^{-6} g/L

_____ 8. Ferrous hydroxide is a slightly soluble base. In which of the following would $Fe(OH)_2$ be most soluble? It is not necessary to know K_{sp} for $Fe(OH)_2$.
(a) 0.1 M HCl   (b) 0.1 M KOH   (c) 0.1 M $Ca(OH)_2$
(d) 0.1 M $FeCl_2$ (e) Equally soluble in all of the preceding.

_____ 9. Values of K_{sp} for some slightly soluble sulfides are as follows:

Sulfide	K_{sp}
CdS	3.6×10^{-29}
CuS	8.7×10^{-36}
PbS	8.4×10^{-28}
MnS	5.1×10^{-15}

Which of the following ions must exist at lowest concentration in a solution in which the sulfide ion concentration had been fixed at some fairly large constant value?
(a) Cd^{2+} (b) Cu^{2+} (c) Pb^{2+} (d) Mn^{2+} (e) Cannot be answered without knowing the sulfide concentration.

_____ 10. If NaCl is added to a 0.01 M solution of $AgNO_3$ in water, at what $[Cl^-]$ does precipitation of AgCl begin to occur? K_{sp} for AgCl is 1.8×10^{-10}.

(a) $1.0 \times 10^{-10} M$ (b) $1.8 \times 10^{-6} M$ (c) $1.8 \times 10^{-8} M$
(d) $1.8 \times 10^{-12} M$ (e) $1.8 \times 10^{-10} M$

Suppose we have a solution that is $0.10 M$ in Ca^{2+} and also $0.10 M$ in Pb^{2+}. We wish to separate these ions by fractional precipitation of one of them as the carbonate. We do this by adding a source of carbonate ion, such as solid Na_2CO_3. Questions 11 through 13 refer to this solution. Use the K_{sp} values 4.8×10^{-9} for $CaCO_3$ and 1.5×10^{-13} for $PbCO_3$. Neglect any change in concentration due to addition of the sodium carbonate.

_____ 11. Which will begin to precipitate from solution first, $CaCO_3$ or $PbCO_3$, and what will be the CO_3^{2-} when this begins (whether or not we can see it)?
(a) $CaCO_3$, $4.8 \times 10^{-8} M$
(b) $CaCO_3$, $4.8 \times 10^{-9} M$
(c) $PbCO_3$, $1.5 \times 10^{-12} M$
(d) $PbCO_3$, $1.5 \times 10^{-13} M$
(e) $PbCO_3$, $7.2 \times 10^{-21} M$

_____ 12. In the solution of Question 11, suppose we keep adding Na_2CO_3. Eventually the second salt will begin to precipitate. When this second salt does begin to precipitate, what will be the concentration of the first metal ion left in solution?
(a) $0.1 M$ (b) $1.5 \times 10^{-12} M$ (c) $3.2 \times 10^5 M$
(d) $3.1 \times 10^{-6} M$ (e) $1.3 \times 10^{-5} M$

_____ 13. When the condition in Question 12 is reached, that is, when the second salt just begins to precipitate, what fraction of the first metal ion will have been removed from the solution?
(a) 4.8 percent   (b) 50 percent   (c) 95.7 percent   (d) 99.997 percent   (e) All of it

_____ 14. We have a solution that is $0.001 M$ Pb^{2+}, $0.005 M$ Ag^+, and $0.002 M$ K^+. If sulfide ion, S^{2-}, is slowly added to this solution, which metal sulfide will precipitate first? Refer to a table of K_{sp} values.
(a) PbS   (b) Ag_2S (c) K_2S (d) All would precipitate together.   (e) None would precipitate at any reasonable sulfide concentration.

_____ 15. K_{sp} for $Fe(IO_3)_3$ is 10^{-14}. We mix two solutions, one containing Fe^{3+} and one containing IO_3^-. At the instant of mixing, $[Fe^{3+}] = 10^{-4} M$ and $[IO_3^-] = 10^{-5} M$. Which of the following statements is true?
(a) A precipitate forms because $Q_{sp} > K_{sp}$.
(b) A precipitate forms because $Q_{sp} < K_{sp}$.
(c) No precipitate forms because $Q_{sp} > K_{sp}$.

(d) No precipitate forms because $Q_{sp} < K_{sp}$.

(e) None of the preceding statements is true.

_____ 16. Magnesium hydroxide is a slightly soluble hydroxide with K_{sp} value $= 1.5 \times 10^{-11}$. What is the pH of a saturated solution of magnesium hydroxide?

(a) 3.51   (b) 10.51   (c) 5.39   (d) 8.60   (e) 7.00

Answers to Preliminary Test

Short Answer

1. molar solubility
2. K_{sp}
3. $[Cu^{2+}][CO_3{}^{2-}]$
4. $[Mn^{2+}][OH^-]^2$
5. $[Mg^{2+}]^3[PO_4{}^{3-}]^2$
6. $>$, $=$
7. more
8. endothermic. Think back to the applications of LeChatelier's Principle as you learned them in Section 15–5. It is very hard to measure the value of ΔH^0 for a reaction that proceeds as slightly as does the dissolution of lead chloride. Can you design an experiment based on measuring solubility of lead chloride at several temperatures to determine ΔH^0 for this reaction? Think about Section 15–11.
9. K_d
10. converting an ion to a weak electrolyte, converting an ion to another species by oxidation or reduction, forming a complex ion involving one of the constituent ions
11. FeS (s) $+ 6CN^-$ (aq) $\rightleftharpoons Fe(CN)_6{}^{4-}$ (aq) $+ S^{2-}$ (aq), 3.8×10^{19}, very easy

    First we write out the equations, reversing the one for the dissociation of $Fe(CN)_4{}^{4-}$:

$$FeS\ (s) \rightleftharpoons Fe^{2+}\ (aq) + S^{2-}\ (aq) \qquad K = 4.9 \times 10^{-18}$$
$$Fe^{2+}\ (aq) + 6CN^-\ (aq) \rightleftharpoons Fe(CN)_6{}^{4-}\ (aq)$$
$$K = 1/(1.3 \times 10^{-37}) = 7.7 \times 10^{36}$$

    (remember to invert K when you reverse the second equation). Then we recall that adding the equations requires that we multiply the values of K:

$$FeS\ (s) + 6CN^-\ (aq) \rightleftharpoons Fe(CN)_6{}^{4-}\ (aq) + S^{2-} \qquad K = 3.8 \times 10^{19}$$

    This very large value of K tells us that the dissolution goes very readily.
12. CdS (s) $+ 4CN^-$ (aq) $\rightleftharpoons Cd(CN)_4{}^{2-}$ (aq) $+ S^{2-}$ (aq), 2.8×10^{-10}, difficult Reason as outlined in the answer to Question 11.

13. less than, removing one of the constituent ions
14. $1.26 \times 10^{-10} M$. The condition for precipitation (barely) is $Q_{sp} = (0.10) [OH^-]^2 = 1.6 \times 10^{-19}$. Solve this for $[OH^-] = 1.26 \times 10^{-10}$. If $[OH^-]$ is kept less than this ($Q_{sp} < K_{sp}$), the precipitate will not form.
15. less than 4.10. In order to keep $[OH^-]$ less than 1.26×10^{-10} we would have to keep $[H_3O^+]$ greater than 7.94×10^{-5}, which corresponds to pH less than 4.10.

Multiple Choice

1. (b). Remember the solubility rules from an earlier chapter. AgCl is one of the examples used in Chapter 18 as an example of a slightly soluble salt.
2. (a). For every mole of Ag^+ that goes into solution, only half of a mole of SO_4^{2-} goes in. Look at the formula of the salt.
3. (e). Each mole of $PbSO_4$ that dissolves gives 1 mole of Pb^{2+} and 1 mole of SO_4^{2-} in solution. So in the saturated solution (that is what solubility means) the concentrations would be $[Pb^{2+}] = 1.14 \times 10^{-4} M$ and $[SO_4^{2-}] = 1.14 \times 10^{-4} M$. Then $K_{sp} = [Pb^{2+}][SO_4^{2-}] = 1.30 \times 10^{-8}$.
4. (e). Did you remember that 2 moles of F^- go into solution for every mole of Pb^{2+}?
5. (b). This would have the highest (Cl^-) to begin with, so less AgCl could dissolve before the value of K_{sp} would be reached by Q_{sp}.
6. (c). Solve by the methods of Section 18–3, such as are illustrated in Example 18–3.
7. (a). Solve as in Question 6, but then remember to convert from moles per liter to grams per liter.
8. (a). The H_3O^+ present in this solution would help to remove OH^- as it is formed by dissolution of $Fe(OH)_2$. According to LeChatelier's Principle, this would help to shift the equilibrium for the dissolution process to the right.
9. (b). No calculation is needed here, since all K_{sp} expressions would have the same algebraic form. If some of the salts had different formulas, for example, some XY and some X_2Y, then you would need to actually calculate concentrations. See text Exercise 19.
10. (c)
11. (c). Calculate the concentration of CO_3^{2-} necessary to begin to precipitate each, using the method shown in Section 18–3, Examples 18–5 and 18–7. This calculation leads to the conclusion that $CaCO_3$ will begin to precipitate when $[CO_3^{2-}] = 4.8 \times 10^{-8} M$ and $PbCO_3$ will begin when $[CO_3^{2-}] = 1.5 \times 10^{-12} M$. Since the latter is the smaller concentration it will be reached first, and so $PbCO_3$ will begin to precipitate first.
12. (d). When $[CO_3^{2-}]$ reaches $4.8 \times 10^{-8} M$ and $CaCO_3$ begins to precipitate, $[Pb^{2+}]$ must be down to $(1.5 \times 10^{-13})/(4.8 \times 10^{-8}) = 3.1 \times 10^{-6} M$.

13. (d). From the results of Question 12, we know that only 3.1×10^{-6} M of the original 0.10 M Pb^{2+} remains. Thus, the percentage of original lead ion removed is $100 \times 3.1 \times 10^{-6}/0.10 = 0.003$ percent; in other terms, 99.997 percent has been removed. This may be referred to as "getting the lead out."

14. (b). Calculate, according to the methods of Section 18–3, the sulfide concentration necessary to begin precipitation of PbS and of Ag_2S — you should remember from the solubility rules that K_2S, like all common salts of the alkali metals, is a soluble salt. To precipitate PbS, $[S^{2-}]$ needed is 8.4×10^{-25} M; for Ag_2S to precipitate, $[S^{2-}]$ needed is 2.0×10^{-47} M. Clearly Ag_2S would precipitate first.

15. (d). If you got answer (a), you forgot to raise $[IO_3^-]$ to the third power.

16. (b). Remember that each mole of $Mg(OH)_2$ that dissolves gives two moles of OH^-. Use K_{sp} and the methods of Section 18–3 to find the molar solubility of $Mg(OH)_2$ to be 1.6×10^{-4} M. Then $[OH^-] = 3.2 \times 10^{-4}$. Since in any aqueous solution $[H_3O^+][OH^-] = 10^{-14}$, $[H_3O^+] = 3.1 \times 10^{-11}$, so pH $= 10.51$.

19

Electrochemistry

Chapter Summary

As we learned in Chapter 7 and studied further in Chapter 11, oxidation-reduction reactions (redox reactions) always involve transfer (actual or apparent) of electrons. The study of this type of reaction, emphasizing the electron transfer, is **electrochemistry.** In **electrochemical cells,** we cause electron transfer to take place through an external circuit rather than directly between reacting species. In Chapter 19, we shall learn about the conceptual aspects of electrochemistry and its relation to the spontaneity of reactions and we shall learn some of electrochemistry's practical aspects.

In our study of electrochemistry, the central ideas are summarized in these questions: How can we tell whether a particular electron transfer process is spontaneous? If it is not, how can we make it occur by supplying electrical energy from an outside source? If it is spontaneous, how can we use this reaction as a source of electrical energy? These questions suggest that our electrochemical studies can conveniently be approached in two parts: (1) those reactions in which we use an external source of electrical energy to cause a nonspontaneous reaction to occur, with such applications as electroplating and electrolytic refining of substances and (2) those reactions in which we use the spontaneity of the reaction to make it serve as a source of electrical energy, with applications such as batteries and fuel cells. Sections 19–1 and 19–2 present some of the basic terminology of electrochemistry— **conduction, electrolytic conduction, electrode, anode, cathode,** and so on. These terms will be used throughout this chapter. A review of Sections 4–12 **(oxidation numbers),** Section 7–7 (introduction to **redox reactions**), and all of Chapter 12, especially the terminology such as oxidation, reduction, oxidizing agent, and reducing agent, with respect to electron transfer, would be a useful prelude to your study of Chapter 19.

Throughout this chapter, we shall be talking about oxidation-reduction reactions in terms of **half-reactions.** In Chapter 12, we saw that the idea of separating the oxidation process from the reduction process was an aid in balancing redox reactions. At that point, we talked about reactions with direct electron transfer between reactant species, so the "separation" was mental, largely a bookkeeping device. In most of the electrochemical studies of this chapter, we actually arrange the experiment so that these half-reactions take place in physically separate parts of the **cell** and the electrons are transferred through an external circuit, such as a wire.

The first major topic of Chapter 19 is **electrolysis,** in which redox reactions that are spontaneous are caused to occur by our supplying electrical energy from outside. As you study the three sections discussing the electrolysis of molten sodium chloride (19–3), aqueous sodium chloride (19–4), and aqueous sodium sulfate (19–5), be sure that you understand how such terms as oxidizing agent, substance oxidized, anode, cathode, oxidation half-reaction, reduction half-reaction, and so on, are used. Given the observations associated with the operation of an electrolytic cell, you should be able to apply these terms.

As we study the three electrolytic processes just mentioned, two types of questions occur: (1) How much electrical charge must be supplied to cause a specified amount of reaction to occur? (2) Why do different reactions take place in the different electrolytic cells? That is, in the electrolysis of aqueous sodium chloride, why is water reduced in preference to sodium ion (which can, however, be reduced in molten NaCl)? Why, in aqueous Na_2SO_4, is water oxidized instead of something else, whereas in aqueous NaCl, chloride ion is oxidized in preference to water? This second type of question, that of relative preference of possible oxidation or reduction processes, will be addressed later in the chapter, beginning in Section 19–15. The first question is the subject of Section 19–6.

The main idea of **Faraday's Law of Electrolysis** is that a specific amount of electrical charge delivered to the cell corresponds to a given number of electrons. Thus, there is a relationship between the amount of electrical charge and the extent of redox reaction that it causes. In particular, 1 **faraday** of charge, which is 96,487 coulombs, corresponds to 1 **mole** of electrons. This amount will cause 1 equivalent weight of oxidizing agent and 1 equivalent weight of reducing agent to react. Section 12–6 will remind you of the determination of equivalent weight in redox reactions. Calculations related to Faraday's Law, including the relation of amount of charge to time and strength of current, are exemplified in Examples 19–1 and 19–2. Applications of the principles of electrolysis are discussed in the next two sections. The charge on an ion in solution may be determined, as in Section 19–7, by applying Faraday's Law to an experiment in which we measure the amount of charge transferred and the amount of substance oxidized or reduced by this charge. In Section 19–8, we see how electrolysis may be used in such processes as electrolytic refining and electroplating.

We now turn to the opposite utilization of electrochemistry, that of using spontaneous reactions to produce electrical energy, in **voltaic** or **galvanic cells.** We accomplish this by separating halves of the redox reaction, forcing the electron transfer to take place through the external circuit. Section 19–9 describes the construction of simple voltaic cells for measurement of voltage (electrical potential). The next two sections illustrate the use of such experimental arrangements to study redox reactions; please notice that for now we are intentionally working only with cells in which all reactants are at standard conditions—solutions are 1 M in each solute, gases are at 1 atm partial pressures. In Section 19–10, we study the zinc-copper cell, sometimes known as the Daniell cell. Think about the *possible* results of redox processes in such a cell: metallic copper could be oxidized ($Cu \rightarrow Cu^{2+} + 2e^-$) or copper(II) ions could be reduced ($Cu^{2+} + 2e^- \rightarrow Cu$); at the same time, this could be accompanied by zinc ions being reduced ($Zn^{2+} + 2e^- \rightarrow Zn$) or metallic zinc being oxidized ($Zn \rightarrow Zn^{2+} + 2e^-$), respectively. From our experiments with this cell, we find that Cu^{2+} is reduced and Zn is oxidized and that the initial cell voltage (i.e., while both solutions are still 1 M) is 1.10 V. By comparison, in the copper-silver cell, Section 19–11, Cu is oxidized and Ag^+ is reduced, with an initial cell voltage of 0.46 V. As a result of such experiments as these, we see that the magnitude of the cell potential is a measure of the spontaneity of the redox reaction, a notion that we will extend later in the chapter. For now, we use these results to allow us to rank the relative strengths of the oxidizing agents and of the reducing agents in the cells.

First, we approach the problem of putting the ranking of oxidizing and reducing strengths on a quantitative basis. We accomplish this with the determination and tabulation of **standard electrode potentials,** discussed and applied in the next eight sections of the chapter. Our first requirement is a reference strength, to which we can refer all other tendencies to be oxidized or reduced. For this, we choose the **standard hydrogen electrode (SHE,** Section 9–12) to have, arbitrarily, an "electrode potential" of exactly 0.0000 . . . V. We can then construct a cell with any other electrode versus the SHE and measure the cell potential. This strategy is applied in Section 19–13 for the Zn/Zn^{2+} electrode and in Section 19–14 for the Cu/Cu^{2+} electrode, each measured against SHE. You should understand that what we are doing is measuring separately against the same reference, the quantitative strength of the oxidizing and reducing agents, by measuring the cell voltages. Since in each case we have some other electrode vs. the SHE (which has exactly 0 V electrode potential), the cell voltage is called the **standard electrode potential (E^0)** for that other electrode or half-cell.

In this way, we build up the **electromotive series** or **activity series,** Section 19–15. You should remember that by convention we always tabulate (Table 19–2) these potentials for half-reactions as *reductions;* the more positive the E^0 value for a particular half-reaction, the easier that reduction is to accomplish. As a way of helping you remember this convention, just look at the table and find some reaction that you know to be easy (or hard) and notice its sign. For instance, in Table 19–2 the reduction of elemental fluorine to fluoride ion is shown as having $E^0 = +2.87$ V. Recall that fluorine has a very high affinity for electrons (Section 6–6) or that it is the most electronegative element (Section 6–8) and you will remember that this reduction is a very easy one. This should enable you to recall that more positive values of E^0 correspond to greater ease of the process. Alternatively, noticing very negative E^0 values for the reduction of alkali metal cations to the metallic elements (a very hard process—remember the low ionization energies denoting ease of positive-ion formation for these elements, Section 6–5) should remind you of the convention. Please be reminded that we are still only talking about standard electrode conditions of 1 M for solutions and 1 atm for gases; corrections for different concentrations or partial pressures will be encountered later in the chapter.

The next four sections of the chapter deal with uses of the knowledge summarized in the electromotive series. One important use, detailed in Section 19–16, is to **determine whether a particular redox reaction would be spontaneous.** We do this by writing E^0 for the possible half-reactions (from the electromotive series) and then adding E^0 for reduction and E^0 for oxidation to determine E^0_{cell} for the overall redox process. The more positive the E^0_{cell} value, the more spontaneous the process would be at these conditions. Notice that we are not necessarily dealing here with the reaction taking place in an electrochemical cell, since the same conclusions apply to the same reaction in a single solution at standard conditions. As you follow Examples 19–4 and 19–5 in this section and in your working of such problems, be very careful of the conventions. Remember to write the half-reaction with the more positive E^0 value as a reduction and reverse the other half-reaction while changing the sign of its E^0 value. The resulting E^0_{cell} will then be positive, indicating the reaction to be spontaneous in the direction written. If a reaction has a negative E^0_{cell}, then the reaction is spontaneous in the reverse direction. It is important to remember, though, that we do not alter the value of E^0 when we multiply the half-reaction by some factor. This is because E^0 is a measure of the *relative tendency* of the reaction to occur. This is different from the case in thermodynamic calculations where, for example, ΔH^0 is a measure of the *amount* of heat produced or consumed when the reaction proceeds by a certain amount.

In Section 19–17, we see how these techniques can also be applied to oxidation and reduction processes that take place in solution at **inert electrodes.** There are no really new ideas here, but you must remember that we are still only able to talk about 1 M solutions. You can see in this section, however, that what we have developed is consistent with all of the observations cited earlier (Sections 19–3 through 19–7) about which reactions occurred preferentially in the various electrolytic cells. The very practical topic of corrosion and corrosion protection is actually an application of electrochemical principles, as emphasized in the discussion of Sections 19–18 and 19–19.

Up to this point in the chapter, all electrode potentials and cell potentials have been standard ones (E^0, E^0_{cell}), corresponding to solution concentrations of 1 M and gas partial pressures of 1 atm. In Section 19–20, we see that we can take these standard conditions as references and then make corrections for the effects of other concentrations. This is accomplished by the

Nernst equation; be sure that you note the exact meaning of the various quantities in this important equation, especially n (the number of electrons transferred in the half-reaction) and Q (the reaction quotient, as in Section 15–4). As you will see in the examples of this section, the approach used is to first apply the Nernst equation to correct each electrode potential to experimental concentrations and then to combine these E (no longer E^0) values to get E_{cell} (not E^0_{cell}) in the manner you learned in Section 19–6. Of course, then E_{cell} is an indication of whether the reaction, at the specified concentrations, will proceed—positive values of E_{cell} indicate that the reaction is spontaneous.

We have now seen three different ways to express the spontaneity of a reaction: (1) the standard Gibbs free energy change, ΔG^0 (Chapter 13), (2) equilibrium constant, K (Chapter 16), and now (3) E^0_{cell} in Chapter 19. You should know the criteria for spontaneity of the forward reaction in terms of all three of these quantities. It should be clear that these are all related quantities; in fact, we have already seen (Section 16–10) the relation between ΔG^0 and K. In Section 19–21, E^0_{cell} is related to the other two indicators of spontaneity. The ideas of this section are important at two levels. First, three important concepts from different areas of chemistry are now connected, which gives an important insight into the fundamental unity of the science and the validity of our descriptions. Second, on a more practical level, it provides us several different ways to derive numerical quantities or results that we may desire. For instance, for some reactions, it may be easier to measure E^0_{cell} than to determine K from experimentally measured concentrations or to determine ΔG^0 from calorimetric measurements or from tables that may not contain all necessary values; for other reactions, one of the latter two determinations may be easier. The relationships in this section then provide us with the means to convert our knowledge of the value of any one of these three quantities into the other two. (Of course, cell potentials apply only to redox reactions.) Examples 19–11 and 19–14 emphasize calculations of this nature.

The final sections of Chapter 19 are concerned with voltaic cells as practical sources of electrical energy. Such cells are referred to as either (1) **primary voltaic cells,** in which the electrochemical reaction cannot be reversed once the reactants have been mixed or (2) **secondary voltaic cells,** also called **reversible cells,** in which the electrochemical reaction can be reversed by the action of a direct current from an external source—"recharging." The applications discussed in the text are the familiar **dry cell** (Section 19–22) as an example of a primary voltaic cell, the automobile **lead storage battery** (Section 19–23), and the rechargeable nickel-cadmium, or **Nicad,** cell (Section 19–24) exemplifying a secondary voltaic cell. When the reactants are continuously supplied to the voltaic cell, it is referred to as a **fuel cell,** of which the hydrogen-oxygen fuel cell (Section 19–25) is an example.

Study Goals

1. Distinguish between: (a) metallic conduction and electrolytic (ionic) conduction; (b) oxidation and reduction; (c) electrolytic cells and voltaic cells; (d) anode and cathode. (Sections 19–1 through 19–3; Key Terms; Exercises 1 through 5)

2. Given the components of the electrodes and observations of what happens at the electrodes when an electrolytic cell is in operation, be able to do the following: (a) Describe the operation of the cell. (b) Write balanced oxidation and reduction half-reactions. (c) Write balanced chemical equations for the overall reaction. (d) Construct a simplified diagram of the cell (such as Figure 19–4), including designation of anode and cathode, positive and negative electrode, direction of electron flow in the external circuit, and direction of migration of ions within the cell. (Sections 19–2 through 19–5; Exercises 11 through 14)

3. State Faraday's Law of Electrolysis and perform calculations to relate the amount of electricity passing through an electrolytic cell to the amount (mass or gas volume) of a specified reactant consumed or product formed in the cell. Relate this information to the charge or atomic weight of an ion consumed or produced. (Sections 19–6 and 19–7; Exercises 15 through 36)

4. Describe the process of electrolytic refining of impure metals. (Sections 19–3 and 19–8; Exercises 6 through 10 and 35)

5. Describe what is meant by standard electrochemical conditions. (Section 19–9; Exercise 42)

6. Be able to perform the same operations as in Study Goal 2 for voltaic cells, including the direction of migration of ions in a salt bridge. (Figure 19–9 is a typical such diagram.) Also be able to write and interpret the short notation of voltaic cells. (Sections 19–10 through 19–14; Exercises 39 through 44 and 51)

7. Describe the standard hydrogen electrode. Illustrate its use in the construction of a table of standard electrode potentials (also known as electromotive series or activity series). (Sections 19–12 and 19–15; Exercise 47 through 50)

8. Assess relative strengths of oxidizing and reducing agents from a table of their standard electrode potentials (the electromotive or activity series). Use these results to assess whether a reaction is spontaneous or nonspontaneous. (Sections 19–16 and 19–17; Exercises 52 through 65)

9. Describe the process of corrosion and methods by which corrosion of a specified metal can be prevented. (Sections 19–18 and 19–19; Exercise 53)

10. Apply the Nernst equation to the determination of electrode potentials

and cell potentials under nonstandard conditions.(Section 19–20; Exercises 66 through 72)

11. Perform calculations to relate standard cell potentials, standard Gibbs free energy changes, and equilibrium constants for redox reactions. (Section 19–21; Exercises 76 through 79 and 82 through 85)

12. Summarize the restrictions on the values of E_{cell}^0, ΔG^0. and the equilibrium constant, K, for (a) spontaneous reactions, (b) nonspontaneous reactions, and (c) reactions at equilibrium under standard electrochemical conditions. (Section 19–21; Exercises 73 through 75)

13. Perform calculations to relate E_{cell} to ΔG for redox reactions under nonstandard conditions. (Section 19–21; Exercises 80 and 81)

14. Describe and distinguish among primary voltaic cells, secondary voltaic cells, and fuel cells. Give examples, balanced electrode half-reactions, and overall reactions for each. (Sections 19–22 through 19–25; Exercises 45 and 46)

Some Important Terms in This Chapter

Write the meanings *in your own words*. Check the Key Terms list and the chapter reading. Then rewrite your definitions, still in your own words, to improve them. Study other new terms and review terms from preceding chapters (especially 9 and 10) if necessary.

oxidation

reduction

electrochemistry

metallic conduction

electrolytic (ionic) conduction

electrode

anode

cathode

electrolysis

electrolytic cell

Faraday's Law of Electrolysis

faraday

voltaic cell

primary voltaic cell

secondary voltaic cell

fuel cell

electrode potential

standard electrode

standard electrode potential

activity series

cell potential

standard cell potential

corrosion

Preliminary Test

As in other chapters, this test will check your understanding of basic concepts and types of calculations. Be sure to practice *many* of the additional textbook exercises, including those indicated in the Study Goals.

True-False

_____ 1. All electrochemical reactions are oxidation-reduction reactions.

_____ 2. In both electrolytic cells and voltaic cells, reduction occurs at the cathode.

_____ 3. One coulomb of electricity is the amount of charge carried when a current of 1 ampere flows for 1 second.

_____ 4. One faraday of electricity is the amount of charge on Avogadro's number of electrons.

_____ 5. According to Faraday's Law of Electrolysis, the same amount of electricity will deposit 1 mole of any metal from a solution of one of its ionic salts.

_____ 6. The same amount of electricity that would deposit 107.87 g Ag from an Ag^+ solution would also liberate 11.2 L of dry H_2 gas, measured at STP.

_____ 7. One faraday of electricity is required to reduce 1 mole of Ag^+ to Ag.

_____ 8. One faraday of electricity is required to oxidize 1 mole of Ag to Ag^+.

_____ 9. One faraday of electricity is required to reduce 1 mole of Cu^{2+} to Cu.

_____ 10. One faraday of electricity is required to produce 8.00 g of O_2 gas by electrolysis of an aqueous solution.

_____ 11. During the electrolysis of aqueous sodium chloride, the solution gradually becomes more basic.

_____ 12. During the electrolysis of aqueous sodium sulfate, the solution gradually becomes more basic.

_____ 13. A battery is an electrolytic cell.

_____ 14. In a voltaic cell, the electrochemical reaction proceeds spontaneously.

_____ 15. In a voltaic cell, we can just mix the reactants together and then dip electrodes of the appropriate metals into the solution.

Short Answer

1. Electrochemical cells in which nonspontaneous reactions are forced to occur by the input of electrical energy are called _____ cells.

2. Electrochemical cells in which a spontaneous reaction serves as a source of electrical energy are called _____ cells.

3. An electrode that provides a surface for the oxidation or reduction half-reaction to occur at, but which is not itself a reactant or product of the electrochemical reaction, is called a(n) _____.

4. In an electrolytic cell, the electrode at which oxidation takes place is called the _____; in a voltaic cell, the electrode at which oxidation takes place is called the _____.

5. One coulomb is the amount of charge on _____ (a number) electrons.

6. The cell that is used for the commercial electrolytic production of sodium metal is named the _____ cell. In this cell, the processes that occur are as follows: reduction half-reaction _____; oxidation half-reaction _____; overall cell reaction _____.

7. In the commerical electrolysis cell for refining of metals, the purified copper is deposited at the _____.

8. In the commercial electrolytic process for the refining of copper, the net cell reaction is _____.

9. In an electrolysis, we observe that 0.5 mole of palladium is deposited by the same current, flowing for the same duration of time, that can also deposit 1 mole of silver. The charge on the palladium ions in this solution is ___.

10. In simple voltaic cells such as those used for measurement, the electrode that gains in weight would be the _____.

11. In discussions of electrochemistry, the initials SHE stand for _____ _____.

12. In the standard hydrogen electrode, the purpose of the platinum metal is to provide _____.

13. When the standard hydrogen electrode acts as the anode in an electrochemical cell, the half-reaction that takes place at this electrode is _____; when it acts as a cathode, the half-reaction is _____.

14. In the cell $Cr/Cr^{3+}(1.0\ M)//H^+(1.0\ M)/H_2(1\ atm)/Pt$, the SHE acts as the _____.

15. A voltaic cell consists of a standard hydrogen electrode connected by a salt bridge and a wire to an electrode consisting of a strip of Cd metal

dipping into a 1 M solution of $Cd(NO_3)_2$. When the cell produces current, the electrons flow through the wire from the _____ electrode to the _____ electrode. In this cell, the _____ electrode is acting as the cathode.

16. Liquid bromine _____ (will, will not) oxidize silver metal to Ag^+ in aqueous solution.

17. The process in which metals are oxidized by O_2 in the presence of moisture is called _____.

18. Given the standard electrode reduction potentials Cu^+/Cu +0.521 V, Cu^{2+}/Cu +0.337 V, we can calculate that the standard reduction potential for the reduction of Cu^{2+} to Cu^+ is _____.

19. Given the standard electrode reduction potentials Cu^+/Cu +0.521 V, Cu^{2+}/Cu^+ −0.184 V, we can calculate that the standard potential for the reaction $2Cu^+ \rightarrow Cu^{2+} + Cu$ is _____, which tells us that in aqueous solution Cu^+ is _____.

20. If, for a given process, E^0_{cell} can be shown to be positive, then ΔG^0 for that process will be _____, K will be _____, and the process, as written, will be _____.

21. In the dry cell, the carbon rod is the _____, at which the half-reaction taking place is _____; the other electrode is provided by the _____, at which the half-reaction taking place is _____.

22. In the lead storage battery, sulfuric acid acts as the _____.

23. During the operation (discharging) of the lead storage battery, Pb is the _____ and PbO_2 is the _____.

Multiple Choice

____ 1. The substances that we classify as electrolytes will conduct electricity when dissolved in water because
(a) they are covalent polar substances.
(b) they are covalent nonpolar substances.
(c) they dissociate in solution to give ions that are attracted to the electrodes having the same signs as those of the ions.
(d) they dissociate in solution to give ions that are attracted to the electrodes having opposite signs from those of the ions.
(e) they cause water to dissociate into H_3O^+ and OH^- ions.

____ 2. In order to obtain 9,000 coulombs in an electrolytic process, how long would a constant current of 18 amperes be required to flow?
(a) 200 seconds   (b) 500 seconds   (c) 1.6×10^5 seconds
(d) 50 seconds   (e) 0.002 seconds

____ 3. The electrode in an electrolysis cell that acts as a source of electrons to the solution is called the ____; the chemical change that takes place at this electrode is called ____.

(a) anode, oxidation   (b) anode, reduction   (c) cathode, oxidation   (d) cathode, reduction   (e) Cannot tell unless we know what species is being oxidized or reduced.

The next three questions, 4 through 6, refer to the electrolysis of molten sodium bromide. (A diagram of the cell may help.)

_____ 4. During this electrolysis, sodium ions move
   (a) to the anode, which is positively charged.
   (b) to the anode, which is negatively charged.
   (c) to the cathode, which is positively charged.
   (d) to the cathode, which is negatively charged.
   (e) through the wire to the battery.

_____ 5. The half-reaction that takes place at the cathode is
   (a) $2Br^- \rightarrow Br_2 + 2e^-$.
   (b) $Br_2 + 2e^- \rightarrow 2\,Br^-$.
   (c) $Na^+ + e^- \rightarrow Na$.
   (d) $Na \rightarrow Na^+ + e^-$.
   (e) $2H_2O + 2e^- \rightarrow 2OH^- + H_2$.

_____ 6. The half-reaction that takes place at the anode is
   (a) $2Br^- \rightarrow Br_2 + 2e^-$.
   (b) $Br_2 + 2e^- \rightarrow 2Br^-$.
   (c) $Na^+ + e^- \rightarrow Na$.
   (d) $Na \rightarrow Na^+ + e^-$.
   (e) $2H_2O + 2e^- \rightarrow 2OH^- + H_2$.

_____ 7. Which of the following is *not* produced by the electrolysis of an aqueous solution of NaCl?
   (a) Na   (b) NaOH   (c) Cl_2 (d) H_2 (e) All of the preceding are produced in this electrolysis.

_____ 8. During the electrolysis of aqueous sodium chloride, the solution gradually
   (a) disappears.   (b) gets more basic.   (c) gets more acidic.
   (d) dissolves the anode.   (e) dissolves the cathode.

_____ 9. In order to plate out 1.0787 g of Ag from an Ag^+ solution, the number of coulombs needed is
   (a) 96,500.   (b) 96,500/1.0787.   (c) 96.500.
   (d) 96,500 × 1.0787.   (e) 965.

_____ 10. How many faradays of electricity are required to perform the reduction of 2.0 g of Sn^{4+} to Sn^{2+}?
   (a) 0.017   (b) 0.034   (c) 0.068   (d) 0.008   (e) 2.000

_____ 11. In $Cr_2(SO_4)_3$, chromium is in the $+3$ oxidation state. What mass of chromium will be deposited by electrolysis of a solution of $Cr_2(SO_4)_3$ for 60 minutes using a steady current of 10 amps?
   (a) 3.25 g   (b) 6.5 g   (c) 17.3 g   (d) 0.187 g   (e) 0.373 g

_____ 12. An aqueous solution of an unknown salt of ruthenium is electrolyzed by a current of 2.50 amp passing for 50 minutes. This results in the reduction of 2.618 g of ruthenium ions to ruthenium metal at the cathode. What is the charge on ruthenium ions in this solution?
(a) 1+   (b) 2+   (c) 3+   (d) 2−   (e) 3−

_____ 13. The electrolysis of an aqueous solution of a cobalt salt proceeds until exactly 8.000 g of O_2 gas has been liberated at the anode. At this time, 29.467 g of Co has been deposited at the cathode. The charge on the cobalt ion in the solution is
(a) 1+.   (b) 2+.   (c) 3+.   (d) 1−.   (e) 2−.

_____ 14. In a voltaic cell, the salt bridge
(a) is not necessary in order for the cell to work.
(b) acts as a mechanism to allow mechanical mixing of the solutions.
(c) allows ions to flow from one half-cell to the other.
(d) is tightly plugged with a firm agar gel in order to keep the ions separate.
(e) drives electrons from one half-cell to the other.

_____ 15. Refer to the table of standard electrode (reduction) potentials in the text, Table 19–2. The most stable ions of the Group IB metals are Cu^{2+}, Ag^+, and Au^{3+}. Which of the following statements regarding the ease of reduction of these ions to the respective metals is true?
(a) Au^{3+} is easier to reduce than Cu^{2+}, which is easier to reduce than Ag^+.
(b) Cu^{2+} is easier to reduce than Au^{3+}, which is easier to reduce than Ag^+.
(c) Au^{3+} is easier to reduce than Ag^+, which is easier to reduce than Cu^{2+}.
(d) Cu^{2+} is easier to reduce than Ag^+, which is easier to reduce than Au^{3+}.
(e) Ag^+ is easier to reduce than Au^{3+}, which is easier to reduce than Cu^{2+}.

_____ 16. Refer to the table of standard electrode reduction potentials in the text, Table 19–2. Which of the following statements about the Group IB metals is true?
(a) Cu is easier to oxidize than Au.
(b) Au is easier to oxidize than Ag.
(c) Ag is easier to oxidize than Cu.
(d) Au is easier to oxidize than Cu.
(e) Nothing can be decided about ease of oxidation from a table of reduction potentials.

_____ 17. According to the table of standard reduction potentials, which of the following metals is most easily oxidized?
(a) Cd   (b) Cu   (c) Fe   (d) Ni   (e) Zn

_____ 18. Which of the following is the strongest oxidizing agent in 1 M solutions?

(a) MnO_4^- (in aqueous acid solution)   (b) Ag^+ (aq)
(c) Cu^{2+} (aq)   (d) Ca^{2+} (aq)   (e) Li^+ (aq)

____ 19. Which of the following is the strongest oxidizing agent (solutions are 1 M, gases are 1 atm)?
(a) Cl_2 (g)   (b) Br_2 (ℓ)   (c) Li (s)   (d) Li^+ (aq)
(e) NO_3^- (aq)

____ 20. Would there be a reaction if a piece of pure copper were dipped into a 1 M $FeCl_2$ solution?
(a) No   (b) Yes, forming Fe metal   (c) Yes, forming Fe^{3+}

The following five questions, 21 through 25, refer to the electrochemical cell:

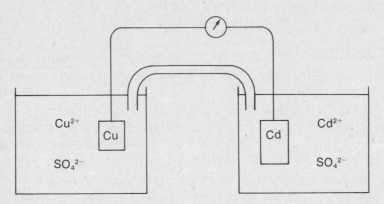

Each half-cell contains an aqueous solution. Necessary values of standard electrode reduction potentials may be obtained from Table 19–2 in the text.

____ 21. What is the standard cell potential for this cell?
(a) $+0.740$ V   (b) -0.740 V   (c) $+0.066$ V
(d) -0.066 V   (e) 0 V

____ 22. Which of the following statements about the half-cell processes is true?
(a) Cu^{2+} is reduced at the anode.
(b) Cu^{2+} is reduced at the cathode.
(c) Cd^{2+} is reduced at the anode.
(d) Cd^{2+} is reduced at the cathode.
(e) This reaction is not an oxidation-reduction reaction.

____ 23. When this cell is in operation, electrons flow
(a) through the wire from the Cu electrode to the Cd electrode.
(b) through the wire from the Cd electrode to the Cu electrode.
(c) through the salt bridge from the Cu half-cell to the Cd half-cell.
(d) through the salt bridge from the Cd half-cell to the Cu half-cell.

____ 24. Which of the following reactions describes the net reaction that takes place in this cell?
(a) $Cu + Cd^{2+} \rightarrow Cu^{2+} + Cd$

(b) $Cu + Cd \rightarrow Cu^{2+} + Cd^{2+}$

(c) $Cu^{2+} + Cd^{2+} \rightarrow Cu + Cd$

(d) $Cu^{2+} + Cd \rightarrow Cu + Cd^{2+}$

_____ 25. What is ΔG^0 for the reaction $Cu^{2+} + Cd \rightarrow Cu + Cd^{2+}$?

(a) -17.05 kcal   (b) -34.10 kcal   (c) -142.82 kcal

(d) -34.10 kcal   (e) $+17.05$ kcal

Answers to Preliminary Test

True-False

1. True
2. True
3. True
4. True
5. False. This would depend on the number of electrons necessary to reduce 1 mole of the metal—that is, on the charge of the ion.
6. True. See Table 19–1; this amount of electricity is 1 faraday. The amount of H_2 liberated is 1.008 g, or $\frac{1}{2}$ mole. At STP, 1 mole of any gas occupies 22.4 L (Chapter 11).
7. True
8. True
9. False. Each Cu^{2+} ion requires 2 electrons in this process.
10. True. The half-reaction is $2H_2O \rightarrow O_2 + 4H^+ + 4e^-$. Thus, 4 faradays are required to produce 1 mole (32.0 g) of O_2. This means that 1 faraday would produce $\frac{1}{4}$ mole O_2, or 8.0 g.
11. True. Remind yourself what the cathode half-reaction is in this cell (Section 19–4).
12. False. At the cathode, OH^- is produced, but H^+ is produced in equal amount at the anode. These neutralize one another (or in the terminology of Chapter 17, the H_3O^+/OH^- balance is not disturbed).
13. False
14. True
15. False. The two half-reactions must be forced to take place in two separate places so that the electrons can be transferred externally. If we just mixed the reactants together and dipped the metals into the solution, the same overall redox reaction would occur, but we would not have an electrochemical cell.

Short Answer

1. electrolytic
2. voltaic

3. inert electrode
4. anode, anode
5. 6.241×10^{18}. Avogadro's number of electrons, 6.022×10^{23}, corresponds to 96,487 coulombs. So one coulomb would correspond to $(6.022 \times 10^{23})/96,487$ electrons.
6. Downs. $Na^+ + e^- \rightarrow Na$ (ℓ); $2Cl^- \rightarrow Cl_2$ (g) $+ 2e^-$; $2Na^+ + 2Cl^- \rightarrow 2Na$ (ℓ) $+ Cl_2$ (g)
7. cathode
8. none. Copper is oxidized from the impure electrode (anode) and redeposited at the cathode.
9. $+2$. You should be able to figure this out *without* calculating by the methods given in Section 19–8; this will test whether you really understand the ideas behind those calculations.
10. cathode. This is the electrode at which metal ions are reduced to metal.
11. standard hydrogen electrode
12. a surface at which the electron transfer can take place
13. (anode): $H_2 \rightarrow 2H^+ + 2e^-$; (cathode): $2H^+ + 2e^- \rightarrow H_2$. Remember that the cathode is the electrode at which reduction occurs.
14. cathode. From the table of standard reduction potentials, we see that H^+ is easier to reduce than is Cr^{3+}, so the SHE is the cathode. At the anode, Cr metal is oxidized to Cr^{3+}.
15. cadmium, hydrogen, hydrogen. From the table of standard reduction potentials, H^+ is more easily reduced than Cd^{2+}. Thus, the electrons are given up by Cd metal, to become Cd^{2+}. These electrons flow through the wire to the SHE, where they reduce H^+ to H_2. Reduction occurs at the cathode.
16. will. We want to see whether the reaction $Br_2 + 2Ag \rightarrow 2Ag^+ + 2Br^-$ will occur. From Table 19–2, we write the half-reactions so that they add to give the reaction we wish to test; we remember that when we reverse the half-reaction for Ag^+/Ag, we change the sign of its E^0. Then we add the reactions, adding the E^0 values to get E^0_{cell}

$$
\begin{array}{ll}
Br_2 + 2e^- \rightarrow 2Br^- & E^0 = +1.08 \text{ V} \\
2(Ag \rightarrow Ag^+ + e^-) & E^0 = -0.799 \text{ V} \\
\hline
Br_2 + 2Ag \rightarrow 2Ag^+ + 2Br^- & E^0_{cell} = +0.28 \text{ V}
\end{array}
$$

Since the E^0_{cell} for this proposed reaction is positive, it is spontaneous in the direction written.
17. corrosion
18. -0.184 V. Same procedure as described for Question 16.

$$
\begin{array}{ll}
Cu^{2+} + 2e^- \rightarrow Cu & E^0 = +0.337 \text{ V} \\
Cu \rightarrow Cu^+ + e^- & E^0 = -0.521 \text{ V} \\
\hline
Cu^{2+} + e^- \rightarrow Cu^+ & E^0_{cell} = -0.184 \text{ V}
\end{array}
$$

19. $+0.705$ V, unstable. Again, apply the procedure described in the answer to Question 16.

$$Cu^+ + e^- \rightarrow Cu \qquad\qquad E^0 = +0.521 \text{ V}$$
$$\underline{Cu^+ \rightarrow Cu^{2+} + e^- \qquad\qquad E^0 = +0.184 \text{ V}}$$
$$2Cu^+ \rightarrow Cu^{2+} + Cu \qquad\qquad E^0_{cell} = +0.705 \text{ V}$$

Since this is a positive value, the reaction is spontaneous. This type of reaction is called disproportionation.

20. negative, greater than 1, spontaneous
21. cathode, $2NH_4^+ + 2e^- \rightarrow 2NH_3 + H_2$;   zinc   container, $Zn \rightarrow Zn^{2+} + 2e^-$.
22. electrolyte
23. anode, cathode

Multiple Choice

1. (d)
2. (b). no. coulombs = (no. amperes) × (no. seconds)
3. (d)
4. (d)
5. (c)
6. (d)
7. (a). See the discussion in Section 19–4. Remember that the alkali metals are much too active (easily oxidized) to exist in contact with water.
8. (b). Remember that the cathode half-reaction in this cell is the reduction of water to H_2 and that this also gives OH^-: $2H_2O + 2e^- \rightarrow 2OH^- + H_2$.
9. (e). This is 0.01 mol Ag^+ to be reduced. Each mole Ag^+ requires 1 faraday or 96,500 coul.
10. (b). The reduction half-reaction is $Sn^{4+} + 2e^- \rightarrow Sn^{2+}$. Thus, 2 faradays are required to reduce 1 mol or 118.7 g of Sn^{4+} to Sn^{2+}. Applying the unit factor $\dfrac{2 \text{ faradays}}{118.7 \text{ g } Sn^{4+} \text{ reduced}}$, we find that 0.034 faraday is required to reduce the desired 2.0 g.
11. (b)
12. (c). The number of coulombs is $250 \dfrac{\text{coul}}{\text{s}} \times 60 \dfrac{\text{s}}{\text{min}} \times 50 \text{ min} = 7{,}500$ coul. If 7,500 coul deposits 2.618 g, 96,500 coul would deposit 33.7 g of ruthenium. This is 33.7/101.07 = 0.333 mol of Ru deposited by 1 mol of electrons, so each Ru^{n+} ion must require three electrons. Thus the ion is Ru^{3+}.
13. (b). In the anode reaction, $2H_2O \rightarrow O_2 + 4H^+ + 4e^-$, it requires $4 \times 96{,}500$ coul to liberate 1 mol or 32.0 g O_2. Thus the reaction involves 1 mol of electrons. Since this liberates 29.467/58.933 = 0.500 mol Co, each Co^{n+} ion must require two electrons. Thus the ion is Co^{2+}.
14. (c)
15. (c). The standard electrode potentials for reduction of each of these ions

to the metal are Au^{3+}, $+1.50$ V; Ag^+, $+0.799$ V; Cu^{2+}, $+0.337$ V. More positive reduction potential means reduction is easier to accomplish.

16. (a). Reasoning from the reduction potentials, the hardest reduction to carry out for the IB ions is Cu^{2+}/Cu. Thus, the reverse of this process, the oxidation, would be the easiest of those listed.

17. (e). Each reaction corresponds to a reduction, as written. The harder the reduction, the easier the reverse reaction (oxidation). Thus, since the half-reaction involving $Zn^{2+} + 2e^- \rightarrow Zn$ is hardest to cary out as reduction, its reverse, the oxidation of Zn metal, would be easiest.

18. (a). Referring to the table of reduction potentials, Table 19–2, we see that all species listed are on the left and are then being reduced in half-reactions as written. Of the species listed, MnO_4^- in acid solution is most easily reduced. When something is reduced, it is acting as an oxidizing agent. Thus, permanganate ion is the strongest oxidizing agent listed here.

19. (a). Same reasoning as for Question 18. The only wrinkle here is to figure out where Li (s) fits as an oxidizing agent. To do so it would have to be reduced and we know that alkali metals rarely gain electrons. Thus, it is a terrible oxidizing agent.

20. (a). Since the Cu metal could only be oxidized ($Cu \rightarrow Cu^{2+} + 2e^-$), Fe^{2+} could not be oxidized to Fe^{3+}, so answer (c) is eliminated. It is possible that Fe^{2+} is reduced ($Fe^{2+} + 2e^- \rightarrow Fe$). For this reduction E^0 is -0.44 V. For the Cu oxidation, E^0 is -0.34 V. Adding these electrode potentials, we see that the only possible reaction, $Fe^{2+} + Cu \rightarrow Fe + Cu^{2+}$, has $E^0_{cell} = -0.78$ V. Since this value is negative, the reaction will *not* occur.

21. (a)

22. (b)

23. (b)

24. (d)

25. (b). Use $\Delta G^0 = -nFE^0_{cell}$. From the answer to Question 21, E^0_{cell} is $+0.740$ V for the reaction as written. The result of this conversion is -34.1 kcal. This value is negative, meaning that this reaction is spontaneous as written. This is also what was indicated by the positive value of E^0_{cell}.

20

Metals and Metallurgy

Chapter Summary

Throughout the first 19 chapters, the emphasis has been on developing a fundamental understanding of chemistry through broad concepts and basic principles. The remainder of the text is concerned in more detail with the specific reactions and properties of various elements and groups of elements —the general area of chemistry called **descriptive chemistry.** As you study each of these chapters, try to keep in mind the basic principles that you have studied and go back whenever necessary to review appropriate earlier chapters or sections. In this way, the principles you have learned will become more meaningful and useful to you as you see how they are related and used in dozens of specific reactions and processes. For instance, in this chapter, we find mention and use of oxidation states, redox reactions, anions and cations, acidity and basicity, amphoterism, basic salts, densities, melting points, solubility rules, crystallization, melting point depression, electrolysis, activity series, relative thermodynamic stability, K_{sp} values, and complex ion formation. In your work on each of these descriptive chemistry chapters, it will probably help you to organize the material in your own words, emphasizing the general reactions or processes of the chapter, the similarities and especially the differences of the various elements or compound types being considered.

In Chapter 20, you will study metals from several aspects—the importance of metals and other trace elements in life processes, the distinctions between properties of metals and nonmetals, the occurrence of metals, the methods of obtaining and using free metals, and conservation of metals. The chapter opens with a discussion of the importance of some metals and nonmetals in trace amounts in living systems, both plants and animals. You should recall (see Study Goal 1) the general distinguishing properties, both physical and chemical, of **metals** and **nonmetals.** Be certain that you remember (Chapter 4) where in the periodic table these general classes of elements are located and review the terminology of representative elements, transition elements, and so on. As pointed out in Section 20–1, some metals have sufficiently high positive reduction potentials (see Section 19–15 for a review of what this means) that they can occur in nature in the uncombined **native state.** Most metals, however, are so easily oxidized that they are found in nature only in compounds; when this is true, they are always in positive oxidation states and methods for obtaining the free metals must involve

reduction. The terms **ore, mineral,** and **gangue,** which will be used many times later in the chapter, are introduced here. Observe (Table 20–2) that we can classify ores according to the anion associated with the metal; methods of extraction of the metals depend on which compounds of the metal are present. Since this may also depend on the solubilities of the compounds, this would be a good time for you to review the solubility rules, Section 7–1.5.

The next portion of the chapter, Sections 20–2 through 20–4, is concerned with the general principles and techniques of **metallurgy**—the commercial purification and use of free metals. You should be reminded that the central chemical process in metallurgy is often one of *reduction* of the metal from a positive oxidation state in a compound, but this must be accompanied by a way of separating components of an extremely complex heterogeneous mixture. As seen in Section 20–2, **pretreatment** of ores to remove the gangue (pronounced like "gang") often involves taking advantage of differences in densities and hydrophilic properties in a **flotation** method, or converting the metal compound to a more easily reduced form, often the oxide (as in the **roasting** of sulfides), or both. A second stage of the metallurgical process is the reduction, or **smelting,** of the metal ores to the free metals (Section 20–3). This can be done in a variety of ways, either by oxidation of the anion away from the metal as in the roasting of cinnabar to produce mercury, by chemical reduction of the ore (which is often an oxide at this stage) with coke or carbon monoxide, by chemical reduction with hydrogen or another reducing agent, or by electrolytic reduction. The general reduction processes are summarized in Table 20–5, with specific applications exemplified in Table 20–6. The reduction process provides impure metals, which are then **refined** or purified by the methods described in Section 20–4. Refining may be followed by the formation of **alloys,** in which metals are mixed with other elements to give desired changes in their physical and chemical characteristics.

Sections 20–5 through 20–9 discuss in detail the metallurgies of five important metals—aluminum, iron, copper, gold, and magnesium. As you study these sections, remember that the metallurgical process described for each metal must involve both (1) manipulations or reactions by which compounds eventually produce the free metals and (2) removal of other unwanted substances, including unwanted components of the ores and the other products of the reduction reaction and other chemical processes. One thing you should realize, in these times of decreasing fuel supplies, is that tremendous amounts of energy must be applied to make many of these processes workable, both for melting huge amounts of material and sometimes for electrolytic reduction.

The final section of the chapter discusses the problem of **depletion** of resources of metals and the fuels necessary to produce energy for the metallurgical processes. Attempts to meet this serious challenge by substitution, recycling, and use of lower grade ores are discussed.

Study Goals

1. Summarize the differences in physical and chemical properties of metals and nonmetals. (Review Sections 4–8, 7–9.2, and 11–8 through 11–11; introduction to Chapter 20)
2. Give several examples of metals that serve biologically important functions and describe these functions. (Section 20–1)
3. Relate the electronic structures of metals to their tendencies to be found combined or uncombined in nature and to the methods that must be used to obtain them from their ores. (Sections 20–1 through 20–4; Exercise 1)
4. Know the anions commonly found combined with metals in ores and give examples of ores containing each. (Section 20–1; Exercise 2)
5. Describe the general sequence of steps used in obtaining metals from their ores. Discuss and illustrate these processes in detail for specific metals. Be able to write balanced equations for important reactions. (Sections 20–2 through 20–4; Exercises 2 through 9 and 12 through 18)
6. Describe in detail the separation processes and chemical reactions involved in the metallurgies of Al, Fe, Cu, Au, and Mg. (Sections 20–5 through 20–9; Exercises 10 through 13)
7. Summarize the ways in which we can conserve important metals. (Section 20–10)

Some Important Terms in This Chapter

Write the Meanings *in your own words.* Check the Key Terms list and the chapter reading. Then rewrite your definitions, still in your own words, to improve them. Study other new terms and review terms from preceding chapters if necessary.

transition metals

native state

ore

metallurgy

flotation

refining

roasting

smelting

zone refining

alloying

Preliminary Test

Be sure to answer *many* of the additional textbook exercises, including those indicated in the Study Goals.

True-False

Mark each statement as true (T) or false (F).

_____ 1. There are more metallic elements than nonmetallic elements.
_____ 2. Metallic character decreases with increasing numbers of electrons in the valence shell.
_____ 3. For elements with the same number of electrons in the valence shell, metallic character decreases with increasing numbers of electron shells.
_____ 4. Metals usually have higher electrical conductivity than nonmetals.
_____ 5. Most metals are solids at room temperature.
_____ 6. Metals are usually fairly electronegative.
_____ 7. Free metals are often good oxidizing agents.
_____ 8. Most metals are found free in nature.
_____ 9. Roasting of sulfide ores is ordinarily one of the most environmentally clean methods used in metallurgy.
_____ 10. The metallurgy of all metals involves reduction of a compound to the free metal.
_____ 11. Since gold occurs in the native state, all that is done to recover it is to carry out a mechanical separation from the other components of the ore.

Short Answer

1. Elements with properties intermediate between those of metals and those of nonmetals are called _____ .
2. The most common human trace element deficiency is a dietary shortage of _____ .
3. The metal that is present in insulin and many enzymes is _____ .
4. The oxides and hydroxides of metals, when they dissolve in water, give solutions that are _____ or _____ .
5. The most common ores of metals, except those in which the element occurs in the native state, have the metal combined with one or more of the following anions: _____ , _____ , _____ , _____ , _____ , _____ .
6. The concentration of an ore before the reduction stage is referred to as _____ of the ore.
7. In the pretreatment of ores in the cyclone separator, the property that is used to effect the separation is differences in _____ .
8. The pretreatment technique in which hydrophobic materials are separated from other components of a mixture by suspending them in water is

called the _____ method; this method usually involves coating the particles with _____ and blowing a stream of _____ through the suspension.

9. In the pretreatment process known as roasting, metal sulfides are converted to _____ by _____.

10. An example of a metal that can be obtained from the sulfide ore by the simple process of roasting is _____; the sulfide ore from which it is obtained is called _____ and has the formula ____.

11. The reduction of metal compounds to the free metal, especially by chemical means, is called _____.

12. The formula of a carbonate that is converted to the oxide by heating to drive off carbon dioxide is _____.

13. The very active metals can only be reduced by _____ methods.

14. The coke that is used in reduction processes in metallurgy is _____ _____.

15. An example of a reaction in which hydrogen is used as the reducing agent in the production of a metal from an oxide is _____ _____.

16. The name of the common ore of aluminum is _____. The commercial process most widely used for the production of aluminum from this ore is called the _____ process.

17. The relatively large amount of sand, soil, clay, rock, and other material that accompanies the minerals in ores is called _____.

18. In the blast furnace process for the metallurgy of iron, limestone is added with the crushed ore. The purpose of this limestone (the flux) is to react with the silica in the gangue to form calcium silicate, which melts at these high temperatures. This molten material is referred to as _____.

19. Two metals that are commercially produced by the electrolytic reduction of the molten chloride salts are _____ and _____.

20. Three general methods that are discussed in the text for conserving metal resources are _____, _____ _____, and _____.

Each of the following equations, Questions 21 through 34, represents a reaction that was discussed in Chapter 20. Each reaction is used in the production of some metal, where M can stand for one or more metals. For each equation, tell what metal or metals M could represent. The possible metals are Al, Au, Ca, Cu, Fe, Hg, Mg, Na, Ni, Pb, and Zn.

21. $MCO_3 \text{ (s)} \xrightarrow{\Delta} MO \text{ (s)} + CO_2 \text{ (g)}$ _____

22. $M(OH)_2 \text{ (s)} \xrightarrow{\Delta} MO \text{ (s)} + H_2O \text{ (g)}$ _____

23. $2MS \text{ (s)} + 3O_2 \text{ (g)} \xrightarrow{\Delta} 2MO \text{ (s)} + 2SO_2 \text{ (g)}$ _____

24. M_2S (s) $+ O_2$ (g) $\xrightarrow{\Delta}$ $2M$ (s) $+ SO_2$ (g) _____

25. MS (s) $+ O_2$ (g) $\rightarrow$ M (ℓ) $+ SO_2$ (g) _____

26. MO_2 (s) $+ C$ (s) $\xrightarrow{\Delta}$ M (ℓ) $+ 2CO$ (g) _____

27. MO (s) $+ C$ (s) $\xrightarrow{\Delta}$ M (s) $+ CO$ (g) _____

28. M_2O_3 (s) $+ 3CO$ (g) $\xrightarrow{\Delta}$ $2M$ (ℓ) $+ 3CO_2$ (g) _____

29. M_2O_3 (s) $+ 3C$ (s) $\xrightarrow{\Delta}$ $2M$ (ℓ) $+ 3CO$ (g) _____

30. $2M_2O_3$ (ℓ) $\xrightarrow[\text{electrolysis}]{\Delta}$ $2M$ (ℓ) $+ 3O_2$ (g) _____

31. $2MCl$ (ℓ) $\xrightarrow[\text{electrolysis}]{\Delta}$ $2M$ (ℓ) $+ Cl_2$ (g) _____

32. $2MCl_3$ (ℓ) $\xrightarrow[\text{electrolysis}]{\Delta}$ $2M$ (ℓ) $+ 3Cl_2$ (g) _____

33. $4M$ (s) $+ 8CN^-$ (aq) $+ O_2$ (g) $+ 2H_2O$ (ℓ) $\rightarrow$
$4[M(CN)_2]^-$ (aq) $+ 4OH^-$ (aq) _____

34. $Ca(OH)_2$ (s) $+ M^{2+}$ (aq) $\rightarrow$ Ca^{2+} (aq) $+ M(OH)_2$ (s) _____

Multiple Choice

1. Which of the following metals is most likely to occur in the native state?
   (a) platinum   (b) sodium   (c) magnesium   (d) iron
   (e) mercury

2. Which of the following metals is produced in large quantities by treatment of its salts as found dissolved in seawater?
   (a) sodium   (b) magnesium   (c) mercury   (d) gold
   (e) iron

3. Which of the following is not a method for reduction of ores?
   (a) electrolysis
   (b) reaction with coke
   (c) reaction with hydrogen
   (d) roasting
   (e) zone refining

4. Which of the following metals is produced primarily by electrolytic reduction of its molten oxide?
   (a) iron   (b) gold   (c) aluminum   (d) zinc
   (e) mercury

5. The purification process known as zone refining depends on the fact that
   (a) many impurities will not fit into the lattice of a pure crystalline substance.
   (b) different substances have different densities.
   (c) some metals are more easily reduced than others.

(d) some salts are soluble in water.

(e) some particles are wet by oil but not by water.

6. Which of the following metals, because of its low density, finds use in lightweight structural alloys?

(a) gold   (b) iron   (c) copper   (d) platinum

(e) magnesium

7. Purification of which of the following metals involves precipitation of a slightly soluble hydroxide?

(a) gold   (b) iron   (c) copper   (d) platinum

(e) magnesium

8. In the metallurgy of iron, the metal obtained from the separation of the slag and the molten metal is called

(a) flux.   (b) pig iron.   (c) cast iron.   (d) steel.

(e) stainless steel.

9. The purpose of adding sand to the roasted copper ore in the reverberatory furnace is to

(a) oxidize the copper oxide to copper metal.

(b) provide structural strength to the copper metal.

(c) aid in the melting for the subsequent electrolytic refining of copper.

(d) react with the limestone impurity to form a molten silicate glass.

(e) cause the metal to conduct so it can be electrolyzed.

Answers to Preliminary Test

True-False

1. True. See Chapter 4 and Section 20–1.

2. True. Remember that metallic character decreases going left to right across a period in the periodic table.

3. False. Remember that metallic character increases going down a group in the periodic table. If you need held in remembering this trend, look at Group IVA, which goes from carbon (a nonmetal) through silicon and germanium (metalloids) to tin and lead (metals). Review Chapter 4, especially Section 4–8.

4. True

5. True. Mercury is a liquid at room temperature and cesium and gallium melt slightly above room temperature. All other metals have higher melting points.

6. False. To be electronegative means to have a tendency to gain electrons; metals tend to lose electrons, having low ionization energies.

7. False. Since metals tend to lose electrons, they are oxidized; hence they act as reducing agents.

8. False. Only a few are sufficiently inactive that they are found in the native state. Can you name some of these metals?
9. False. Read Section 20–2 regarding the SO_2 formed in the process.
10. False. Some metals occur in the free or native state and require no reduction.
11. False. As described in Section 20–8, additional gold can be recovered by amalgamation with mercury followed by distillation of the mercury, or by oxidation in the presence of cyanide ion to form the soluble complex ion $[Au(CN)_2]^-$, followed by electrolytic reduction.

Short Answer

1. metalloids
2. iron
3. zinc
4. basic, amphoteric
5. oxide, sulfide, chloride, carbonate, sulfate, silicate (sometimes phosphate)
6. pretreatment
7. density
8. flotation, oil, air
9. oxides, heating in the presence of oxygen
10. mercury, cinnabar, HgS
11. smelting. In such processes, the metal is often obtained in molten (liquid) form.
12. $CaCO_3$. This conversion is used both in the production of calcium (Section 20–3) and to produce CaO for use in the production of magnesium (Section 20–9).
13. electrochemical (or electrolytic). You may wish to reread Section 19–3 regarding the production of sodium metal by electrolysis of molten sodium chloride in the Downs cell. This method is used to produce the metals of Groups IA and IIA, as well as some others.
14. impure carbon
15. $WO_3 + 3H_2 \rightarrow W + 3H_2O$. See Table 20–6. This method is also used for molybdenum.
16. bauxite, Hall
17. gangue. Can you pronounce this word?
18. flux
19. magnesium, sodium. These two have been discussed, magnesium in Section 20–9 and sodium in Section 19–3. As pointed out in Table 20–6, this method is also used for calcium and the other active Group IA and IIA metals.
20. substitution of other materials, recycling, using lower grade ores.

21. Ca
22. Mg
23. Zn, Ni, Pb
24. Cu
25. Hg
26. Sn
27. Zn
28. Fe
29. Fe. Both this reaction and that in Question 28 take place in the blast furnace.
30. Al
31. Na (and the other Group IA metals)
32. Al
33. Au
34. Mg

As you think about the reactions in Questions 21 through 34, remember to take into account the stoichiometry in identifying them. For example, even though the Group IIA metals are produced by electrolysis of their molten chlorides, neither the equation in Question 31 nor that in Question 32 could represent this process since these metal chlorides have the formula MCl_2.

Multiple Choice

1. (a). This is discussed in Section 20-1. Recall that the way to tell is by comparing reduction potentials for the cations of these metals. Metals with higher reduction potentials are less active and are more likely to occur in the native state. The list of metals inactive enough to occur in the native state is sufficiently short that you should remember which metals are included.
2. (b)
3. (e). This is a method for purifying metals once they have been reduced.
4. (c). The metallurgy of aluminum is discussed in detail in Section 20-6.
5. (a)
6. (e)
7. (e)
8. (b)
9. (d). The calcium silicate that is formed also dissolves the ferrous oxide impurity.

21

The Representative Metals

Chapter Summary

In this descriptive chemistry chapter, we discuss the **representative metals**, leaving a coverage of the transition metals until Chapters 26 and 27. All members of Group IA (the alkali metals) and Group IIA (the alkaline earth metals), as well as some of the lower (heavier) members of Groups IIIA, IVA and VA, have predominantly metallic properties. Each group of metals is discussed in this chapter from three aspects—(1) **properties and occurrence,** (2) **reactions,** and (3) **uses of the elements and their compounds.**

Descriptive chemistry contains much detail, but it is presented in such a way that you can learn it with the right systematic approach. Some suggestions that may help you in organizing and remembering the material in each of the remaining chapters are presented here. First, do not just read the entire chapter in detail, front to back—go over it first lightly, just to see the main points of the presentation. Then outline the chapter for yourself, perhaps one group of elements at a time, noting particular examples and more details of the main ideas that were pointed out. Second, try to remember something about the occurrence of the elements in each group—at least which are the most common and which are quite rare—and the major sources of the elements of the group. Third, as you study each group, try to see trends in the general chemical and physical properties, such as those summarized in Table 21–1 for the alkali metals. Such trends and similarities are more important to remember and to understand than the particular numerical values. For example, it is not as significant to remember that sodium metal melts at 97.5°C as it is to recall that all alkali metals melt at relatively low temperatures and that the melting points decrease with increasing atomic number— and to relate these observations to atomic properties. Also, be sure that you see and understand exceptions to these trends. Often, even the exceptions are systematic enough to aid in remembering them; e.g., the somewhat anomalous properties of the first members of many groups and the resulting **diagonal similarities** discussed in the latter part of Section 21–2. Try to organize your study of the specific chemical reactions of the elements of each group along these same general lines. In the discussion of each group of elements, a table summarizes the reactions of the metals of that group (e.g.,

Table 21 – 2 for the alkali metals), but you also need to remember when one or two members of a group display a different reactivity than other elements in the group.

The **alkali metals, Group IA,** are discussed in Sections 21 – 1 through 21 – 3. You should be able to name these metals without reference to the text. All of these melt at relatively low temperatures and are relatively low-density metals whose properties are dominated by their ns^1 outer shell configurations. All are very electropositive, with low first ionization energies and very negative reduction potentials. These metallic properties all increase going down the group. Thus, all alkali metals are very reactive elements, often reacting so vigorously and with evolution of so much heat that they can be dangerous, as in their reactions with water. They are never found free in nature, but occur in many stable salts, all with the metals in the $+ 1$ oxidation state. In their reactions (Section 21 – 2), the alkali metals are all strong reducing agents. The oxides and hydroxides of all of these metals are strongly basic. In your study of Group IA, be sure to notice that the properties of lithium, both physical and chemical, are anomalous in almost all respects, presumably as a consequence of its very small size and resulting high charge density. The many uses of the alkali metals compounds, especially those of sodium, are listed in Section 21 – 3.

The metals of **Group IIA,** the **alkaline earth metals** (can you name them?) are discussed in Sections 21 – 4 through 21 – 6. All of these metals have the outer configuration ns^2. They are not as reactive as the alkali metals, but are still sufficiently reactive that they are never found free in nature. The lighter elements, especially Be, have more tendency to form covalent substances than any of the alkali metals. Calcium and magnesium are the especially abundant members of the group. As you see in Section 21 – 5, the types of reactions of these elements are similar to those of the alkali metals, except for stoichiometry. Notice especially the trends in basic and amphoteric nature of the oxides of Groups IA to IIIA, summarized in this section. Several important uses of compounds of the Group IIA metals, especially of the very common calcium and magnesium, are mentioned in Section 21 – 6.

Each of the other groups of elements in this chapter is a post-transition metal group—i.e., it is to the right of the transition metals in the periodic table. Each of these groups ranges from predominantly nonmetallic elements at the top of the group to the metallic ones at the bottom. Only elements with significantly metallic properties are discussed in this chapter, the nonmetallic elements of these groups appearing in detail in Chapters 24 (N, P, and As) and 25 (C, Si, and B).

Periodic Table Groups IIIA and IVA each consist of elements ranging from nonmetallic to metallic properties. Section 21 – 7 deals with periodic trends in these two groups. You should be aware that gradations in properties in the post-transition metal groups are more extreme than they are in Group IA or IIA. All Group IIIA metals can exhibit $+ 3$ oxidation state, but with predominantly covalent bonding. The elements of this group that are beyond a transition metal series (Ga, In, Tl) also exhibit increasingly stable +1 oxidation states going down the group, often with marked ionic character. This is due to the tendency, which increases going down the group, for the elements to lose or share only their outer p electrons, with the s electrons remaining nonionized or unshared. This **inert pair effect** is common to all post-transition metals Section 21–8 discusses the properties and chemistry of **aluminum,** the most important of the post-transition metals. As you will see, many of its important properties depend on its intermediate, or metalloid, character. The hydrolysis reactions (Chapter 17) play an important role in the aqueous chemistry of aluminum.

The two true metals of Group IVA, **tin** and **lead,** are discussed in Section 21–9. The primary oxidation states exhibited by these metals are +4 (invariably covalent compounds) and +2 (usually covalent, some ionic compounds for Pb). Complex octahedral anions are also formed by all IVA elements except carbon, by use of vacant d orbitals in sp^3d^2 hybridization. The reactions of the metals of this group are summarized in Table 21–11. The discussion in Section 21–11 emphasizes the amphoterism of their oxides and hydroxides. Note that the acidity and covalent nature of each element's oxides and hydroxides increase with higher oxidation state; this generalization extends to other groups of elements. This final section also discusses the chemistry of **bismuth,** the most metallic element of Group VA. This metal occurs mainly in the +3 oxidation state; in its +5 oxidation state it is a powerful oxidizing agent.

Study Goals

1. Review the general physical and chemical characteristics of metals. Know where the representative metals are located in the periodic table. Be able to write electronic configurations for metals and their ions. (Review Sections 3–15, 4–8, 7–9.2, and 11–8 through 11–11; introduction to Chapter 21; Exercises 1 through 5)
2. Account for the trends in periodic properties of the alkali metals, Group IA. Give several examples of typical reactions of the Group IA metals. Know some of the uses of the alkali metals and their compounds. (Sections 21–1 through 21–3; Exercises 6 through 12 and 14)
3. Account for the trends in properties of the alkaline earth metals, Group IIA. Compare the properties of these metals with those of the alkali metals. Give several examples of typical reactions of the Group IIA metals. Know some of the uses of the alkaline earth metals and their compounds. (Sections 21–4 through 21–6; Exercises 6 and 9 through 14)
4. Summarize and illustrate, with properties and reactions, the trends in

metallic and nonmetallic characteristics of the Group IIIA elements. Summarize and illustrate the trends in basic and acidic characteristics of their oxides, hydroxides, and salts. (Section 21–7; Exercises 15 through 17)

5. Be able to carry out the summary and illustrations listed in Study Goal 4 for the Group IVA metals. (Section 21–7; Exercises 15 through 19)

6. Know some examples of the properties and reactions of Al, Sn, Pb, and Bi and their compounds. Know some of the uses of these metals and their compounds. (Sections 21–8 and 21–9; Exercises 17 through 19)

Some Important Terms in This Chapter

Write the meanings *in your own words.* Check the Key Terms list and the chapter reading. The rewrite your definitions, still in your own words, to improve them. Study other new terms and review terms from preceding chapters if necessary.

alkali metals

alkaline earth metals

post-transition metals

diagonal similarities

acidic anhydride

basic anhydride

amphoterism

Preliminary Test

Be sure to answer *many* of the additional textbook exercises, including those indicated in the Study Goals.

True-False

Mark each statement as true (T) or false (F).

_____ 1. All transition elements are metals and all representative elements are nonmetals.

_____ 2. Of the alkali metals, only the heavier ones are sufficiently inactive to be found free in nature.

_____ 3. Alkali metals can easily form either $1+$ or $2+$ ions since they have such low ionization energies.

_____ 4. Francium is so rare an element that its properties have not even been characterized well.

_____ 5. Because they are easily oxidized by atmospheric oxygen, the alkali metals are usually stored under water.

_____ 6. In many ways, the compounds of lithium resemble those of magnesium more than they do those of the other alkali metals.

_____ 7. Since they have only ns^1 electrons in the outer shell, alkali metals generally show the $+1$ oxidation state and never the $+2$.

_____ 8. Since they have ns^2 configurations in their outer shell, alkaline earth metals frequently show either the $+1$ or the $+2$ oxidation state in their compounds.

_____ 9. All alkali metals react readily with water at room temperature to produce hydroxides and hydrogen.

_____ 10. All alkaline earth metals react readily with water at room temperature to produce oxides or hydroxides and hydrogen.

_____ 11. All Group IIIA metals react readily with water at room temperature to produce oxides or hydroxides and hydrogen.

_____ 12. Because of its ease of oxidation, aluminum is rarely used in the pure state.

_____ 13. The Group IIIA metals are sufficiently less reactive than those of Groups IA and IIA that they (Group IIIA) frequently occur free in nature.

_____ 14. The elements of Group IIIA are much more alike within the group than are the elements of either Group IA or Group IIA.

_____ 15. All of the representative metals are solids at room temperature.

_____ 16. All of the tripositive ions of Group IIIA hydrolyze readily.

_____ 17. Germanium, tin, and lead are all easily oxidized to the $+4$ oxidation state by nitric acid.

_____ 18. Oxides and hydroxides of an element in a higher oxidation state are always more acidic and covalent than oxides and hydroxides of the same element in a lower oxidation state.

_____ 19. Nonmetallic character decreases as the oxidation state of a particular metal increases.

Short Answer

1. The names and symbols of the metals of Group IA are _____, _____, _____, _____, _____, and _____.

2. As a common group name, the elements of Group IA are referred to as the _____.

3. The names and symbols of the metals of Group IIA are _____, _____, _____, _____, _____, and _____.

4. As a common group name, the elements of Group IIA are referred to as the _____.

5. The names and symbols of the metals of Group IIIA are _____, _____, _____, and _____.

6. The names and symbols of the metals of Group IVA are _____ (a metalloid), _____, and _____.

7. The names and symbols of the metals of Group VA are _____ (a metalloid) and _____.

8. The two most commonly occurring metals of Group IA are _____ and _____.

9. The melting points of the alkali metals _____ going down the group.

10. All of the metals of Group IA have quite _____ reduction potentials, which tells us that they are very _____ to reduce to the metallic state.

11. Denoting the metal by M, the formula of the normal oxides of the Group IA metals is _____, the formula for the peroxides of these metals is _____, and the formula for their superoxides is _____.

12. The only Group IA metal that combines with nitrogen to form a nitride is _____ .

13. When burned in limited O_2, the heavier alkali metals form oxides called _____ , having formula _____ ; in the presence of excess O_2, the metal compounds formed are called _____ and have formula _____ .

14. The formulas and uses of two compounds of sodium are _____ (formula, use) and _____ (formula, use).

15. Aqueous solutions of the oxides and hydroxides of all Group IA elements are strongly _____ .

16. The two most abundant alkaline earth metals (on earth) are _____ and _____ ; the most rare element of this group is _____ , all of whose isotopes are radioactive.

17. Of the hydroxides of the Group IIA elements, _____ , _____ , and _____ are water-soluble strong bases, _____ is quite insoluble in water and is amphoteric, and _____ is only slightly soluble in water.

18. In general, oxides of the representative metals become decreasingly acidic going _____ across the periodic table and going _____ within a group of the periodic table.

19. One use of beryllium is _____ _____ .

20. The substance that is used to coat the gastrointestinal tract for obtaining x-ray photographs is _____ .

21. Until recently, the metal used in electrical wiring was primarily _____ , but it is probable that _____ will ultimately replace it.

Each of the following equations, Questions 22 to 32, represents a reaction of one or more of the representative metals, as discussed in Chapter 21. For each reaction, tell whether the reaction is typical of the metals of Group IA, IIA, IIIA, IVA, or VA. Some reactions may be limited to only one or a few of the metals of the group; if so, you should indicate that. Some other reactions may be applicable to metals from more than one group. Be careful of the stoichiometry.

22. $M(OH)_3 + 3[H^+ + Cl^-] \rightarrow [M^{3+} + 3Cl^-] + 3H_2O$
23. $M(OH)_3 + [Na^+ + OH^-] \rightarrow [Na^+ + M(OH)_4^-]$
24. $4M + O_2 \rightarrow 2M_2O$ (limited O_2)
25. $6M + N_2 \rightarrow 2M_3N$
26. $M + O_2 \rightarrow MO_2$
27. $2M + 2H_2O \rightarrow 2MOH + H_2$
28. $M + 2H_2O \rightarrow M(OH)_2 + H_2$
29. $M + X_2 \rightarrow MX_2$ (X = halogen, Group VIIA)

30. $2M + 3X_2 \rightarrow 2MX_3$ (X = halogen, Group VIIA)
31. $2M + X_2 \rightarrow 2MX$ (X = halogen, Group VIIA)
32. $M_2O + H_2O \rightarrow 2[M^+ + OH^-]$

Questions 22 to 32 have emphasized only a few of the fairly general reaction types of the representative elements. Tables 21–2 and 21–4 in the text include many more reactions of some generality. In addition, the reactions that may be specific to one or a few metals should also be studied — e.g., the many reactions demonstrating acidic, basic, or amphoteric behavior of oxides, hydroxides, and salts.

Multiple Choice

_____ 1. Which of the following oxides is most basic?
   (a) B_2O_3 (b) Ga_2O_3 (c) BeO   (d) CaO   (e) K_2O
_____ 2. Which of the following oxides is most acidic?
   (a) B_2O_3 (b) Ga_2O_3 (c) BeO   (d) CaO   (e) K_2O
_____ 3. Which of the following is not a substance that includes calcium?
   (a) quick lime   (b) gypsum   (c) slaked lime   (d) mortar
   (e) baking soda
_____ 4. Which of the following is not a use of magnesium or one of its compounds?
   (a) heat insulator in ovens
   (b) drying agent
   (c) stomach antacid
   (d) lithopone, a white paint pigment
   (e) photographic flash accessories
_____ 5. The most abundant metal in the earth's crust is
   (a) aluminum.   (b) sodium.   (c) silicon.   (d) oxygen.
   (e) iron.
_____ 6. The metal with the largest liquid-state temperature range of any element is
   (a) gallium.   (b) mercury.   (c) aluminum.   (d) potassium.
   (e) bromine.
_____ 7. The tendency for the post-transition metals to retain their s electrons nonionized or unshared is referred to as
   (a) the diagonal similarity.
   (b) the heat of hydration.
   (c) the inert pair effect.
   (d) amphoterism.
   (e) stoichiometry.
_____ 8. Which of the following is not a use of lead or one of its compounds?
   (a) protective absorber of x-rays

(b) battery plates
(c) low-melting alloys such as solder
(d) antiknock additive in fuels
(e) semiconductor

Answers to Preliminary Test

True-False

1. False. It is true that all transition elements are metals, but not that all representative elements are nonmetals. All of the elements of Groups IA and IIA, as well as several of those of Groups IIIA, IVA, and VA have pronounced metallic character.
2. False. All alkali metals are far too reactive to ever occur in the native state. The heavier ones are even more active than the lighter ones.
3. False. These metals have low first but very high second ionization energies. Thus, they do not form $2+$ ions by ordinary chemical means. Think about what electron configuration would need to be disturbed for one of these metals to go from a $1+$ to a $2+$ ion!
4. True
5. False. They react with water to form hydrogen in a manner ranging from "readily" for Li, through "vigorously" for Na, to "explosively" for K, Rb, and Cs. They are stored under anhydrous nonpolar liquids such as mineral oil.
6. True. Do you know why this is so? (Do not answer "diagonal similarity" —this is just another way of saying that it is so, but not why.)
7. True
8. False. Alkaline earth metals (Group IIA) do not exhibit the $+1$ oxidation state since the second ionization energy is also quite low.
9. True
10. False. The Group IIA metals are sufficiently less reactive than those of Group IA that only the heavier alkaline earth metals react with water at room temperature. Magnesium reacts with water only as steam and beryllium will not react with pure water even when red hot. See Section 21–5.
11. False. None of the Group IIIA metals is active enough to react readily with water.
12. False. In fact, the easily formed, hard, unreactive, transparent oxide surface acts to protect the underlying metal from further oxidation.
13. False. These are still so reactive that they never occur in the native state. Aluminum occurs mainly in aluminosilicate minerals (from which it cannot easily be extracted) and as the oxide; gallium, indium, and

thallium occur mainly as the sulfides, but are much rarer than aluminum.

14. False. The differences are greater and the gradations in properties and reactivities are less regular in Group IIIA than in IA or IIA.
15. True. Mercury is the only metal that is liquid at room temperature and it is in Group IIB.
16. True. Of these, Al^{3+}, having the highest charge density, hydrolyzes most readily. Do you need to review Section 17–6, concerning hydrolysis of small highly charged metal ions?
17. False. Lead is oxidized only to the $+2$ state by HNO_3 while the others do attain the $+4$ oxidation state in GeO_2 and SnO_2. See Table 21–8.
18. True. To help you remember and understand this, read Section 17–6 again, where you learned that the hydrolysis of small highly charged metal ions (i.e., the action of their hydrates as acids) is facilitated by the strong pull of the more highly charged metal ion for the electrons in the water molecule bonded to the metal.
19. False. This is discussed in Section 21–11 and examples appear several times throughout the chapter.

Short Answer

1. lithium (Li), sodium (Na), potassium (K), rubidium (Rb), cesium (Cs), francium (Fr)
2. alkali metals
3. beryllium (Be), magnesium (Mg), calcium (Ca), strontium (Sr), barium (Ba), radium (Ra)
4. alkaline earth metals
5. aluminum (Al), gallium (Ga), indium (In), thallium (Tl). Boron is not considered to have significant metallic properties.
6. germanium (Ge), tin (Sn), lead (Pb). Carbon and silicon are not metals.
7. antimony (Sb), bismuth (Bi). The lighter elements of this group are not metals.
8. sodium (Na), potassium (K)
9. decrease
10. negative, difficult. Do you need to review the meaning of reduction potentials, Section 19–15?
11. M_2O, M_2O_2, MO_2. Do you remember which metals form which of these oxides and under what conditions? See Table 21–2.
12. lithium, Li
13. normal oxides, M_2O; superoxides, MO_2. Remember that only K, Rb, and Cs form superoxides.
14. Nine possible answers to this question appear in the first paragraph of Section 21–3.
15. basic

16. calcium (Ca), magnesium (Mg); radium (Ra)
17. $Ca(OH)_2$, $Sr(OH)_2$, $Ba(OH)_2$ [water-soluble strong bases], $Be(OH)_2$ [amphoteric, insoluble], $Mg(OH)_2$ [slightly soluble].
18. right to left, down
19. There are several uses described in Section 21–6, including use as a structural material, alloyed with copper for use in electrical contacts in springs, in tools, and as windows for x-ray tubes. Beryllium and many of its compounds, including the oxide, are extremely toxic.
20. $BaSO_4$
21. copper, aluminum
22. Group IIIA. (All—Al, Ga, In, Tl—can act as bases in this way.)
23. Group IIIA. (Al and Ga only—these two are amphoteric, but the corresponding In(III) and Ga(III) hydroxides are distinctly basic.)
24. Group IA, all metals
25. Group IA (Li only). Magnesium also reacts with nitrogen to form nitrides, but the stoichiometry is different. Can you write that equation and the formulas of the Group IIA nitrides?
26. Group IA (K, Rb, Cs only, in the presence of excess O_2—these are the Group IA superoxides); Group IIA (Ba only—this is barium peroxide); Group IVA (all metals—these are the normal oxides of Group IVA). Be sure you see that the formulas for the various oxides (normal, per-, and super-) differ for different groups.
27. Group IA (The heavier alkali metals undergo this reaction in a dangerous, explosive manner.)
28. Group IIA (Ca, Sr, Ba at room temperature, Mg only at high temperature, Be not at all.)
29. Group IIA; Group IVA (Pb only)
30. Group IIIA (Al, Ga, In)
31. Group IA
32. Group IA

Multiple Choice

1. (e)
2. (a)
3. (e). Can you write the formulas for each of these substances?
4. (d). This involves barium sulfate in combination with zinc sulfide. You should know in what form, elemental or the specific compound, magnesium is used in the other four answers.
5. (a). Both silicon and oxygen are more abundant than aluminum in the earth's crust (Chapter 25), but neither is classified as a metal.
6. (a)
7. (c)
8. (e)

22

The Nonmetallic Elements, Part I: The Noble Gases and Group VIIA

Chapter Summary

Chapters 22 through 25 are devoted to a discussion of the descriptive chemistry of some remaining representative elements, all of which are **nonmetals.** In Chapter 22, we shall learn about two groups at the extreme right of the periodic table. One of these, the **noble gas group,** consists of extremely nonreactive elements, discussed in Sections 22–1 through 22–4. Group VIIA, or the **halogen group,** which consists of quite reactive nonmetals, is the subject of Sections 22–5 through 22–15.

Because of their rarity (they were formerly called the rare gases) and their lack of occurrence in any natural compounds due to their very low reactivity, the noble gases were quite late to be discovered. The discovery, isolation, and occurrence of these gases are described in Section 22–1. It is interesting to observe that argon, a noble gas, is actually the third most abundant element in the earth's atmosphere at about one percent, many times more abundant than hydrogen. (Of course, hydrogen is a very abundant element on earth, but most of it appears in compounds, of which the vast bulk is water.) Several uses of the noble gases are also described in Section 22–1. As might be expected, most of these uses depend on the relative chemical inertness of these elements. Some uses involve the emission of light under the influence of an electric field. You may recall (Section 1–8) that the unit of length in both the metric and the SI systems is defined in terms of the wavelength of light emitted by krypton, one of the noble gases. Some of the uses of helium are based on its unusually low density. Hydrogen, the only gas that is less dense than helium at the same conditions, has many disadvantages due to its high reactivity, especially with oxygen.

Section 22–2 details the physical properties of the noble gases. Because of their very low interatomic attractions, all have low melting and boiling points, increasing with increasing atomic number (i.e., going down the group). The discovery in the 1960s that some of these elements, previously thought to be totally inert to chemical reaction, could form compounds is described in Section 22–3. It is to be noted, however, that the only known reactions of the noble gases are with extremely powerful oxidizing agents, and that their compounds (Section 22–4) all involve the noble gas elements in positive oxidation states. The first compounds of noble gases to be made, and those most extensively studied to date, are the **xenon-fluorine compounds.** In all of the known compounds of this class, XeF_2, XeF_4, and XeF_6, the hybrid orbitals involve Xe d orbitals, which accounts for the violation of the octet rule. No compounds are known of argon, neon, or helium, the lighter members of the group.

The remainder of the chapter concerns the properties, reactions, and compounds of the elements of Group VIIA, the **halogens.** As is described in Section 22–5, the halogens are all nonmetals, displaying a greater similarity in properties than any other group except the noble gases and possibly the Group IA metals. Table 22–5 emphasizes the quite regular gradation in properties of the halogens. In most of their compounds, these elements exhibit the −1 oxidation state, but, except for F, they can also show +1, +3, +5, and +7 states.

The occurrence, production, and uses of the individual halogens are detailed in Section 22–6. As you should expect from their quite high reactivity, these elements do not occur free in nature; they appear most commonly as halide salts containing X^- (X is the halogen). (1) **Fluorine** is produced mostly by the electrolysis of molten potassium hydrogen fluoride. The free element is used as a powerful oxidizing agent. Many fluorocarbons, compounds involving C—F bonds, are extremely stable, leading to a variety of uses as refrigerants, lubricants, plastics, aerosol propellants, and coating agents. The chemistry of the well-known use of fluoride in preventing tooth decay is explained. (2) **Chlorine,** produced primarily by electrolysis, is used extensively in extractive metallurgy, as a disinfectant, in making chlorinated hydrocarbons, and in bleaching agents. (3) **Bromine,** one of the two liquid elements at room temperature, is a very volatile, corrosive substance. It is produced in the free state primarily by extraction from seawater and by displacement of Br^- by Cl^- (previously discussed in Section 7–3). Compounds of bromine find use in leaded gasolines, as light-sensitive substances (such as silver bromide) in photographic emulsions, as a sedative, and as a fire extinguisher. (4) **Iodine,** a volatile black crystalline solid, is obtained from dried seaweed or from $NaIO_3$ impurities in nitrate deposits. Its biological importance in the function (and dysfunction) of the thyroid gland has been discussed in Section 20–1. Iodine is used as an antiseptic, while its compounds find use as antiseptics, germicides, and agents for cloud seeding.

Section 22–7 describes the reactions of the free halogens. These are sufficiently strong oxidizing agents to react with most other elements ranging in strength from F_2, a very vigorous agent, to I_2, a quite mild one. The reactions with iron and copper detailed early in this section exemplify this, but you can see the same trend by studying the remarks in Table 22–6. For example, Cl_2 and Br_2 oxidize elemental sulfur to $+1$; Cl_2 also oxidizes it to $+4$; and F_2 can oxidize it to $+6$. You should study this table for other similar trends. Notice that the displacement reaction with other halogens, $X'_2 + 2X^- \rightarrow 2X'^- + X_2$, is limited to X' being lighter than X, consistent with the order of oxidizing power of the diatomic free elements.

The similar **interhalogen** compounds, XX'_n, are discussed in Section 22–8. Remember that X must be a heavier halogen than X'—thus, BrF_3 exists, but not FBr_3. Observe how oxidation states are assigned in these compounds so that the more electronegative halogen (higher in the table) has -1 oxidation state. This section describes the advantages of use of the interhalogen compound BrCl rather than Cl_2 as a disinfectant.

The most important and generally useful compounds of the halogens are the **hydrogen halides, HX,** which are the subject of the next four sections. The properties of the hydrogen halides are summarized in Section 22–9. These compounds can be prepared by direct reaction of the elements H_2 and X_2, but at greatly varying rates, ranging from the fastest for F_2 to the slowest for I_2. Numerous other methods of preparation of the hydrogen halides are given in Section 22–10. As we have seen for many properties throughout the text, we can correlate the bonding and acidities of anhydrous hydrogen halides with the electronegativity trends within this group (Section 22–11). When these hydrogen halides, which are covalent substances, are dissolved in water, they give the **hydrohalic acids** (Section 22–12), of which HF (aq) is a weak acid and HCl (aq), HBr (aq), and HI (aq) are strong. The strengths of these last three, which cannot be discriminated in water, are seen to increase going down the group. Uses of some of the hydrohalic acids are also described in this section.

Almost all other elements can also form binary compounds with the halogens. These compounds, known as **halides,** are discussed in Section 22–13. They can range from quite ionic (with active metals) to quite covalent (with nonmetals). The long Section 22–14 is concerned with the other important class of inorganic halogen compounds, the **oxyacids (ternary acids)** and their salts. Table 22–9 provides a useful summary of the oxidation states, formulas, names, stabilities, and oxidizing powers of these acids and their salts. You may wish to review the naming of ternary acids and their salts, Section 5–24. These compounds are conveniently organized and studied according to the oxidation state of the halogen. Note that fluorine seldom exists in an oxidation state other than -1 in a compound; this is because the most electronegative element in a compound is always assigned the negative oxidation number (Section 6–12) and fluorine is the most electronegative element. Stability of higher oxidation states increases with increasing halogen size and atomic number.

Several inorganic ions form both covalent and ionic compounds resembling those of the halogens. These ions are known as the **pseudohalide** ions.

Some of these groups can form dimeric molecules, analogous to F_2, Cl_2, and so on, called **pseudohalogens.** These ions and their compounds are discussed briefly in Section 22–15.

Study Goals

1. Give a few practical uses of the noble gases and the physical and chemical properties on which they depend. (Sections 22–1 through 22–3; Exercises 1 through 5)
2. Describe some compounds of the noble gases. Be able to describe the formation of these compounds and the bonding of the noble gas element in each. (Sections 22–3 and 22–4; Exercises 6 through 10)
3. Describe the trends in such properties of the halogens as electronegativities, standard reduction potentials, atomic and ionic radii, polarizabilities, and melting and boiling points. Give reasons for the trends. (Section 22–5; Exercises 11, 12, and 14 through 17)
4. Describe the occurrence, production, and uses of the halogens. (Section 22–6; Exercises 13 and 18 through 22)
5. Give several typical reactions of the free halogens. (Section 22–7; Exercises 23 and 25)
6. Give several examples of interhalogens and their structures, properties, and uses. Compare the properties of diatomic interhalogens with those of the halogens. (Section 22–8; Exercises 26 and 27)
7. Describe and account for trends in the properties of the hydrogen halides. (Section 22–9; Exercises 28 and 29)
8. Give several methods of preparation of the hydrogen halides. (Section 22–10; Exercise 30)
9. Compare and explain the trends in acid strengths of the hydrogen halides, both in anhydrous form and in aqueous solution. Describe some uses of these solutions. (Sections 22–11 and 22–12; Exercises 31 and 32)
10. Compare the preparations and general properties of metal halides with those of nonmetal halides. (Section 22–13; Exercise 33)
11. Know the names and formulas of the halogen oxyacids and their salts. Draw representative structures of perhalate, halate, halite, and hypohalite ions. (Review Section 5–24; Section 22–14; Exercises 34 through 37)
12. Give representative preparations and reactions of the perhalic, halic, halous, and hypohalous acids. Explain the trend in acid strengths of the chlorine oxyacids. (Section 22–14; Exercises 38 and 39)
13. Give several examples of pseudohalogens and pseudohalide ions. Compare their properties with those of the halogens and the halide ions. (Section 22–15; Exercise 40)
14. Be able to apply principles learned earlier to perform calculations con-

cerning the halogens and their compounds. (Review appropriate earlier chapters—especially Chapters 2, 8, and 10; Exercises 41 through 51)

Some Important Terms in This Chapter

Here are some important terms that are used in this chapter. Several of them were first used in earlier chapters. Write the meanings of these terms in your own words. Then look them up in the Key Terms list or in previous chapters.

nonmetal

noble gases

halogens

ionization energy

bond energy

reduction potential

displacement reaction

oxyacid

ternary acid

interhalogen

pseudohalogen

Preliminary Test

Be sure to answer additional textbook exercises. Many of these are indicated in the Study Goals.

True-False

Mark each statement as true (T) or false (F).

_____ 1. All of the noble gases are chemically inert.
_____ 2. Most of the nonmetals are found at the right-hand end of the periodic table.
_____ 3. All of the noble gases are gaseous at all conditions of temperature and pressure.
_____ 4. In their compounds, the noble gases always obey the octet rule.
_____ 5. The noble gases react only with very strong reducing agents.
_____ 6. Reactivity of the noble gases increases going down the group.
_____ 7. The general formula of the hydrides of the noble gas elements (denoting these elements as G) is GH.

_____ 8. All of the halogens exist as stable diatomic gases at room temperature and atmospheric pressure.

_____ 9. Even though they are in the same group, the halogens display widely varying properties.

_____ 10. Generally, small ions are harder to polarize than large ones.

_____ 11. The halogens are generally nonmetallic in their properties.

_____ 12. Because of their strengths as oxidizing agents, halogens always show negative oxidation states in their compounds.

_____ 13. Because of its strength as an oxidizing agent, fluorine cannot be produced by electrolysis.

_____ 14. The most abundant sources in nature of the halogens are halide salts.

_____ 15. Fluorine, in the form of fluoride ion, is effective in preventing dental caries.

_____ 16. Any of the halogens is capable of oxidizing iron metal to Fe(II).

_____ 17. Any of the halogens is capable of oxidizing iron metal of Fe(III).

_____ 18. Generally, only the heavier halogens are able to oxidize another element to high oxidation states.

_____ 19. Halogens are so reactive that their binary compounds with other elements are all ionic.

Short Answer

1. The noble gas whose uses often depend on its low density is _____.

2. All known noble gas compounds involve one of the two other elements _____ or _____.

3. There are more compounds of _____ than of any other of the noble gases.

4. The order of decreasing electronegativity of the halogens is _____.

5. The halogens have _____ standard reduction potentials.

6. The order of increasing strength of the halogens as oxidizing agents is

_____.

7. All halogens have the outer-shell electronic configuration _____.

8. The order of increasing atomic size of the halogen atoms is

_____.

9. A convenient way of storing bromine is to bubble it through a saturated solution of Na_3CO_3, in which it is trapped as a concentrated solution of two bromine-containing ions with formulas _____ and _____; then when bromine vapor is desired, it may be obtained by treating this solution with _____.

10. A reaction in which some of an element is oxidized while the same element is also reduced is referred to as a _____ reaction.

11. Binary compounds involving two different halogens are called

_____.

12. Binary compounds involving a halogen and one other element are called
_____.

13. The binary compounds of hydrogen and halogen are called _____
_____.

14. The degree of covalent nature of the halides _____ going left to right
across a period of the periodic table.

15. The oxidation numbers exhibited by halogens in the halogen oxyacids
and their salts are ___, ___, ___, and _____.

16. The interhalogen compounds XX'_3 and XX'_7 are more likely to exist
when the element X' is _____   _____.

17. The name of the compound ClF is _____
_____.

18. The name of the compound ClF_5 is _____
_____.

19. Negative ions involving more than one halogen atom are called
_____ ions.

20. The hydrogen halides, arranged in order of increasing acidity (pure
anhydrous compounds) are _____.

21. The hydrogen halides, arranged in order of increasing acidity in aqueous
solution are _____.

22. The hydrogen halides, arranged in order of increasing acidity (in solution
in a not-too-basic solvent), are _____.

23. An example of a pseudohalogen is _____ (name, formula).

24. Most of the pseudohalogens are _____ oxidizing agents than are the
lighter halogens.

25. The oxyacids of chlorine, arranged according to increasing acidity, are
_____.

As you have seen, we often discuss descriptive chemistry according to the
oxidation numbers that the elements of a group display. In each of the next
forty questions, 26 through 65, tell the oxidation number (oxidation state) of
any noble gas or halogen contained in the element, compound, or ion.

26. Xe _____

27. Cl_2 _____

28. PtF_6 _____

29. XeF_2 _____

30. XeF_4 _____

31. XeF_6 _____

32. $RbXeF_7$ _____

33. XeO_3 _____

34. $XeOF_4$ _____

35. XeO_6^{4-} _____

36. $HXeO_4^-$ _____

37. XeO_4 _____

38. AgI _____

39. $MgBr_2$ _____

40. KF _____

41. $MnCl_2$ _____

42. HClO _____

43. NaClO _____

44. Br^- _____

45. BrO_3^- _____

46. Br_2 _____

47. IO_3^- _____

48. SO_2F_2 _____
49. IBr _____
50. $BrCl_3$ _____
51. BrF_5 _____
52. IF_7 _____
53. I_3^- _____
54. HCl _____
55. SiF_4 _____
56. $CuCl_2$ _____

57. $HClO_4$ _____
58. $NaBrO_3$ _____
59. HOF _____
60. H_5IO_6 _____
61. OCl^- _____
62. ClO_2^- _____
63. $Zn(ClO_4)_2$ _____
64. $NaBrO_4$ _____
65. $NaClO_3$ _____

Multiple Choice

_____ 1. The halogen that is conveniently purified by sublimation is
(a) F_2.   (b) Cl_2.   (c) Br_2.   (d) I_2.

_____ 2. Which of the halogens has the lowest melting point?
(a) F_2 (b) Cl_2 (c) Br_2 (d) I_2

_____ 3. Which of the halogens has the strongest X—X bond in the diatomic element?
(a) F_2 (b) Cl_2 (c) Br_2 (d) I_2

_____ 4. Which of the halogens has the shortest X—X bond?
(a) F_2 (b) Cl_2 (c) Br_2 (d) I_2

_____ 5. Which of the following is not a common use of fluorine or one of its compounds?
(a) purification of uranium   (b) refrigerant   (c) plastics
(d) oxidizing agent   (e) dietary supplement to aid in thyroid function

_____ 6. Which of the following is a likely method for preparing a free halogen?
(a) $Cl_2 + 2Br^- \rightarrow 2Cl^- + Br_2$
(b) $Br_2 + 2Cl^- \rightarrow 2Br^- + Cl_2$
(c) $I_2 + 2F^- \rightarrow 2I^- + F_2$
(d) $2HF \rightarrow H_2 + F_2$
(e) $2KBr + I_2 \rightarrow 2KI + Br_2$

_____ 7. Which of the following is not a likely product of oxidizing a Group VA element with a halogen?
(a) PCl_5 (b) SbF_5 (c) $AsBr_5$ (d) BiF_5 (e) PF_5

_____ 8. Which of the following is not described in the chapter as a common use of some compound of bromine?
(a) photographic film
(b) sedative
(c) soil fumigant
(d) component of leaded gasolines
(e) plastic

_____ 9. Compounds of which of the halogens are commonly used as bleaching agents?
(a) F   (b) Cl   (c) Br   (d) I

_____ 10. Which of the interhalogen compounds is commonly used as a disinfectant?
(a) Cl_2 (b) BrCl   (c) IF_7 (d) I_3^- (e) ClF_3

_____ 11. Which hydrohalic acid is most widely used in industry?
(a) HF   (b) HCl   (c) HBr   (d) HI

_____ 12. A principal use of hydrofluoric acid is
(a) as a disinfectant.
(b) as a bleaching agent.
(c) as a dietary supplement.
(d) as an agent for etching glass.
(e) as an oxidizing agent.

_____ 13. The name of $NaClO_2$ is
(a) sodium hypochlorite.   (b) sodium chlorite.
(c) sodium chlorate.   (d) sodium perchlorate.
(e) sodium paraperchlorate.

_____ 14. What is the formula for sodium iodate?
(a) NaI   (b) NaIO   (c) $NaIO_2$ (d) $NaIO_3$ (e) $NaIO_4$

_____ 15. What is the formula of the only oxyacid that contains fluorine?
(a) HF   (b) HFO   (c) HFO_2 (d) HFO_3 (e) HFO_4

_____ 16. Which of the following is not a pseudohalide ion?
(a) CN^- (b) OCN^- (c) ONC^- (d) S^{2-} (e) N_3^-

_____ 17. Which of the following is the formula for the isocyanate ion?
(a) CN^- (b) OCN^- (c) ONC^- (d) SCN^- (e) $SCSN_3^-$

_____ 18. What is the formula for the anhydride of perchloric acid?
(a) Cl_2O (b) ClO_2 (c) ClO_3 (d) Cl_2O_5 (e) Cl_2O_7

_____ 19. Which of the elements studied in this chapter is necessary to aid thyroid function?
(a) fluorine   (b) chlorine   (c) bromine   (d) iodine
(e) xenon

_____ 20. Which of the following salts are used as bleaching agents?
(a) halides   (b) halites   (c) hypohalites   (d) halates
(e) xenates

Answers to Preliminary Test

True-False

1. False. The heavier ones have been shown to form compounds.
2. True
3. False. All have quite low boiling and melting points, but all can be condensed and solidified.

4. False. Almost all of the compounds of the noble gases involve d orbitals of that element, and thus violate the octet rule.

5. False. They react only with very strong oxidizing agents.

6. True

7. False. The noble gas hydrides have never been prepared. The only known compounds of the noble gases involve very electronegative elements (F, O).

8. False. All are diatomic, but bromine is a liquid and iodine and astatine are solids.

9. False. The properties show more similarity within this group than in most others of the periodic table.

10. True. See the discussion of the relative polarizability of fluoride and iodide in Section 22–5.

11. True

12. False. All form many stable halides (-1), but all except fluorine commonly exhibit oxidation numbers of $+1$, $+3$, $+5$, and $+7$. Fluorine shows $+1$ in a few compounds. These higher oxidation states are discussed, for instance, in Section 22–14 for the oxyacids and oxyanions of the halogens.

13. False. It is because of its strength as an oxidizing agent that no other chemical agent can oxidize fluoride ions to fluorine gas, so it must be prepared electrochemically. See Section 22–6 for details of its preparation.

14. True

15. True. (Dental caries means tooth decay.)

16. False. F_2 is so strong an oxidizing agent that it oxidizes Fe to Fe(III).

17. False. I_2 is so weak an oxidizing agent that it can oxidize Fe only to Fe(II).

18. False. Fluorine is the strongest oxidizing agent; oxidizing power decreases going down the group.

19. False. They range from quite ionic, with active metals, to quite covalent, with nonmetals.

Short Answer

1. helium
2. fluorine, oxygen
3. xenon
4. $F > Cl > Br > I$
5. high. This means that the elements are good oxidizing agents.
6. $I_2 < Br_2 < Cl_2 < F_2$
7. ns^2np^5
8. $F < Cl < Br < I$
9. Br^-, BrO_3^-; acid. This is discussed in the part of Section 22–6 dealing with the preparation and properties of bromine.

10. disproportionation. The reaction described in Question 9 is an example of such a reaction. Can you find others in this chapter?
11. interhalogens
12. halides
13. hydrogen halides
14. increases
15. $+1, +3, +5, +7$. Be aware of which halogens can exhibit which oxidation states. See Table 22–9.
16. fluorine. See Table 22–7.
17. chlorine fluoride. Observe that the more electronegative element is considered to be in the -1 oxidation state, and thus gets the "-ide" ending.
18. chlorine pentafluoride
19. polyhalide, interhalide
20. $HF < HCl < HBr < HI$
21. $HF < HCl = HBr = HI$. Notice that water is such a strong base that it does not distinguish among the acid strengths of HCl, HBr, and HI. Read about the leveling effect, Section 11–5.
22. $HF < HCl < HBr < HI$. Can you name such a solvent that would be able to distinguish among the acidities of the "strong" acids HCl, HBr, and HI?
23. Several examples are listed in Table 22–10. Probably the most common is cyanogen, $(CN)_2$.
24. weaker
25. $HClO < HClO_2 < HClO_3 < HClO_4$. You learned in Chapter 11 (and again in Chapter 16) that perchloric acid, $HClO_4$, is one of the few common strong acids. For any element, acidity of the oxyacids increases with increasing oxidation number of the central atom.

In answering Questions 26 through 65, it may be helpful for you to remember the following: In free elements, the oxidation number is always zero. In the interhalogens, the more electronegative element has an oxidation number -1. You may wish to review the determination of oxidation numbers, Section 4–12.

26. Xe 0	37. Xe $+8$	48. F -1
27. Cl 0	38. I -1	49. I $+1$; Br -1
28. F -1	39. Br -1	50. Br $+3$; Cl -1
29. Xe $+2$; F -1	40. F -1	51. Br $+5$; F -1
30. Xe $+4$; F -1	41. Cl -1	52. I $+7$; F -1
31. Xe $+6$; F -1	42. Cl $+1$	53. I $-\frac{1}{3}$
32. Xe $+6$; F -1	43. Cl $+1$	54. Cl -1
33. Xe $+6$	44. Br -1	55. F -1
34. Xe $+6$; F -1	45. Br $+5$	56. Cl -1
35. Xe $+8$	46. Br 0	57. Cl $+7$
36. Xe $+6$	47. I $+5$	58. Br $+5$

59. F -1
60. I $+7$
61. Cl $+1$

62. Cl $+3$
63. Cl $+7$

64. Br $+7$
65. Cl $+5$

Multiple Choice

1. (d)
2. (a)
3. (b). This is one of the exceptions to the very regular trends in properties of the elements of Group VIIA. See Table 22–5.
4. (a)
5. (e)
6. (a). Remember that in the displacement reactions, the heavier halogens replace the lighter ones from halides. Of course, this is consistent with our observation that the lighter the halogen, the greater the oxidizing power. As you learned in Section 22–10, the equation shown in (d) is a very unlikely reaction for the halogens, especially so for fluorine.
7. (c). See Table 22–6.
8. (e)
9. (b)
10. (b)
11. (b). The only acid used to a greater extent in industry than HCl is H_2SO_4.
12. (d)
13. (b)
14. (d). This is one of the principal naturally occurring sources of iodine.
15. (b)
16. (d). All pseudohalide ions have negative charge of -1. (Of course, this is *not* to say that all negative ions with -1 charge are pseudohalides.)
17. (c)
18. (e)
19. (d)
20. (c)

23

The Nonmetallic Elements, Part II: Group VIA

Chapter Summary

Chapter 23 is concerned with the three most common heavier Group VIA elements: **sulfur, selenium,** and **tellurium.** (Polonium, a quite rare radioactive element, is not well characterized by chemists.) As is the case when we move further from the extreme ends of the periodic table, there is considerable variation in the properties of this group of elements, much more so than for the halogens. By consideration of the group properties presented in Table 23–1, you can see that although most properties undergo a trend within the group, the big jump in properties is between oxygen (which has no valence shell d orbitals) and sulfur (which does). For instance, oxygen is the only gas—the other members of the group are solids; the other elements of the group only differ by about 0.5 electronegativity units altogether, whereas oxygen is one full unit higher than sulfur; the boiling point changes by more than 600 degrees from oxygen to sulfur and much less after that; oxygen exhibits almost exclusively the -2 oxidation state, whereas for the other members of the group, $+2, +4,$ and $+6$ are also common. No doubt you can see other such irregularities in this table and as you study the chapter in more detail. You will recall that the chemistry of the most nonmetallic Group VIA element, oxygen, was a topic of Chapter 7. This chapter discusses the other common elements of the group together.

The occurrence, properties, and uses of these elements are discussed in Section 23–1. Because of its ability to bond to itself, sulfur can exist in several forms in each of the three physical states. As you can see in this section, the properties of the two solid and the various liquid forms of sulfur depend on the extent of S—S bonding present. Selenium, a much rarer element, can also exhibit several different solid forms and exists in various molecular forms in the vapor phase. Several uses of elemental selenium are mentioned, including some that depend on its sensitivity to light. Not surprisingly, selenium, like the even rarer tellurium, occurs mainly in sulfide ores.

The general reactions of the Group VIA nonmetals are summarized in

Table 23–2, Section 23–2. Be sure that you notice, when studying this table, that not all elements of the group undergo all of these reactions. All of the Group VIA elements form covalent hydrides H_2E (E representing a Group VIA element), with E in the -2 oxidation state. The properties of these hydrides, summarized in Table 23–3, Section 23–3, show the expected general trend, except for the anomalous properties of H_2O, which are attributable to its hydrogen bonding (review Section 9–9.3). Sections 23–3 through 23–6 are concerned with the preparation, properties, and reactions of the heavier Group VIA hydrides, both as compounds and in aqueous solution. As with the hydrogen halides, acidity of the Group VIA hydrides increases going down the group. These hydrides are reducing agents (Section 23–5), with strengths that increase going down the group (again, compare with the hydrogen halides, discussed in Chapter 22.) Many metals displace hydrogen from H_2S, to form metal sulfides. These sulfides (containing S^{2-}) and hydrosulfides (containing HS^-), along with the analogous Se and Te compounds, are discussed in Section 23–6. The wide range of water solubility of metal sulfides provides a basis for separation of metal ions from one another. Recall the discussion of separations, fractional precipitation, and simultaneous equilibria involving slightly soluble compounds in Chapter 18.

A number of binary compounds that Group VIA elements form with halogens (halides) are discussed in Section 23–7. These illustrate the variety of oxidation states that the Group VIA elements (except oxygen) can have in compounds. It may help you to observe that all of the common oxidation states of the halogens, Group VIIA, are odd, whereas the most common oxidation states of these Group VIA elements are even $(-2, +2, +4, +6)$. The quite high reactivity of the halides of the VIA elements in lower oxidation states is related to the presence of unshared valence electrons on the central atom, whereas the relative chemical stability of the EX_6 species is attributed in part to the absence of nonbonding valence electrons around the central atom.

All of the heavier Group VIA elements form oxides, which are discussed in Sections 23–8 through 23–12. The most important VIA oxides are the dioxides, EO_2, and the trioxides, EO_3. The tendency toward increasing metallic character going down a group is very dramatically shown by the stable dioxides of the VIA elements, discussed in Section 23–8. As has been mentioned earlier (Section 20–2), SO_2 is a serious atmospheric pollutant formed by the combustion of sulfur-containing fossil fuels and by the roasting of sulfide ores. Some of the chemistry of this noxious, dangerous gas and some of the methods for removing it from flue gases are discussed in Section 23–9. The preparation of sulfur trioxide by the highly exothermic metal-catalyzed oxidation of SO_2 is described in Section 23–11.

The oxides of the Group VIA elements are acid anhydrides: (1) the dioxides, EO_2, which dissolve in water to give the "-ous" acids and (2) the trioxides, EO_3, which dissolve in water to give the "-ic" acids. The remainder of this chapter is concerned with the chemistry of the oxyacids of sulfur, selenium, and tellurium. Sections 23–13 through 23–15 discuss sulfurous acid and its salts, the sulfites, and the corresponding selenium and tellurium compounds. H_2SO_3 and H_2SeO_3 are weak diprotic acids; H_2TeO_3 can ionize either as a weak diprotic acid or as a weak base.

The chemistry of a commercially very important substance, sulfuric acid, and its salts, the sulfates, is the topic of Section 23–16. Further emphasis is put here on the environmental effects of the "acidic rain" produced by dissolution of oxides of sulfur in atmospheric water. The analogous selenic and telluric acids are discussed in the next two sections, 23–17 and 23–18. You should notice that in all of the "-ic" acids, the oxidation state of the Group VIA element is +6 but the formulas are H_2SO_4, H_2SeO_4, and H_6TeO_6. Thiosulfuric acid, $H_2S_2O_3$, and thiosulfate salts, which contain $S_2O_3{}^{2-}$, are briefly mentioned in Section 23–19.

Study Goals

1. Account for the trends in properties of the Group VIA elements given in Table 23–1. Summarize the occurrence, properties, uses, and general reactions of sulfur, selenium, and tellurium. (Chapter introduction, Sections 23–1, and 23–2; Exercises 1 through 11)
2. Write equations for the preparations of the Group VIA hydrides. Compare the properties of the VIA hydrides, including the acidic nature of their aqueous solutions. (Sections 23–3 through 23–5; Exercises 12 through 15 and 24)
3. Be familiar with the formulas of the metal sulfides and hydrosulfides and their Se and Te analogs. (Section 23–6)
4. Summarize the oxidation states and formula types exhibited by S, Se, and Te in their halides. Know the relative stabilities and some of the reactions of these compounds. (Section 23–7; Exercise 16)
5. Compare the structures, properties, preparations, and reactions of the Group VIA dioxides. (Sections 23–8 through 23–10; Exercises 17 and 18)
6. Describe the air pollution problems associated with the oxides of sulfur. (Sections 23–9 and 23–16; Exercise 23)
7. Write equations for the preparation of sulfur trioxide and describe the preparation of concentrated sulfuric acid from sulfur trioxide. Compare SeO_3 and TeO_3 with SO_3. (Sections 23–11 and 23–12; Exercise 19)
8. Write equations for the preparations of, and draw representative structures of, the following oxyacids and their salts: (a) sulfurous acid and sulfite salts; (b) sulfuric acid and sulfate salts. (Sections 23–13 and 23–16; Exercises 20 and 21)
9. Compare the preparations and structures of sulfurous and sulfuric acids

(and their salts) with those of the Se and Te analogs. (Sections 23–14, 23–15, 23–17, and 23–18)

10. Be familiar with the properties and reactions of the acids and salts listed in Study Goals 8 and 9. (Sections 23–13 through 23–18; Exercises 21, 22, 25, and 26)

11. Know the formulas, structures, and some uses of thiosulfuric acid and the thiosulfates. Know how these are related to the acids and salts of Study Goal 8. (Section 23–19; Exercise 27)

Some Important Terms in This Chapter

Here are some important terms that are used in this chapter. Some of them were first used in earlier chapters. Write the meanings of these terms in your own words. Then look them up in the Key Terms list or in previous chapters.

nonmetal

ionization energy

reduction potential

Frasch process

polymer

acidic anhydride

ternary acid

contact process

Preliminary Test

Be sure to answer *many* of the additional textbook exercises, including those indicated in the Study Goals. In this test, as in the chapter, it is sometimes convenient to represent a Group VIA element as E.

True-False

Mark each statement as true (T) or false (F).

_____ 1. The elements of Group VIA are much more alike than are the elements of Group VIIA.
_____ 2. All of the elements of Group VIA form covalent compounds in which they exhibit the oxidation number -2.
_____ 3. All of the elements of Group VIA form covalent compounds in which they exhibit the oxidation number $+6$.
_____ 4. The hydrides of the Group VIA elements are often used as perfumes in soaps and cosmetics.
_____ 5. Aqueous solutions of hydrogen sulfide, selenide, and telluride are acidic.
_____ 6. The metallic character of the elements studied in this chapter increases in the order sulfur $<$ selenium $<$ tellurium.
_____ 7. Sulfur is too reactive to occur as the free element, occurring almost exclusively in compounds.
_____ 8. The major source of sulfur in naturally occurring compounds is as metal sulfides.
_____ 9. Pure sulfur is always bright yellow, whether solid, liquid, or gas.
_____ 10. Selenium is so rare that it has no significant use.
_____ 11. All Group VIA hydrides are liquid at room temperature and atmospheric pressure.

____ 12. Sulfur dioxide is a gas at room temperature and atmospheric pressure.

____ 13. Sulfur trioxide is a gas at room temperature and atmospheric pressure.

____ 14. Sulfurous acid is a diprotic acid.

____ 15. Sulfuric acid has never been isolated in pure form.

____ 16. Selenic acid, H_2SeO_4, is prepared by dissolving SeO_3 in water.

Short Answer

1. The names and symbols for the elements of Group VIA are _____, _____, _____, _____, and the quite rare element _____.

2. Because it does not have available d orbitals in its outermost shell, oxygen can bond covalently to a maximum of ___ other atoms.

3. Because of the availability of d orbitals in their outer shell, the heavier VIA elements sulfur, selenium, and tellurium, can bond covalently to as many as ___ other atoms.

4. The outermost electronic configuration of all Group VIA elements is _____.

5. Of the Group VIA elements heavier than oxygen, _____ is by far the most abundant.

6. All of the Group VIA elements form covalent hydrides having the formula _____, in which the VIA element is represented as E.

7. The major natural source of selenium and tellurium is in _____ ores.

8. The oxidation number of sulfur in the sulfides is ____; in the hydrosulfides it is ____.

9. The sulfide and hydrosulfide salts may be considered the analogs of salts of the _____, O^{2-}, and the _____, OH^- ions.

10. The dioxides of sulfur, selenium, and tellurium, arranged according to increasing covalent (decreasing ionic) character, are _____ (Write the formulas).

11. Sulfur dioxide is the anhydride of the acid _____ (name, formula), whereas sulfur trioxide is the anhydride of the acid _____ _____ (name, formula).

12. Pyrosulfuric acid, $H_2S_2O_7$, may be formed by dissolving _____ _____ in _____; when it is added to water, it produces _____. (Fill in a name and a formula in each blank.)

13. The salts of sulfurous acid, depending on the number of acidic hydrogens replaced (neutralized), are called _____ and _____.

14. The salts of sulfuric acid, depending on the number of acidic hydrogens replaced (neutralized), are called _____ and _____.

15. The only single acid that can dissolve gold is _____ (name, formula).

16. When we see the prefix "thio-" in a compound or ion name, we know that _____.
17. The formula for sulfur, in its two most stable solid forms, is ___.
18. The formula for hydrogen selenide is _____.
19. The name of the compound CH_3CSNH_2, which is often hydrolyzed in the laboratory to provide a source of H_2S, is _____.
20. The name of the ion S^{2-} is _____.
21. The name of the ion HS^- is _____.
22. The formula for sodium selenide is _____.
23. The name of the ion S_2^{2-} is _____.
24. The formula for sulfur hexafluoride is _____.
25. The name of the compound SO_2 is _____.
26. The formula for sodium sulfite is _____.
27. The formula for sodium thiosulfate is _____.
28. The formula for sodium sulfate is _____.
29. The formula for sulfurous acid is _____.
30. The formula for sulfuric acid is _____.
31. The formula for selenic acid is _____.
32. The formula for telluric acid is _____.
33. The formula for the sulfate ion is _____.
34. The name of $H_2S_2O_3$ is _____.
35. The name of the ion $S_2O_3^{2-}$ is _____.

Multiple Choice

____ 1. Which of the Group VIA elements is not a solid at room temperature and atmospheric pressure?
(a) oxygen   (b) sulfur   (c) selenium   (d) tellurium
(e) polonium

____ 2. The element oxygen, in the form O_2, accounts for which of the following percentages by volume of dry air?
(a) about 20 percent   (b) about 40 percent   (c) about 50 percent   (d) about 60 percent   (e) about 80 percent

____ 3. Which of the following Group VIA elements has the highest first ionization energy?
(a) O   (b) S   (c) Se   (d) Te

____ 4. Which of the following is a major method for obtaining the element sulfur from deposits of free sulfur?
(a) strip mining
(b) pumping out the sulfur after melting with very hot water
(c) deep shaft mining
(d) treatment in a blast furnace
(e) electrolysis

____ 5. Which of the following is not mentioned in the chapter as a use of selenium?

    (a) as a coloring agent in glass

    (b) in photocopying machines

    (c) in solar cells

    (d) as an additive to stainless steel

    (e) as a component of gunpowder

_____ 6. Which of the following Group VIA hydrides has the lowest melting point?

    (a) H_2O (b) H_2O_2 (c) H_2S (d) H_2Se (e) H_2Te

_____ 7. Which of the following is most stable?

    (a) S_2F_2 (b) SF_2 (c) SF_4 (d) SF_6

_____ 8. Sulfur dioxide is environmentally significant because

    (a) it is depleting the ozone layer.

    (b) it helps protect streams from excessive contamination by phosphates.

    (c) it dissolves in atmospheric water to produce "acidic rain."

    (d) it helps to absorb ultraviolet light that could attack the ozone layer.

    (e) it is formed by the rotting of eggs.

_____ 9. The process in which sulfur dioxide is catalytically oxidized to sulfur trioxides is called the _____ process.

    (a) contact   (b) Frasch   (c) Hall   (d) Downs

    (e) Ostwald

Answers to Preliminary Test

True-False

1. False. The differences in the properties within a group are more pronounced near the middle of the periodic table than they are near the ends.
2. True
3. False. Oxygen never exhibits an oxidation number as high as $+6$. Can you tell why? The higher oxidation states $+2$, $+4$, and $+6$ are quite common, however, for the heavier members of Group VIA.
4. False. H_2O is odorless. H_2S, H_2Se, and H_2Te are poisonous, bad-smelling gases. For instance, H_2S is the smell of rotten eggs.
5. True. As discussed in Section 23–4, the strength of these substances as acids increases as we descend within the group.
6. True. Remember that the trend throughout the periodic table is that metallic properties increase going down within a group.
7. False. There are large deposits of free sulfur, predominantly as S_8 molecules, for instance, along the US Gulf Coast.
8. True. The major sulfide ores are galena (PbS), iron pyrites (FeS_2), and cinnabar (HgS).

9. False. At some temperatures, liquid sulfur is dark brown. Read in the first part of Section 23–1 how the properties of sulfur in the solid and liquid phases change with temperature.
10. False. Read the second part of Section 23–1.
11. False. All of these compounds except water are gases. Remember that water has very unusual properties because of its ability to form hydrogen bonds.
12. True
13. False. It is a liquid.
14. True
15. False. Its properties are described in Section 23–16.
16. False. SeO_3 is too unstable. H_2SeO_4 is prepared by oxidation of H_2SeO_3, selenous acid, with hydrogen peroxide.

Short Answer

1. oxygen (O), sulfur (S), selenium (Se), tellurium (Te), polonium (Po)
2. 4
3. 6
4. ns^2np^4
5. sulfur
6. H_2E
7. sulfide. It should not surprise you that these elements are found together in the same chemical state.
8. $-2; -2$
9. oxide, hydroxide
10. $TeO_2 < SeO_2 < SO_2$
11. sulfurous acid (H_2SO_3), sulfuric acid (H_2SO_4)
12. sulfur trioxide (SO_3), concentrated sulfuric acid (H_2SO_4); sulfuric acid (H_2SO_4)
13. sulfites, hydrogen sulfites
14. sulfates, hydrogen sulfates
15. selenic acid (H_2SeO_4)
16. an oxygen atom has been replaced by a sulfur atom
17. S_8. This is a ring containing eight sulfur atoms.
18. H_2Se
19. thioacetamide
20. sulfide
21. hydrosulfide
22. Na_2Se
23. disulfide
24. SF_6
25. sulfur dioxide

26. Na_2SO_3
27. $Na_2S_2O_3$
28. Na_2SO_4
29. H_2SO_3
30. H_2SO_4
31. H_2SeO_4
32. H_6TeO_6. Notice that this is different from the formula for the corresponding acids of sulfur and selenium.
33. SO_4^{2-}
34. thiosulfuric acid
35. thiosulfate ion

Multiple Choice

1. (a)
2. (a)
3. (a). This trend of decreasing first ionization energy going down the group prevails in all representative groups of the periodic table. Review Section 4–4.
4. (b). This is called the Frasch process, described in Section 23–1.
5. (e)
6. (c). The anomalously high melting point of water is due to its extensive hydrogen bonding.
7. (d). As is discussed in Section 23–7, the EX_6 species is the most chemically stable of all of the Group VIA halides due to its absence of nonbonding electrons around the element E.
8. (c)
9. (a). Can you identify the processes mentioned in the other answers?

24

The Nonmetallic Elements, Part III: Group VA

Chapter Summary

In Group VA, sometimes referred to as the **nitrogen family,** the properties of the elements range from the quite nonmetallic **nitrogen** and **phosphorus,** through predominantly nonmetallic arsenic and more metallic **antimony,** to metallic **bismuth.** The latter was discussed with the other representative metals in Chapter 21. Chapter 24 is concerned with the nonmetallic members of this group: nitrogen, phosphorus, and arsenic.

As you can see in Table 24-1, the elements of this group show the expected trends in properties. All of the elements of Group VA, including nitrogen, show an unusually large range of oxidation states in their compounds. Thus, their chemistry is quite varied and you will find it convenient to organize your study of these elements by oxidation number of the Group VA elements. Chemical trends exist with which you are probably familiar by now—for instance, the regular variation from acidic to basic properties of the oxides formed from Group VA elements in the same oxidation state. This trend is illustrated by the oxides N_2O_3, P_4O_6, As_4O_6, Sb_4O_6, and Bi_2O_3. The first 16 sections of this chapter deal with the chemistry of nitrogen and the last eight with phosphorus and arsenic.

It is interesting to note, Section 24-1, that although nitrogen is the most abundant element in the atmosphere it occurs in the form of its compounds as only a minor fraction of the earth's crust. All living matter contains nitrogen, especially in proteins and in nucleic acids. The nitrogen cycle, by which atmospheric nitrogen is converted by bacteria into a form that is chemically accessible to higher living systems, is described in Section 24-2. As is the case with oxygen (Section 7-9), the most common preparation of nitrogen gas (Section 24-3) is by fractional distillation of liquid air, followed, if necessary, by further removal of residual oxygen and water vapor. Smaller amounts of very pure nitrogen are available from the decomposition of azides.

Nitrogen in the form of N_2 is one of the most stable elements except for the noble gases and the noble metals. It does, however, have a very rich and interesting chemistry, forming a wide variety of compounds. The versatility of the chemistry of nitrogen is demonstrated by the observation that it can exhibit all oxidation states from -3 to $+5$ (Section 24–4).

Of the binary compounds of nitrogen with hydrogen, undoubtedly the most important, both commerically and chemically, is **ammonia,** NH_3 (Section 24–5). The industrial production of ammonia by the Haber process was discussed in detail in Section 15–5 in connection with the concepts of chemical equilibrium and kinetics; this would be a good time for you to review that discussion. As we have seen (Chapters 11 and 16), aqueous solutions of ammonia are weakly basic and, when neutralized by acids, form **ammonium salts.** Ammonia can also act as a Lewis base, both with metal ions (as we shall discuss in more detail in Chapter 27) and with other electron-pair acceptors. Oxidation of ammonia to form NO as a step in producing nitric acid and the use of liquid ammonia as a solvent that is in many ways similar to water further exemplify the varied utility of this important compound. Organic compounds called **amines,** which are structurally related to ammonia but have one or more hydrogens replaced by organic groups, are mentioned in Section 24–6. These have already been encountered in Section 16–4 as weak bases and will be discussed more generally in Sections 30–9 and 30–10, in the chapter on functional groups in organic chemistry. Another binary compound containing hydrogen and nitrogen, hydrazine (N_2H_4), is discussed in Section 24–8. It acts as a weak base, ionizing in two steps in aqueous solution and forming unstable salts by neutralization with acids; it is also a powerful reducing agent in aqueous solution.

The variety of the chemistry of nitrogen is further shown by the number of oxides it forms, with nitrogen having all positive oxidation states from 1 to 5 in these binary compounds. The preparations, properties, reactivities, and uses of these, as well as their interconversions, are described in detail in Sections 24–8 through 24–12. These compounds and their rather involved chemistry are of great environmental significance in atmospheric processes, especially those related to the production of photochemical smog, Section 24–13.

In the nitrogen **oxyacids** and their salts (Sections 24–14 through 24–16), nitrogen displays oxidation states $+1$ (**hyponitrous acid** and **hyponitrites**), $+3$ (**nitrous acid** and **nitrites**), and $+5$ (**nitric acid** and **nitrates**). Of these, the most important is **nitric acid** (HNO_3) (Section 24–15). The commercial production of nitric acid by the **Ostwald process** is described in this section. Much of the useful chemistry of nitric acid depends on its oxidizing power. You should observe that the reduction products of nitric acid in such reactions depend on the concentration of this acid, with increasing acid concentration generally leading to products with nitrogen in higher oxidation states. Oxidation of metals produces solutions of the metal ions, whereas oxidation of nonmetals yields a preparation of oxyacids of the nonmetal. Neutralization of nitric acid with hydroxides, carbonates, or oxides produces water-soluble **nitrate salts,** of which several examples are mentioned in the third part of Section 24–15. Some of these are thermally unstable, decomposing to give oxygen and other products that differ, depending on the metal present. The use and possible danger of nitrates and nitrites as food additives are discussed in Section 24–16.

The occurrence, production, and uses of phosphorus and arsenic are the topic of Sections 24–17 and 24–18. Commercially, the most important use of phosphorus is in **fertilizers** since phosphorus is an essential nutrient to all living organisms and since the natural phosphorus cycle that produces soluble phosphorus compounds is extremely slow. The production of superphosphate of lime also represents the biggest single use of sulfuric acid. The highly poisonous nature of most arsenic compounds has eliminated most of the former practical uses of this element and its compounds. Both arsenic and phosphorus exist in several allotropic forms (Section 24–19), with two of each being most important. Each element can be present in either a nonmetallic-type lattice, consisting of discrete tetrahedral molecules, P_4 or As_4, or in a polymeric metal-like structure.

Both phosphorus and arsenic, like nitrogen, form **binary compounds with hydrogen** in which they exhibit the -3 oxidation state, PH_3 and AsH_3 (Section 24–20). These compounds react in ways similar to ammonia but both are considerably more unstable than ammonia. Phosphorus and arsenic form many **binary halides** (Section 24–21), the most important of which are the **trihalides** and the **pentahalides** (VA elements in $+3$ and $+5$ oxidation states, respectively). The trihalides can be formed either by direct reaction of elements or by indirect methods. The pentahalides are prepared either by direct reaction of the VA element with excess halogen or by reaction of a trihalide with halogen. The acidic nature of these VA halides is demonstrated by their reaction with water.

Of the several oxides of phosphorus and arsenic, the most important are those in which the Group VA element has the oxidation state $+3$ or $+5$. The preparations and formulas of these are given in Section 24–22. Many **oxyacids** and **oxysalts** of phosphorus are known (Section 24–23), of which the most important are given in Table 24–3. You should observe that in these compounds hydrogen atoms bonded to oxygen are acidic, whereas those bonded to phosphorus are not. For some of these, the acids themselves have been prepared, although for others only salts have been isolated. Several oxyacids with phosphorus in oxidation state $+5$ exist, of which the most common and important is **orthophosphoric acid,** H_3PO_4, usually called simply phosphoric acid, a weak triprotic acid. The problems that phosphate detergents can cause to vegetation and animal life in rivers, streams, and lakes are also described in this section. Organic polyphosphates such as **adenosine triphosphate (ATP)** and **adenosine diphosphate (ADP)** play extremely important metabolic roles in the storage and release of energy in living organisms. The oxyacids of arsenic and their similarity to the corresponding phosphorus compounds are briefly mentioned in Section 24–24.

Study Goals

These goals will help you to focus on the most important features of this long chapter. Use them to help organize your class notes and reading.

1. Compare the Group VA elements. Account for the unusual stability of elemental nitrogen and the differences in its chemical properties from those of other VA elements. (Chapter introduction and Section 24–1; Exercises 1 through 6 and 12)
2. Summarize the occurrence, properties, preparation, and importance of nitrogen. (Sections 24–1 and 24–3; Exercise 1)
3. Describe the nitrogen cycle in nature. (Section 24–2; Exercise 8)
4. Give example of species containing nitrogen in all oxidation states from −3 to +5. (Section 24–4; Exercises 10 and 11)
5. Describe the structure and bonding of ammonia and the Haber process for its preparation. Describe (with equations) ammonia as a Brønsted-Lowry base and as a Lewis base. Know the important reactions of ammonia and its salts. (Section 24–5; Exercises 9, 13, 16, 18, 19, 31, 33, and 34)
6. Compare the properties of liquid ammonia and liquid water. (Section 24–4; Exercises 18, 19, and 31)
7. Be able to draw the general structural formulas for typical amines. Know their most important chemical property. (Section 24–6)
8. Know the structure and some properties of hydrazine. (Section 24–7; Exercises 13 and 33)
9. Give dot formulas and structures and assign oxidation numbers for the oxides of nitrogen. Know the preparations and some reactions of these compounds. (Sections 24–8 through 24–13; Exercises 14, 22, 23, 32, and 35)
10. Describe the role of oxides of nitrogen in the problem of photochemical smog. (Section 24–13; Exercises 22 and 25)
11. Describe, with equations, the preparations of the following oxyacids of nitrogen and their salts: (a) nitrous acid and nitrite salts, (b) nitric acid and nitrate salts. Give dot formulas, structures and uses of these compounds. (Sections 24–14 through 24–16; Exercises 14, 21, 24, 26 through 28, and 30)
12. Summarize the occurrence, production, and uses of phosphorus and arsenic. (Sections 24–17 and 24–18; Exercises 1, 7, and 29)
13. Describe the allotropes of phosphorus and arsenic in words and structural representations. (Section 24–19; Exercise 15)

14. Be familiar with the formulas, structures, preparations, and reactions of the hydrides and the halides of phosphorus and arsenic. (Sections 24 – 20 and 24 – 21)
15. Give the structures of P_4O_6 and P_4O_{10}. (Section 24 – 22; Exercise 15)
16. Give structures of and equations for preparations of (a) hypophosphorous acid and hypophosphite salts, (b) phosphorous acid and phosphite salts, and (c) orthophosphoric acid and phosphate salts. Assign oxidation numbers to phosphorus in each compound. Compare the corresponding arsenic oxyacids. (Sections 24 – 23 and 24 – 24; Exercises 15, 24, 29, and 36 through 39)

Some Important Terms in This Chapter

Write the meanings *in your own words.* Check the Key Terms list and the chapter reading. Then rewrite your definitions, still in your own words, to improve them. Study other new terms and review terms from preceding chapters if necessary.

nitrogen cycle

Haber process

photochemical smog

photochemical oxidants

PANs

Ostwald process

allotropes

Preliminary Test

True-False

Mark each statement as true (T) or false (F).

_____ 1. Nitrogen, N_2, is a very reactive molecule because it contains a highly reactive unsaturated triple bond.

_____ 2. Like O_2, N_2 is paramagnetic.

_____ 3. No other element exhibits more oxidation states than does nitrogen.

_____ 4. Hydrazine is a weak base, ionizing in two steps.

_____ 5. Hydrazine is a powerful oxidizing agent.

_____ 6. Amines can be considered as derivatives of ammonia.

_____ 7. Dinitrogen oxide, N_2O, has the two nitrogen atoms equivalently bonded to a central oxygen atom.

_____ 8. Gaseous nitrogen oxide, NO, is paramagnetic.

_____ 9. The oxidizing power of the nitrogen oxides decreases as the oxidation state of the nitrogen increases.

_____ 10. The reduction product of nitric acid when it acts as an oxidizing acid is nearly always NO.

_____ 11. The atmospheric reaction in which nitrogen dioxide reacts with water vapor to produce nitric acid and nitrogen oxide is a disproportionation reaction.

_____ 12. Phosphorus is so reactive that it must be stored under oil to keep it from reacting with water vapor in the air.

_____ 13. All of the trihalides of phosphorus and arsenic can be prepared by the direct union of the elements with the appropriate halogens.

_____ 14. The structure of P_4O_6 can be visualized as a loosely linked dimer of P_2O_3.

_____ 15. The reason nitrogen can form so many oxides is the availability of d orbitals on nitrogen for bonding.

_____ 16. Phosphorus can exist in more than one solid form.

_____ 17. Arsenic resembles phosphorus in many of its properties.

____ 18. Ammonia can act both as a Brønsted-Lowry base and as a Lewis base.

____ 19. Ammonia can act as a Brønsted-Lowry acid.

Short Answer

1. The three nonmetallic (or predominantly nonmetallic) elements of Group VA are _____, _____, and _____; the two more metallic elements of this group are _____ and _____.

2. Each of the Group VA elements can exhibit at least some of the oxidation states ranging from ____ to ____.

3. The formulas for oxides in which the Group VA elements exhibit the $+3$ oxidation state, arranged according to increasing acidity (decreasing basicity), are _____.

4. The equation for the autoionization reaction of liquid ammonia is _____.

5. The organic compounds in which one or more of the hydrogen atoms of ammonia have been replaced with organic groups are called _____; like ammonia, these compounds are all _____ bases.

6. The names and formulas of two binary compounds of nitrogen and hydrogen are _____ and _____.

7. The name of the major commercial process for producing nitric acid is the _____ process.

8. The oxide of nitrogen that can be considered as the anhydride of hyponitrous acid, $H_2N_2O_2$, is _____ (name, formula).

9. The oxide of nitrogen that is the anhydride of nitrous acid, HNO_2, is _____ (name, formula).

10. The two oxysalts of nitrogen that are often used as meat additives to retard oxidation are _____ (name, formula) and _____ (name, formula).

11. Nitric acid is prepared by dissolving _____ (name, formula) in water; nitric acid is a _____ acid and a _____ oxidizing agent (strong or weak?).

12. The formula for the oxide of phosphorus that is often used as a very powerful dehydrating agent is _____.

13. Most of the former practical uses of arsenic and its compounds are now banned because _____.

14. The existence of elements in several different forms in the same physical state, as exemplified by phosphorus and arsenic, is called _____.

15. The formulas for the two most common classes of compounds between phosphorus and a halogen (call it X) are _____ and _____.

16. The formulas for the two most common classes of compounds between arsenic and a halogen (call it X) are _____ and _____.

17. The pentahalides of phosphorus and arsenic can be prepared using either

the reaction of the elements with excess halogen or by the reaction of _____ with _____.

18. The trihalides and pentahalides of phosphorus all hydrolyze readily to give solutions that are _____.

19. The anhydride of (ortho)phosphorous acid is _____ (name, formula). However, the acid is more easily prepared by hydrolysis of _____ (name, formula).

20. The anhydride of orthophosphoric acid is _____ (name, formula).

21. Phosphoric acid, H_3PO_4, is an acid that ionizes in ___ stage(s).

22. Hypophosphorous acid, H_3PO_2, is an acid that ionizes in ___ stage(s).

23. Trimetaphosphate salts can be prepared by _____.

In each of the following questions, 24 through 46, supply either the name or the formula of the compound or ion and tell the oxidation state of nitrogen in that compound or ion.

Formula	Name	Oxidation State of Nitrogen
24. NH_3	_____	___
25. HNO_3	_____	___
26. ___	nitrogen oxide	___
27. ___	nitrogen	___
28. ___	nitrous acid	___
29. N_2O	_____	___
30. NH_2OH	_____	___
31. ___	nitrogen dioxide	___
32. ___	dinitrogen tetroxide	___
33. ___	dinitrogen trioxide	___
34. NO_3^-	_____	___
35. ___	amide ion	___

36. N_2O_5 _____   ___

37. ___   hydrazine   ___

38. ___   calcium nitride   ___

39. ___   ammonium nitrate   ___

40. NH_4^+ _____   ___

41. $Ca(NO_3)_2$ _____   ___

42. ___   potassium nitrite   ___

43. ___   potassium nitrate   ___

44. $H_2N_2O_2$ _____   ___

45. BaN_2O_2 _____   ___

46. ___   lead(II) nitrate   ___

In each of the following questions, 47 through 68, supply either the name or the formula of the compound or ion and tell the oxidation state of phosphorus or arsenic in that compound or ion.

Formula	Name	Oxidation State of Phosphorus or Arsenic
47. $Ca_3(PO_4)_2$	_____	___
48. P_4	_____	___
49. ___	calcium dihydrogen phosphate	___
50. ___	arsenic(III) sulfide	___
51. As_4	_____	___
52. $(P_4)_n$ [polymeric]	_____	___

Formula	Name	Oxidation State of Phosphorus or Arsenic
53. ___	phosphine	___
54. ___	arsine	___
55. P_2H_4	_____	___
56. ___	arsenous acid	___
57. ___	arsenic trichloride	___
58. PF_5	_____	___
59. P_4O_6	_____	___
60. ___	hypophosphorous acid	___
61. H_3PO_3	_____	___
62. H_3PO_4	_____	___
63. $H_4P_2O_7$	_____	___
64. ___	pyrophosphate ion	___
65. ___	trimetaphosphate ion	___
66. Ca_3P_2	_____	___
67. H_3AsO_4	_____	___
68. ___	phosphate ion	___

Multiple Choice

___ 1. The Group VIA element with the highest melting point is
(a) nitrogen.   (b) phosphorus.   (c) arsenic.
(d) antimony.   (e) bismuth.

___ 2. Nitrogen is made available to living organisms primarily by

(a) bacterial action in the nitrogen cycle.
(b) the Haber process.
(c) the Ostwald process.
(d) the use of detergents.
(e) the oxidizing action of nitric acid.

_____ 3. The principal method of preparation of nitrogen, N_2, is
(a) decomposition of nitrates.
(b) decomposition of azides.
(c) fractional distillation of liquid air.
(d) electrolysis of nitride salts.
(e) roasting of nitride ores.

_____ 4. The oxide of nitrogen called "laughing gas" that is used by some dentists as a mild anesthetic is
(a) N_2O.   (b) NO.   (c) N_2O_3.   (d) NO_2.   (e) N_2O_5.

_____ 5. The multistep procedure by which nitric acid is produced commercially from ammonia is called
(a) the Haber process.   (b) the Ostwald process.
(c) respiration.   (d) eutrophication.   (e) the Frasch process.

_____ 6. Commercially, the most important oxyacid of nitrogen is
(a) HNO_3.   (b) HNO_2.   (c) $H_2N_2O_2$.   (d) H_3NO_4.
(e) HN_3.

_____ 7. Commercially, the most important oxyacid of phosphorus is
(a) HPO_3.   (b) H_3PO_2.   (c) H_3PO_3.   (d) H_3PO_4.
(e) $H_4P_2O_7$.

_____ 8. The only element of Group VA that does not occur in a free form in nature is
(a) nitrogen.   (b) phosphorus.   (c) arsenic.
(d) antimony.   (e) bismuth.

_____ 9. The largest single use of phosphorus compounds is in
(a) the fertilizer industry.
(b) the detergent industry.
(c) rocket propellants.
(d) insecticides and other poisons.
(e) smog preventive agents.

_____ 10. The Marsh test for the presence of arsenic in criminological investigations is based on
(a) the decomposition of arsine gas in a heated tube.
(b) the formation of arsine gas in a heated tube.
(c) the dissolving of As_2O_5 to form arsenic acid, H_3AsO_4.
(d) the conversion of yellow arsenic to gray arsenic.
(e) the vaporization of As_4.

_____ 11. Which of the following oxidation states of phosphorus is not shown in one of its important oxyacids?
(a) -3 (b) $+1$ (c) $+3$ (d) $+5$

Answers to Preliminary Test

Do not just look up answers. Think about them and study related sections in the chapter.

True-False

1. False. This triple bond has a very high bond energy, 225 kcal/mol or 941 kJ/mol. This means that it is very stable and unreactive.
2. False. It is diamagnetic, all electrons being paired. You may wish to review the discussion of bonding in O_2 and N_2 in terms of molecular orbitals, Chapter 6.
3. True. It exhibits all oxidation states from -3 to $+5$.
4. True. Each of these steps involves one of the nitrogen atoms providing a lone pair of electrons for reactions, just as does the nitrogen atom in ammonia.
5. False. It is a powerful reducing agent in basic solution, usually being oxidized to N_2. It is the expansion from production of this N_2 gas that makes hydrazine useful as a rocket propellant.
6. True
7. False. See Section 24–8 for a description of the bonding in this compound.
8. True. Any molecule that contains unpaired electrons is paramagnetic, and NO, which contains an odd number of electrons, must have an unpaired electron.
9. False. If you think about it, this statement just makes no sense, whether you know anything about oxides of nitrogen or not. In order to act as an oxidizing agent, the substance must already be in a higher oxidation state and be able to be reduced.
10. False. The nature of the reduction product depends on the concentration of the nitric acid and on the nature of the substance being oxidized. Read Section 24–15 for further information on this point.
11. True. The reaction is $3NO_2 + H_2O \rightarrow 2HNO_3 + NO$. Determine the oxidation state of nitrogen in these compounds.
12. False. It is reactive with regard to oxidation by atmospheric oxygen, but it is not reactive with water, so it is stored under water to protect it from air.
13. True. See Section 24–21 for the equations for these reactions.
14. False. See the description of this structure in Section 24–22.
15. False. There are no d orbitals in the valence shell ($n = 2$) of nitrogen.
16. True. This is discussed in Section 24–19. Can you visualize the structures of these two allotropic forms?
17. True
18. True. The accepting of H^+ from H_2O is Brønsted-Lowry basic behavior.

The providing of the lone pair for this reaction and many others is also Lewis basicity.

19. True. In its autoionization, some NH_3 molecules give up H^+, which is Brønsted-Lowry acidic behavior.

Short Answer

1. nitrogen, phosphorus, arsenic; antimony, bismuth
2. $-3, +5$
3. $Bi_2O_3 < Sb_4O_6 < As_4O_6 < P_4O_6 < N_2O_3$. This is the same trend you have seen for many other groups—the acidity decreases (basicity increases) for the oxides going down the group. This question asked for the reverse trend. Remember how this correlates with metallic character.
4. $2NH_3(\ell) \rightarrow NH_4^+ + NH_2^-$. This reaction takes place to a much smaller extent than the corresponding one for water ($K_{H_2O} = 10^{-14}$, $K_{NH_3} = 10^{-30}$), so ammonia is a more basic solvent than is water. Liquid ammonia is a very useful solvent for some reaction systems.
5. amines, weak
6. ammonia (NH_3), hydrazine (N_2H_4), hydrazoic acid (HN_3)
7. Ostwald
8. dinitrogen oxide, N_2O. However, read the first paragraph of Section 24–16, which tells you the evidence on which this conclusion is based.
9. dinitrogen trioxide, N_2O_3
10. sodium nitrite ($NaNO_2$), sodium nitrate ($NaNO_3$). There is, however, considerable concern recently about the possibility of the formation of carcinogenic (cancer-causing) compounds from these additives.
11. nitrogen dioxide, NO_2; strong, strong. Dissolving NO_2 in water is part of the Ostwald process. Be sure that you are aware, however, that this is an oxidation-reduction reaction, so that NO_2 is not to be considered the "anhydride" of nitric acid in the usual sense. You should also be aware that, although nitric acid can be prepared by dissolving N_2O_5 (the oxide that already has nitrogen in the proper oxidation state) in water, it is not the major method of preparation.
12. P_4O_{10}. This is used, for example, in the preparation of N_2O_5 by dehydration of nitric acid (Section 24–11).
13. arsenic and most of its compounds are quite poisonous
14. allotropism. The various forms are called allotropes or allotropic forms.
15. PX_3, PX_5
16. AsX_3, AsX_5
17. the trihalide, a halogen
18. acidic. These reactions are described in Section 24–21.
19. tetraphosphorus hexoxide (P_4O_6); phosphorus trichloride (PCl_3)
20. tetraphosphorus decoxide (P_4O_{10})

21. 3. All of these ionizations are relatively weak (and of course successive ionizations are increasingly weaker).
22. 1. Two of the hydrogen atoms are bonded to phosphorus and are thus not acidic. See the structural formula in Section 24–23.1.
23. heating salts containing $H_2PO_4^-$ or HPO_4^{2-} ion.
24. ammonia, -3
25. nitric acid, $+5$
26. NO, $+2$
27. N_2, 0. Sometimes this is called "dinitrogen," though not in this text.
28. HNO_2, $+3$
29. dinitrogen oxide, $+1$
30. hydroxylamine, -1
31. NO_2, $+4$
32. N_2O_4, $+4$
33. N_2O_3, $+3$
34. nitrate ion, $+5$
35. NH_2^-, -3
36. dinitrogen pentoxide, $+5$
37. N_2H_4, -2
38. Ca_3N_2, -3
39. NH_4NO_3, -3 in the ammonium ion, $+5$ in the nitrate ion
40. ammonium ion, -3
41. calcium nitrate, $+5$
42. KNO_2, $+3$
43. KNO_3, $+5$
44. hyponitrous acid, $+1$
45. barium hyponitrite, $+1$
46. $Pb(NO_3)_2$, $+5$
47. calcium phosphate, $+5$
48. white phosphorus, 0
49. $Ca(H_2PO_4)_2$, $+5$
50. As_2S_3, $+3$
51. yellow arsenic, 0
52. red phosphorus, 0
53. PH_3, -3
54. AsH_3, -3
55. diphosphine, -2
56. H_3AsO_3, $+3$
57. $AsCl_3$, $+3$
58. phosphorus pentafluoride, $+5$
59. tetraphosphorus hexoxide, $+3$
60. H_3PO_2, $+1$
61. phosphorous acid (or orthophosphorous acid), $+3$
62. phosphoric acid (or orthophosphoric acid), $+5$

63. pyrophosphoric acid, $+5$
64. $P_2O_7^{4-}$, $+5$
65. $P_3O_9^{3-}$, $+5$
66. calcium phosphide, -2
67. arsenic acid, $+5$
68. PO_4^{3-}, $+5$

Multiple Choice

1. (c). The melting points of the elements of Group VA reach a maximum in the middle of the group.
2. (a). This is sometimes accomplished with the aid of an enzyme called nitrogenase.
3. (c). Method (b) is used in the production of limited amounts of very pure N_2.
4. (a)
5. (b)
6. (a). This is nitric acid. HN_3 is not an oxyacid and there is no such acid as H_3NO_4.
7. (d). Which of the other answers are compounds that actually exist?
8. (b)
9. (a)
10. (a). This decomposition to metal-like arsenic results in the formation of a mirror on the inside of the tube.
11. (a)

25

The Nonmetallic Elements, Part IV: Carbon, Silicon, and Boron

Chapter Summary

In this, the last of four chapters dealing with the nonmetallic elements, we study the three elements carbon, silicon, and boron. As the introduction to this chapter points out, carbon and silicon form compounds with analogous formulas since they are in the same group; however, in another example of the "diagonal similarity" principle which you have seen before, silicon resembles boron more than it does carbon in its own properties and those of its compounds. Silicon and boron are both more metallic than carbon and are considered metalloids. The first five sections of Chapter 25 deal with the "inorganic" chemistry of carbon. Sections 25–6 through 25–12 are concerned with silicon and Sections 25–13 through 25–19 with boron.

Carbon forms no monatomic ions since it is in the middle of the representative elements. (That is, carbon is quite far from attaining a stable configuration like that of the noble gases, by either gain or loss of electrons.) Carbon does, however, form very stable covalent bonds, especially with other carbon atoms and with hydrogen, which has nearly the same electronegativity. As a consequence of this ability to form stable covalent bonds, carbon has a strong tendency to form chains and rings in which carbon atoms are bonded to other carbon atoms and to hydrogen atoms. The branch of chemistry that studies such compounds is called, somewhat arbitrarily, **organic chemistry**. The present chapter is concerned with **inorganic** compounds of carbon, most of which contain only one carbon atom per formula unit and no C—H bonds.

Section 25–1 discusses the occurrence of carbon, whose major compounds in the crust of the earth are calcium or magnesium carbonates in rocks. Other occurrences include deposits of free carbon, carbon dioxide gas in the atmosphere, and the organic compounds in plants and animals. Like several other nonmetallic elements in this region of the periodic table, carbon occurs in two **allotropic** forms, which are **diamond** and **graphite.** Probably no other element, however, exhibits such a dramatic difference in the properties of its allotropes as does carbon in graphite and diamond. Section 25–1 describes these differences in terms of the arrangements by which the carbon atoms are bonded. **Coal** and its conversion to **coke** are also discussed in this section. In its reactions, which must take place at elevated temperatures, carbon acts as a reducing agent, with either oxygen, metal oxides, nonmetal oxides, or steam, as discussed in Section 25–2.

The only two important oxides of carbon (Section 25–3) are carbon monoxide (CO) and carbon dioxide (CO_2). The first of these, carbon monoxide, is a very toxic gas that is particularly dangerous because it is odorless; it acts by interfering with the ability of the blood to carry oxygen. Some of the other reactions of CO are described here, with a mention of **metal carbonyls,** which will be discussed more fully in Chapter 27 along with other coordination compounds of transition metals. When carbon or a hydrocarbon is burned in the presence of sufficient oxygen (complete combustion), carbon dioxide rather than carbon monoxide is formed. This gaseous substance is important in the **photosynthesis** that takes place in green plants, a process in which carbon dioxide and water are converted into sugars. Section 25–3 closes with a discussion of the changes in the earth's climate that are resulting from the increased amount of atmospheric CO_2 caused by burning of fossil fuels — the so-called **greenhouse effect.** Carbon dioxide dissolves in water to form carbonic acid, salts of which are the hydrogen carbonates (bicarbonates) and the carbonates, Section 25–4. The calcium and magnesium carbonate deposits mentioned earlier are abundant in areas formerly covered by bodies of water, having been formed by the neutralization of basic oxides by the carbonic acid formed when CO_2 dissolves in water.

Even though carbon can form four **tetrahalides** (Section 25–5), only carbon tetrachloride, CCl_4, is commercially important. Many of its former uses are now discouraged or prohibited because of its toxicity and high vapor pressure and the toxicity of its combustion product, phosgene.

Silicon is the second most abundant element in the earth's crust, occurring in vast quantities in **silica** and the **silicate minerals.** It does not occur free in nature. Pure silicon has a structure like that of diamond, but it is less dense and less hard than diamond. Uses of elemental silicon (Section 25–6) include semiconductors, transistors, solar cells, additives to steel and aluminum alloys, and as the source of silicon in silicone polymers. Even though silicon is in the same group as carbon, it has quite different chemical properties because of (1) its inability to form double bonds, (2) its tendency not to form Si—Si bonds under most circumstances, and (3) the availability of $3d$ orbitals for bonding (Section 25–7). Silicon is not a very reactive element, reacting with the more active metals to form silicides, with halogens to form tetrahalides, and with a mixture of nitric and hydrofluoric acids.

The preparations and properties of the silicon halides are discussed in Section 25–8. All hydrolyze completely to produce silicon dioxide and silicic acids.

The only important oxide of silicon is silicon dioxide (silica), Section 25–9. However, unlike carbon dioxide, which is a gaseous molecular substance, silicon dioxide is a polymeric substance, occurring as a solid at room temperature. The structures of the two familiar natural forms of silicon dioxide, quartz and flint, are described in this section. The very slow reaction of strong bases of silica to form **metal silicates,** Section 25–10, is the basis for the discussion in Section 25–11 of the **natural silicates.** These include a large variety of compounds, all having SiO_4 tetrahedra linked into chains, sheets, or three-dimensional networks, but with metal ions occupying spaces between the tetrahedra. These silicate minerals can adopt a wide variety of structural arrangements, summarized in Table 25–1. Section 25–11 also includes a brief discussion of the formation of **glass** and the dependence of its properties on other elements that may be present with the silicates. Section 25–12 describes the constitution of the **silicones,** an important class of polymers whose various uses depend on their pliability and relative chemical inertness.

The discussion of boron begins with a description of the occurrence of the element, primarily in the form of the minerals borax and kernite (Section 25–13). Boric oxide, B_2O_3, is the anhydride of three common boric acids, as discussed in Section 25–14. Elemental boron (Section 25–15) exists in several different allotropic modifications, all consisting of very complex clusters of boron atoms in geometrically regular arrangements. The bonding in these boron "cages" is quite unusual. The covalent bonds you have seen for all other elements involve the sharing of two electrons between two atoms. Boron is one of the few elements able to share two electrons over three atoms by the appropriate overlap of orbitals, giving rise to the **three-center two-electron bond,** described in Section 25–16. All of the allotropic forms of boron, as well as the **boron hydrides** or **boranes** (Sections 25–17 and 25–18) involve both this type of bonding and the more familiar type in which the electron pair is shared between only two atoms. Some of the three-center two-electron bonds in the boranes involve three boron atoms and some involve two boron atoms and one hydrogen atom. The more complex boranes, of which there are many, also have polyhedral structures. These boranes can react by hydrolysis with halogens or halides to give halogenated boranes and with some reducing agents to give the borohydride anions, e.g., BH_4^-.

The **boron trihalides,** Section 25–19, all four of which are known, are covalent molecular substances. Since boron does not satisfy the octet rule in these compounds, it is not surprising that their principal reactivity is as Lewis acids.

Study Goals

These goals will help you to focus on the most important features of this chapter. Use them to help organize your class notes, reading, and study.

1. Know the general chemical properties of carbon and the electronic reasons for these properties. Describe and distinguish among graphite, diamond, coal, and coke. (Sections 25–1 and 25–2; Exercises 1 through 4, 6, and 10)
2. Write equations for the reactions of carbon with (a) oxygen, (b) metal oxides, (c) nonmetal oxides, and (d) steam. Know some uses of these reactions and their products. (Section 25–2; Exercises 5 and 7)
3. Compare the structures, properties, and typical reactions of carbon monoxide and carbon dioxide. (Section 25–3; Exercises 11 through 13 and 17)
4. Describe the importance of carbon dioxide. Describe its role in the greenhouse effect. (Section 25–3)
5. Give equations showing the preparation and reactions of carbonic acid and of bicarbonate and carbonate salts. (Section 25–4; Exercises 8, 14, 15, and 18)
6. Know the preparations and some uses of carbon tetrachloride. (Section 25–5; Exercises 9 and 16)
7. Describe the physical properties, production (with equations), and uses of silicon. Know some reactions of the free element. (Sections 25–6 and 25–7; Exercises 20 through 22 and 26)
8. Compare the structure of silicon dioxide (silica) with carbon dioxide. Understand reasons for differences in structures and properties. (Section 25–9; Exercises 19, 23, and 24)
9. Describe the natural silicates. (Sections 25–10 and 25–11)
10. Describe the general structures and properties of the silicone polymers. (Section 25–12; Exercise 25)
11. Describe the occurrence and uses of boron and its compounds. (Sections 25–13 through 25–15, 25–18, and 25–19; Exercises 27 through 30 and 33 through 36)
12. Describe two kinds of three-center two-electron bonds in boron and boron hydrides. Explain why boron enters into this kind of bonding. (Sections 25–16 and 25–17; Exercises 31 and 32)
13. Compare the properties of carbon, boron, and silicon, and those of their corresponding compounds (e.g., their oxides or their halides). This will involve a recognition of the principle of "diagonal similarity." Be able to account for the similarities and differences. (Chapter introduction; Sections 25–3, 25–9, and 25–14 regarding oxides; 25–5, 25–8, and 25–19 regarding halides, etc.; Exercise 2)

Some Important Terms in This Chapter

Write the meanings *in your own words*. Check the Key Terms list and the chapter reading. Then rewrite your definitions, still in your own words, to improve them. Study other new terms and review terms from preceding chapters if necessary.

diagonal similarity

catenation

hydrolysis

fossil fuels

combustion

greenhouse effect

three-center two-electron bond

Preliminary Test

Be sure to answer *many* of the additional textbook exercises, including those indicated in the Study Goals.

True-False

Mark each statement as true (T) or false (F).

_____ 1. Since it is in Group IVA, carbon can readily form ions with charge of either 4 − or 4 +.

_____ 2. Even though carbon and silicon are in the same group, silicon resembles boron more than it does carbon in many of its properties.

_____ 3. Carbon monoxide is a toxic gas that is especially dangerous because it is odorless.

_____ 4. Carbon dioxide is only slightly less poisonous than carbon monoxide.

_____ 5. Carbon monoxide acts as a poison by binding strongly to the oxygen-carrying protein in the blood, prohibiting this protein from carrying oxygen to the cells.

_____ 6. Carbon in the form of graphite is a fairly reactive substance at room temperature, but diamond reacts only at elevated temperatures.

_____ 7. When CO_2 dissolves in water, it all reacts to form carbonic acid.

_____ 8. Carbonic acid can act as a diprotic acid.

_____ 9. Because of its relatively low reactivity, most of the silicon in the earth's crust occurs in the native, or uncombined, form.

_____ 10. Like carbon dioxide, SiO_2 is a gas.

_____ 11. Because of the availability of d orbitals, silicon can form some stable species in which its coordination number exceeds four.

_____ 12. Silicon reacts with active metals to produce silicides, which are similar to carbides but somewhat more reactive.

_____ 13. Since it is in the same group as carbon, silicon forms silicon-halogen compounds analogous to those of carbon.

_____ 14. The silicon halides are much more reactive with water than are the carbon halides.

_____ 15. Silicones are a useful class of compounds because of their unusually high reactivity compared with other silicon compounds.

_____ 16. Elemental boron is diatomic.

_____ 17. Like the hydrocarbons, the boron hydrides consist of chains of boron atoms bonded to hydrogens.

_____ 18. Like the boron hydrides, the boron halides are polyhedral cage structures.

_____ 19. The boron halides can act as Lewis acids.

Short Answer

1. The usual, but arbitrary, distinction between "organic" and "inorganic" compounds of carbon is that the inorganic compounds contain only _____ and do not contain _____ _____.

2. In the earth's crust, carbon occurs mainly in the form of carbonates of the two elements _____ and _____.

3. The principal occurrence of carbon in the earth's atmosphere is in the form of the substance _____ (name, formula).

4. The two allotropic forms of the element carbon are called _____ and _____.

5. In graphite, each carbon atom is strongly covalently bonded to ___ other carbon atoms, and may be thought of as being _____ hybridized.

6. In diamond, each carbon atom is strongly covalently bonded to ___ other carbon atoms, and may be thought of as being _____ hybridized.

7. The ease with which the layers of carbon atoms of _____ slide over one another accounts for its utility as a lubricant.

8. The ability of graphite to conduct electricity is accounted for by its having electrons in _____.

9. The fossil material having a graphite-like framework in which some of the carbon atoms are bonded to hydrogen is called _____.

10. When coal is destructively distilled to release hydrocarbons, the residue of impure carbon that remains is called _____.

11. In all of its reactions, elemental carbon acts as a(n) _____ agent.

12. When elemental carbon reacts with metal oxides or nonmetal oxides of other elements, its reaction product is usually _____ (name, formula).

13. When elemental carbon reacts with oxygen, its reaction product can be either _____ (name, formula) or _____ depending on _____.

14. Silicon carbide has the same structure as _____, except that it contains alternating silicon and carbon atoms.

15. The equation for the "water gas" reaction, which accounts for much of the industrial production of _____ gas, is _____ _____.

16. When hydrocarbons are burned in the presence of sufficient oxygen, the two chemical products are _____ and _____.

17. The formula of carbonic acid is _____; its anhydride is _____ (name, formula).

18. When carbonic acid is neutralized by metal hydroxides or metal oxides, the salts that are formed contain the anion _____ (name, formula) or the anion _____ (name, formula).

19. The structure of the carbonate ion may be described as _____ , with all three O—C—O angles equal to _____ .

20. A compound, described in this chapter, that was formerly widely used in dry cleaning is _____ (name, formula).

21. The element that is second to oxygen in abundance in the earth's crust is _____ .

22. The much higher rate of hydrolysis of silicon tetrahalides than of carbon tetrahalides is believed to be due to _____ on silicon.

23. The general name for the binary compounds between boron and hydrogen is the _____ .

24. Some gems and semiprecious stones are crystals of the compound _____ in the form of _____, but containing colored impurities.

25. The reaction in which silica (often in the form of glass) is attacked by hydrofluoric acid is represented by the equation _____ .

26. The class of minerals in which aluminum atoms replace some silicon atoms in the silica structure is called _____ .

27. The glass used in bottles and window panes is a fused mixture of _____ (name, formula) and _____ (name, formula).

28. The formulas and names of the three common silicic acids are _____, _____, and _____ .

29. The names and formulas of the three common boric acids are _____, _____, and _____ .

30. In all of the common boric acids, the oxidation state of boron is ____ .

31. In all of the common silicic acids, the oxidation state of silicon is ____ .

32. In a type of bonding that is common for boron but relatively uncommon for many other elements, three boron atoms can bond by overlapping ____ (a number) orbitals and sharing in these overlapped orbitals ____ (a number) electrons; these bonds are referred to as _____ .

Multiple Choice

Select the one best answer for each question.

_____ 1. The climatic changes we refer to as the greenhouse effect are due to
   (a) the absorption of sunlight by atmospheric CO_2, which causes heat to get to the earth's surface.
   (b) the trapping of infrared radiation given off by the earth, which causes the atmospheric temperature to rise.
   (c) the trapping of heat from burning hydrocarbons, which causes the temperature to rise.

      (d) the destruction of the ozone layer, which lets more ultraviolet
light in and causes the temperature to rise.

      (e) the reflection of light by the particulate matter in the atmo-
sphere, which causes the climate to cool.

____ 2. Of the four tetrahalides of carbon, which is most important com-
mercially?

      (a) CF_4 (b) CCl_4 (c) CBr_4 (d) CI_4

____ 3. Which of the elements discussed in this chapter is obtained primar-
ily by mining in evaporated lake beds?

      (a) carbon   (b) silicon   (c) boron

____ 4. Which of the following is not a common use of silicon?

      (a) in alloys with aluminum

      (b) in alloys with iron

      (c) in semiconductors

      (d) in soldering and welding

      (e) in solar cells

____ 5. The silicon-containing substance that is used as a drying agent and
dehumidifier is

      (a) silica in the form of quartz.

      (b) aluminosilicate minerals.

      (c) silicones.

      (d) silica gel.

      (e) silicon tetrafluoride.

____ 6. Which of the following classes of silicon-containing compounds is
often used in the manufacture of plastics?

      (a) silicones

      (b) silica

      (c) silicic acid

      (d) silicon halides

      (e) silicates

Answers to Preliminary Test

True-False

1. False. It does not form ions with positive charges. Only in combination
with the most metallic elements can it form the carbide ion, C_2^{2-}, its only
simple negative ion.
2. True. This is an example of diagonal similarity.
3. True
4. False. Carbon dioxide is not poisonous.
5. True
6. False. Both allotropic forms are quite unreactive at room temperature.

7. False. Only a small percentage of the dissolved CO_2 forms carbonic acid (Section 25–4).
8. True
9. False. This element does not occur free in nature. About 87% of the silicon in the earth's crust is in the form of silica (SiO_2) or the silicate minerals.
10. False. It has a polymeric structure, occurring in several solid forms. SiO_2 does not exist as discrete molecules.
11. True. Not many such compounds actually form, one of the few stable specics being the hexafluorosilicate ion, SiF_6^{2-}.
12. True
13. True. However, the properties of these two classes of compounds differ markedly.
14. True. This is so because of the availability of d orbitals in silicon. See Section 25–8.
15. False. Most silicones are quite resistant toward chemical attack and thermal decomposition.
16. False. It exists in very complex polyhedral structures, in each of its several allotropic modifications. These are described in Section 25–15.
17. False. The boron hydrides (boranes) are nearly all cage or polyhedral structures, some of which are described in Section 25–17.
18. False. The boron halides have molecular structures.
19. True. This is their principal mode of reaction.

Short Answer

1. one carbon atom per formula unit, C—H bonds
2. calcium, magnesium
3. carbon dioxide (CO_2)
4. graphite, diamond
5. 3, sp^2
6. 4, sp^3
7. graphite
8. overlapping p orbitals. Read the first part of Section 25–1.
9. coal
10. coke
11. reducing
12. carbon monoxide (CO)
13. carbon monoxide (CO), carbon dioxide (CO_2), the relative amounts of carbon and oxygen present. Carbon dioxide is formed in excess oxygen.
14. diamond
15. carbon monoxide, $C + H_2O \rightarrow CO + H_2$. This reaction must be carried out at very high temperatures.

16. carbon dioxide, water
17. H_2CO_3, carbon dioxide (CO_2)
18. carbonate (CO_3^{2-}), bicarbonate (HCO_3^-)
19. planar, 120°
20. carbon tetrachloride, CCl_4
21. silicon
22. vacant outer d orbitals. These can accept an electron pair from an attacking water molecule. Carbon has no such d orbitals, so it reacts much more slowly. This difference is described in more detail in Section 25–8.
23. boron hydrides (or boranes)
24. SiO_2, quartz
25. $SiO_2 + HF \rightarrow 2H_2O + SiF_4$
26. aluminosilicates. These are described in Section 25–11, with a few examples. The main classes of aluminosilicate minerals are summarized in Table 25–1.
27. sodium silicate (Na_2SiO_3), calcium silicate ($CaSiO_3$). The chemistry of glass is somewhat complicated, but the major features are indicated in Section 25–11.
28. metasilicic acid (H_2SiO_3), orthosilicic acid (H_4SiO_4), pyrosilicic acid ($H_6Si_2O_7$). The last of these is also called disilicic acid.
29. orthoboric acid (H_3BO_3), metaboric acid (HBO_2), tetraboric acid ($H_2B_4O_7$). The first of these is usually just referred to as boric acid and the last of these is also called pyroboric acid.
30. +3
31. +4
32. 3, 2; three-center two-electron bonds

Multiple Choice

1. (b)
2. (b). However, most of the former uses of carbon tetrachloride are now discouraged or prohibited because of its toxicity. See Section 25–5.
3. (c)
4. (d)
5. (d). This is a spongy form of silica produced by partial dehydration of a silicic acid. See Section 25–10.
6. (a)

26

The Transition Metals

Chapter Summary

In Chapter 26, we undertake a survey of the major aspects of the properties and chemistry of the **transition metals.** Since there are so many of these elements and each has a quite varied chemistry, we will not study all of the elements in detail; that would (and does!) require several quite large volumes. Rather, we are concerned here with summarizing the major trends in properties of these elements. We will study in detail some of the compounds of only two of them, manganese and chromium. The major portion of the chapter covers the *d*-transition metals, the last section being devoted to the *f*-transition metals, or **rare earth metals.**

The general properties of the *d*-transition elements (usually called just the transition metals) are summarized in Section 26–1. These are the ten columns of elements located between Groups IIA and IIIA in the periodic table. The general properties enumerated here are the subject of discussion later in the chapter on the basis of electronic configurations. As you recall from Chapters 3 and 4, the electronic configurations of these elements (Section 26–2) all involve the filling of *d* orbitals one energy level below the highest occupied level; thus each element has a noble gas core of electrons, followed by one to ten electrons in the $(n-1)^{th}$ set of *d* orbitals and one or two electrons in the nth *s* orbital. That is, the transition metals in Period 4 are filling the 3*d* orbitals and are often called the 3*d*-transition metals, respectively. Because the energies of 4*d* and 5*d* are close to those of 5*s* and 6*s*, respectively, the electron configurations are somewhat harder to predict for these two series than for the 3*d*-transition metals. Remember the special stability of half-filled and filled sets of orbitals and the resulting apparent anomalies in the configurations of Cr and Cu.

When a group of elements has such a widely varied chemistry as do the transition elements, we need to organize the reactions or compounds of the elements in some way; as we have seen before, a very convenient organization is in terms of the **oxidation state** of the element. You should pay attention to the discussion in Section 26–5 with regard to the existence of several oxidation states for each transition metal and the relative reducing and oxidizing tendencies of the element in its various oxidation states. It will help you to remember that in its simple ions, each of the transition metals loses its outer s electrons (or sometimes electron, as in Cu^+), and often then loses one or more d electrons as well. It may also be helpful to observe that, for most odd-numbered groups, at least some of the most important oxidation states are odd, whereas for even groups, several of the principal oxidation states are even (though this is by no means an infallible rule but only a guide to your memory). As is very clear from Table 26–3, the tendency to form several different oxidation states is much higher near the middle of each series of transition metals than near the ends. Moving down within a group, higher oxidation states become more stable and common, which is an opposite trend from that observed among the representative elements. Other trends regarding correlations of acidity, basicity, and covalent character with oxidation state and with position in the group are parallel to those already seen for the representative elements.

One of the properties of the transition elements that distinguishes them from the representative elements is the common occurrence of **colors** in the transition-metal compounds, contrasted with the rarity of colored compounds of the representative metals. The origin of these colors, together with some typical examples, is discussed in Section 26–3. As is pointed out in Section 26–4, the classification of the transition metals into groups, identified with a Roman numeral and the suffix "B," is based primarily on the similarity in stoichiometry (composition by numbers of atoms) of compounds of these elements to those in the corresponding "A" group; the chemical properties are usually quite different. Be sure that you are familiar with the **triad** terminology used to identify the three sets of elements in Group VIIIB.

Some rough generalizations regarding the trends in several physical properties of the transition metals are discussed and rationalized in terms of trends in electronic configurations (Section 26–5). These trends are usually not as smooth with respect to position in the periodic table as is the case with the representative elements. The properties discussed in general terms in this section are **atomic radii, densities, magnetism, melting points,** and **oxidation states.** Do not be concerned with remembering individual values or details of properties here, but rather with understanding and remembering the trends. It will probably help you to notice that the trend in each of these properties, going across the transition metal series, involves either a maximum or a minimum of the property concerned.

As mentioned earlier, the chemistry of the transition metals is far too vast and varied to cover in detail in any one chapter. However, it is illustrative to look a little more closely at a few of these metals. The next two sections do this, going into some detail regarding the reactions and properties of the oxides and hydroxides of manganese (Section 26–6) and of chromium (Section 26–7). It can be seen from the discussion of these two sections that the variations of acidity of hydroxides of an element with oxidation states follow just the same trend as was seen for the representative elements. The hydroxides of transition metals in high oxidation states are acidic, with acidity increasing with oxidation state, just as was seen earlier for the representative nonmetals. For both manganese and chromium, the higher oxidation states are very powerful oxidizing agents; stability with respect to reduction for a given high oxidation state increases going down within either of the groups involved.

One of the most useful features of transition metal chemistry is the great tendency of these elements to effectively **catalyze** many reactions, both homogeneous and heterogeneous. Reactions typifying those catalyzed by transition metals or their ions appear in Section 26–8.

The remainder of the chapter is devoted to a brief survey of the rare earth metals–the lanthanides (4f-transition elements) and the actinides (5f-transition elements). Since all of these have two electrons in their outermost shell and either eight or nine in the next shell inward, differing from one another only in the second shell from the highest, these elements all are quite similar chemically and physically. All exhibit predominantly +3 oxidation state but can have other positive oxidation states. Because of their similarities in most chemical properties, the lanthanides and actinides are very difficult to separate by physical methods such as fractional crystallizations. All of the actinides are radioactive; this aspect of their behavior will be discussed in more detail in Chapter 28.

One of the most common chemical properties of the d-transition metals and their ions is their ability to function as Lewis acids, accepting one or more lone pairs from other atoms, ions, or groups to form coordinate covalent bonds. The resulting **coordination compounds** will be studied in Chapter 27.

Study Goals

1. Summarize the general properties of the d-transition metals. Explain why the properties of successive transition metals in one period vary less dramatically than those of representative metals. (Section 26–1; Exercises 1 through 3)

2. Write out the electronic configurations of the first row (Period 4) transition metals and their common ions. Explain why the Period 5 and Period 6 transition metals contain more exceptions to the expected, or Aufbau, electronic configurations than do the Period 4 metals. (Review Section 3–15; Section 26–2; Exercises 4 and 5)

3. Relate the degree of covalent and ionic character of transition metal compounds containing the same elements to the oxidation number of the metal. Do the same for acidic and basic properties of oxides and hydroxides of the same metal in different oxidation states. (Review Sections 4–12 and 11–8; Exercises 11 through 14, 23, and 27)

4. Explain why many compounds of the transition metals are colored. (Section 26–3; Exercise 6)

5. Summarize the significance and limitations of the Roman numeral designations of the subgroups of the transition metals in the periodic table. (Section 26–4; Exercises 7 through 9)

6. Describe and account for the trends in (a) atomic radii, (b) densities, (c) magnetic properties, and (d) melting points of the transition metals. (Section 26–5; Exercises 10 and 15 through 17)

7. Show how the properties and reactions of the oxides and hydroxides of manganese and chromium demonstrate the ideas of this chapter. Be familiar with the structures, properties, and reactions of compounds of manganese and chromium. (Sections 26–6 and 26–7; Exercises 14, 18, 21, 22, 24, and 25)

8. Give equations for reactions in which transition metals or their compounds act as catalysts. (Section 26–8; Exercise 19)

9. Summarize the general properties of the rare earths (f-transition metals). Explain why the properties of the f-transition metals vary even less than do those of the d-transition metals. (Unnumbered section "The Rare Earths")

10. Be able to apply calculations of earlier chapters to reactions of transition metals. (Review appropriate sections of Chapters 2, 8, 16, and 19; Exercises 20 through 22 and 26 through 29)

Some Important Terms in This Chapter

Write the meanings *in your own words*. Check the Key Terms list and the chapter reading. Then rewrite your definitions, still in your own words, to improve them. Study other new terms and review terms from preceding chapters if necessary.

transition metal

atomic radii

triad

oxidation state

acid anhydride

amphoterism

paramagnetism

ferromagnetism

catalyst

rare earth

lanthanide

actinide

Preliminary Test

True-False

Mark each statement as true (T) or false (F).

_____ 1. The transition metals are generally more reactive than the Group IA and IIA representative metals.

_____ 2. All of the d-transition metals discussed in this chapter are in B groups of the periodic table.

_____ 3. The ions and compounds of transition metals are often colored.

_____ 4. In terms of the numbers of atoms present, the compositions of compounds of the corresponding A- and B-group elements are often alike.

_____ 5. The chemical properties of compounds of the corresponding A- and B-group elements are often alike.

_____ 6. The rare earth elements vary more in their properties than do the d-transition elements.

_____ 7. The actinides are all radioactive.

_____ 8. The actinides are all artificially produced elements, prepared by nuclear reactions.

Short Answer

1. The first ionization energy of the $3d$-transition metals generally _____ going left to right across this series.

2. The electronic configuration of Ti (atomic number 22) is _____ _____.

3. The electronic configuration of V (atomic number 23) is _____ _____.

4. The electronic configuration of Cr (atomic number 24) is _____ _____.

5. The three elements of the iron triad are _____, _____, and _____.

6. The three elements of the palladium triad are _____, _____, and _____.

7. The three elements of the platinum triad are _____, _____, and _____.

8. The phenomenon in which the transition metals of the sixth period have nearly the same radii as the metals above them in the fifth period is known as the _____; it may be explained by the _____ by the 14 f-electrons that are one shell inside the set of d-orbitals being filled in the transition series.

9. Since many transition metals and metal ions have one or more unpaired electrons, they are _____ .

Each of the next ten questions, 10 through 19, is to be answered with words such as larger, smaller, higher, lower, more, less, fewer, and so on.

10. Among the transition metals in a given period, the atomic radii are generally _____ in the center of the period than at the two ends; the atomic radii are also _____ at the beginning than at the end of the transition metal series.

11. The densities of the metals in a transition series are generally _____ in the center of the series and are _____ at the beginning than at the end.

12. For the transition metal ions with a charge of 2+, the magnetic moment is _____ for ions with d^5 configuration than it is for ions with fewer d electrons; the magnetic moment is _____ for 2+ ions with d^5 than it is for ions with a larger number of d electrons.

13. Among the transition metals in a given period, the melting points are generally _____ in the center of the period than at the two ends.

14. Elements near the middle of a transition series generally exhibit a _____ number of oxidation states than those at the ends of the series; the highest oxidation state available to the metal is usually _____ for elements near the middle of the transition series than for those at the ends.

15. As we move down within a group of transition metals, the _____ oxidation states become more stable and more common.

16. As we move down within a group of transition metals, the ionic character of corresponding compounds becomes _____ for the metals in the same oxidation state.

17. As we increase the oxidation state of a transition metal in a series of its oxides or hydroxides, the acidity of the oxide or hydroxide becomes _____ .

18. For a given transition metal, as we increase the oxidation state, the oxidizing power of that species becomes _____ and the reducing power becomes _____ .

19. As we move down within a group of transition metals, the stability of the higher oxidation states becomes _____ .

20. The five common oxidation states of manganese are ___, ___, ___, ___, and ___.

21. An example of a compound in which manganese has an oxidation state of +4 is _____ .

22. An example of a compound in which manganese has an oxidation state of +7 is _____ .

23. The formula for manganic acid is _____ .

24. The formula for permanganic acid is _____ .

25. The name of the compound $MnSO_4$ is _____.
26. The three common oxidation states of chromium are ___, ___, and ___.
27. An example of a compound in which chromium has an oxidation number of $+2$ is _____.
28. An example of a compound in which chromium has an oxidation number of $+3$ is _____.
29. Two common ions in which chromium has an oxidation state of $+7$ are _____ and _____. (name and formula for each.)
30. Chromate and dichromate ions exist in a pH-dependent equilibrium in solution, for which the reaction equation is _____.
31. A common (but potentially hazardous) laboratory glassware cleaning solution is made by adding concentrated _____ to a concentrated aqueous solution of _____.
32. Two reactions that are typical of those catalyzed by transition metals or transition metal ions or compounds are _____ and _____.
33. Some transition metals that are quite unreactive are used as catalysts in finely divided form. Examples of such metals are _____, _____, and _____; such reactions are termed _____.
34. The two series of f-transition elements are collectively called the _____.
35. The $4f$-transition metals are often called the _____.
36. The $5f$-transition metals are often called the _____.
37. The lanthanides all appear in Period ___.
38. The most common oxidation state exhibited by the rare earth metals is ___.

Multiple Choice

1. Which of the following is not a general property of the transition elements?
   (a) They form many complex ions.
   (b) They often exhibit multiple oxidation states.
   (c) They are metals.
   (d) They form their most stable ions by attaining a noble gas configuration.
   (e) Their ions and compounds are often colored.
2. The colors exhibited by many transition metal ions and compounds are caused by
   (a) light absorption of wavelengths in the visible region of the spectrum.
   (b) light emission of wavelengths in the visible region of the spectrum.
   (c) inability to form positive ions.
   (d) the different color of electrons in a d-orbital from those in a p-orbital.
   (e) the large number of oxidation states available to these elements.

3. Which $3d$-transition element exhibits the largest number of oxidation states?
   (a) Mn   (b) Cr   (c) Fe   (d) Zn   (e) Ni
4. Which of the following is the strongest acid?
   (a) $Mn(OH)_2$ (b) $Mn(OH)_3$ (c) H_2MnO_3 (d) H_2MnO_4
   (e) $HMnO_4$
5. Which of the following oxides of manganese is the strongest oxidizing agent?
   (a) MnO   (b) Mn_2O_3 (c) MnO_2 (d) MnO_3 (e) Mn_2O_7

Answers to Preliminary Test

True-False

1. False
2. Truc
3. True
4. True
5. False
6. False. They are more similar. The rationale for this observation is presented in the last section of the chapter.
7. True
8. False. Many of them are, but some are naturally occurring, such as uranium.

Short Answer

1. increases. Can you rationalize this in terms of the progressions in the electronic configurations?
2. $[Ar] 3d^2 4s^2$
3. $[Ar] 3d^3 4s^2$
4. $[Ar] 3d^5 4s^1$. Remember that this irregularity in electronic configuration is due to the special stability of the d^5 configuration. Copper is an analogous exception to the usual order, as a result of the stable d^{10} configuration.
5. iron (Fe), cobalt (Co), nickel (Ni)
6. ruthenium (Ru), rhodium (Rh), palladium (Pd)
7. osmium (Os), iridium (Ir), platinum (Pt)
8. lanthanide contraction, poor shielding. See the discussion in the first part of Section 26-5.
9. paramagnetic. The relationship between unpaired electrons and paramagnetism, first discussed in Section 3-15, is a useful aid in determining electron configurations.
10. lower, higher. Look, for instance, at the values in each row of Table

26–6. This trend is illustrated graphically in Figure 26–1 in Section 26–5.

11. higher, lower. This is illustrated in Figure 26–2 and is discussed in the second part of Section 26–5.

12. higher, higher. Remember that once an atom or ion has more than five d electrons, it has fewer than five unpaired d electrons. That is, the maximum number of unpaired electrons that can be in a set of d orbitals is five. See Figure 26–3 for an illustration of the relation between magnetic moment and number of unpaired electrons, and examples of ionic species ranging from d^0 to d^{10}.

13. higher. This is related to the number of unpaired electrons available to be delocalized over the metallic lattice. A larger number of unpaired electrons results in stronger bonding in the metal lattice and higher melting points.

14. larger, higher. It will be very instructive for you to study Table 26–3 in some detail, looking for trends.

15. higher

16. greater. Another way of saying this is that the compounds become less covalent going down the group — but remember that this is for the metals in the same oxidation state.

17. greater. Again, this is the same trend as for the representative elements. Recall, for instance, that sulfuric acid, with S in the +6 oxidation state, is the strongest of the various oxyacids of sulfur. A similar comparison between the oxyacids of chlorine and manganese appears in Table 26–9.

18. stronger, weaker. This is shown in Table 26–3, and is discussed for manganese in Section 26–6 and for chromium in Section 26–7.

19. greater. This is opposite to the trend for the representative elements.

20. $+2, +3, +4, +6, +7$

21. Several examples were mentioned in the text in Section 26–6. Among these are MnO_2, H_2MnO_3 (unstable), and $CaMnO_3$.

22. Among the several examples appearing in Section 26–6 are Mn_2O_7 (quite unstable), $HMnO_4$, and the various permanganate salts such as $KMnO_4$.

23. H_2MnO_4

24. $HMnO_4$

25. manganese(II) sulfate

26. $+2, +3, +6$

27. Examples are encountered in Section 26–7 and some are listed in Table 26–9. Some of these are CrO, $Cr(OH)_2$, and various salts such as $CrCl_2$.

28. See Section 26–7. Examples are Cr_2O_3, $Cr(OH)_3$, various salts such as $CrCl_3$, and oxysalts such as $KCrO_2$.

29. chromate (CrO_4^{2-}), dichromate ($Cr_2O_7^{2-}$)

30. $2CrO_4^{2-} + 2H^+ \rightarrow Cr_2O_7^{2-} + H_2O$

31. H_2SO_4, $K_2Cr_2O_7$. Note the warning about the danger associated with the analogous manganese solutions, Section 26–7.

32. Six examples of such reactions are listed in Section 26–8 of the text. Refer to that section.
33. platinum, palladium, gold; heterogeneous
34. rare earth elements (or metals)
35. lanthanides
36. actinides
37. 6
38. +3

Multiple Choice

1. (d). Very few of the stable ions of transition metals have noble gas configurations. Can you find some that do?
2. (a)
3. (a)
4. (e). Remember that for a series of oxyacids (or oxides or hydroxides) of the same element, the acid strength increases with increasing oxidation number.
5. (e). This is such a strong oxidizing agent that it decomposes explosively. Remember that strengths of oxidizing agents increase with increasing oxidation number for the same element.

27

Coordination Compounds

Chapter Summary

Many compounds are formed by **coordinate covalent bond** formation, a process in which one of the atoms provides the pair of electrons to be shared, the other atom providing a vacant orbital. As we saw in Section 11–12, this process can be described in acid-base terms, using the Lewis acid-base theory. Transition metal ions have vacant d orbitals, as well as vacant s and p orbitals, so they can often act as Lewis acids, reacting by coordinate covalent bond formation with molecules or ions that have unshared electron pairs. The compounds or polyatomic ions thus formed are referred to as **coordination compounds, coordination complexes,** or **complex ions.** Some representative metal ions can also bond in this way—e.g., Al^{3+}, Sn^{2+}, Sn^{4+}—but even these often use d orbitals in their formation of coordination compounds. In Chapter 27, we shall study some aspects of the formation, nomenclature, structures, and properties of coordination compounds.

Section 27–1 is an introduction to this topic, with many examples illustrating the importance and some of the history of coordination chemistry. You might recall that the stability of these complexes with respect to dissociation is described by the value of K_d, the **equilibrium constant** for the dissociation reaction; you have already encountered and used this quantity in Section 18–6.3.

Several transition metals whose hydroxides are amphoteric can dissolve in an excess of strong soluble base. Ammonia, however, is such a weak base that it cannot dissolve most such amphoteric hydroxides by the usual method of formation of hydroxo complexes. Yet the hydroxides of some metals do dissolve in an excess of aqueous ammonia, by the formation of soluble **ammine complexes,** which are discussed in Section 27–2.

Several important terms in coordination chemistry are defined and illustrated in Section 27–3. A molecule or ion that acts as the Lewis base in complex formation is called a **ligand;** within a ligand, the atom that actually provides the electron pair is the **donor atom.** A ligand is termed **unidentate, bidentate,** and so on, to describe the number of different atoms that ligand can use as donor atoms simultaneously. The metal atom or ion and the ligands (but not any uncoordinated counter-ions) constitute the **coordination**

sphere. The **coordination number** is the number of donor atoms (not ligands) to which the metal is bonded. Study the examples in Tables 27 – 3 and 27 – 4, which illustrate the use of these terms.

Likewise, a knowledge of and careful adherence to the rules for *naming* coordination compounds (Section 27 – 4) along with much practice with examples and exercises, will enable you to write formulas from names and vice versa. Notice that the naming system frequently specifies the oxidation state of the metal. You will probably want to review the rules for assignment of oxidation numbers in polyatomic molecules and ions (Section 4 – 12). It will help you to remember that the sum of the oxidation numbers of atoms in a neutral molecule (or now also a neutral ligand) is equal to *zero* and that the sum of the oxidation numbers of the atoms in a polyatomic ion (or in an ion acting as a ligand) is equal to the *charge* on that ion.

Once we know the coordination number of the metal in a coordination compound, we can use the **VSEPR theory** (do you recall what these letters mean? — see Section 5 – 8) to predict the arrangement of donor atoms in the coordination sphere — the structure of the complex. You may wish to review how the VSEPR theory is applied (Sections 5 – 10 through 5 – 17) before you study Section 27 – 5, which deals with the structures of coordination compounds. The heart of this discussion is Table 27 – 5, which is quite similar to Table 5 – 4 in the earlier applications of VSEPR theory. Please notice, though, that in coordination chemistry there may be different structures possible for some coordination numbers, especially 4 (tetrahedral or square planar) and 5 (trigonal bipyramidal or square pyramidal). Each of the different geometries around the metal ion corresponds, of course, to a different set of hybrid orbitals. One other trivial but common point of confusion for some students involves the way structural formulas of coordination compounds are represented. Look, for instance, at the representation of the hexachlorostannate(IV) ion, at the beginning of Section 27 – 1. The lines linking one Cl^- ligand to another are not bonds, but are drawn merely to help visualize the shape of the coordination sphere and the arrangement of the ligands; however, the lines drawn from each Cl^- to the tin(IV) ion are bonds (coordinate covalent bonds). Similar comments apply to the common representations of square planar, trigonal bipyramidal, and square pyramidal structures.

The next portion of the chapter, consisting of Sections 27 – 6 and 27 – 7, deals with the existence of **isomers,** which are substances having the same number and kinds of atoms, but arranged differently. There are several ways in which the atoms can differ in their arrangements, so several different kinds of isomers can exist. These are broadly classified into two major categories: (1) **structural isomers,** involving differences in the bonding arrangement of different donor atoms on the same ligand or differences in bonding beyond a single coordination sphere and (2) **stereoisomers,** involving only one coordination sphere and the same ligands and donor atoms. Section 27 – 6 breaks the topic of structural isomers into four subclasses—**ionization isomers, hydrate isomers, coordination isomers,** and **linkage isomers**—with several examples of each. The two subclasses of stereoisomers, known as **geometrical isomers** and **optical isomers** (or **enantiomers**) are described in Section 27–6. The following distinctions between structural isomers and stereoisomers may be helpful to you in recognizing the broad categories. In structural isomers, the pattern or order of bonds is different, so you should be able to find at least one atom that is bonded to different atoms in the isomers. (Notice how the rules already given for naming compounds serve to distinguish among various structural isomers.) In stereoisomers, on the other hand, the order of bond linkages is the same, but the spatial arrangements of the atoms are different; if this is due to the atoms being linked in different relative positions on the central metal atom, the isomers are geometrical isomers, and if it is due only to the "handedness" of the entire arrangement, they are optical isomers. As you will find out when studying stereoisomerism, additional terms are used to describe such isomers, so be sure you understand and can use properly such terms as **cis, trans, dextro, levo,** and **racemic.**

The remainder of the chapter is concerned with the bonding in coordination compounds. Two ways of describing this bonding, the **Valence Bond theory** and the **Crystal Field theory,** are discussed here, with each applied to cases of coordination number 6 and coordination number 4. The Valence Bond theory assumes that the bonding is entirely covalent and discusses this bonding in terms of **hybrid orbitals,** just as was done in Chapter 5 for other types of compounds. The Crystal Field theory, on the other hand, takes the view that the bonding is entirely (or at least predominantly) ionic and that the d orbitals of the metal, which in an isolated ion would be at the same energy, have their energies disturbed (**degeneracy** is removed) by the presence of the ligands. The amount by which these energies change, called the **crystal field splitting,** depends on the nature and arrangement of the ligands. As you study these two theories in detail, in Sections 27–8 and 27–9, you should be aware that each of them has its advantages and disadvantages, but that both are intended to lead to the same result—an understanding of how the electrons are arranged in complexes. It would be good for you to pay special attention to the complexes that are discussed from both points of view, such as the octahedral $[CoF_6]^{3-}$ and $[Co(NH_3)_6]^{3+}$ ions. Notice that the magnetic nature of the complex, that is, whether it is diamagnetic or paramagnetic (and the degree of paramagnetism), is often used to aid in proposing or verifying the bonding description for that complex. As you study these sections, you will need to become familiar with the meaning of such terms as e_g, t_{2g}, **inner orbital complex, outer orbital complex,** the difference between d^2sp^3 and sp^3d^2 hybrid orbitals, **crystal field splitting, low spin complex, high spin complex,** Δ_{oct}, and Δ_{tet}.

The great variety of *colors* exhibited by transition metal coordination compounds can be interpreted in terms of the Crystal Field theory, as in Section 27–10. According to this interpretation, the different crystal field strengths of various ligands cause different e_g vs. t_{2g} splitting. Thus, in order to promote an electron from one d orbital to another, the various complexes must absorb light of different energy, that is, a different color. The common ligands have been ranked in order of increasing crystal field strength, based on a study of the colors of light that they absorb. This ordered list of ligands is called the **spectrochemical series.**

The great stability of octahedral coordination complexes of the transition metals compared with the free metal ions can be accounted for quantitatively by considering the energies of the e_g and t_{2g} orbitals when they are occupied in the complex compared with those of the unperturbed d orbitals in the free metal ion. This **crystal field stabilization energy (CFSE)** is discussed in Section 27 – 11.

Study Goals

It may help you to write out a brief summary of the ideas of each study goal, summarizing the applicable portions of your class notes and text readings. Be sure to answer many of the suggested questions related to the study goals.

1. Account for the tendency of the d-transition metals to form coordination compounds. (Section 27 – 1; Exercise 1)
2. Describe the experiments and reasoning of Werner that allowed him to determine which species of a complex were in the metal's coordination sphere, and therefore, what were the true formulas for coordination compounds. (Section 27 – 1; Exercises 2 and 3)
3. Write equations that account for the solubility of water-insoluble hydroxides in aqueous ammonia. (Section 27 – 2; Exercises 10 through 13)
4. Distinguish among the terms ligand, donor atom, polydentate, unidentate, chelate complex, coordination number, and coordination sphere. (Section 27 – 3; Exercises 4 and 5)
5. Know the names and formulas of common ligands as well as their donor atoms. (Section 27 – 4)
6. Know the general IUPAC rules for naming coordination compounds. Name coordination compounds if given their formulas, and supply formulas if given names. (Section 27 – 4; Exercises 6 through 9)
7. Sketch structures of coordination compounds of the types ML_2, ML_4 (square planar and tetrahedral), ML_5 (trigonal bipyramidal and square pyramidal), and ML_6, and give hybridizations of the metal in each case. (Sections 27 – 5 and 27 – 8; Exercises 14 and 15)
8. Distinguish between structural isomers and stereoisomers. (Sections 27 – 6 and 27 – 7; Exercise 16)
9. Describe and give examples of the following kinds of isomers: (a) ioniza-

tion, (b) hydrate, (c) coordination, (d) linkage, (e) geometric, and (f) optical. Name the isomers, using appropriate prefixes where necessary. (Sections 27–6 and 27–7; Exercises 16 through 25)

10. Describe and relate the following: (a) dextro and levo isomers, (b) racemic mixture, (c) plane polarized light, (d) polarimeter, and (e) optical activity. (Section 27–7; Exercises 17 and 23 through 25)

11. Given the name and formula of an octahedral coordination compound and information regarding its magnetic properties, predict and sketch the shape of the complex molecule or ion, draw electron diagrams to show the hybridization at the metal, and designate it as an "inner orbital" or and "outer orbital" complex. (Section 27–8; Exercises 26 through 31)

12. Draw and distinguish between the t_{2g} and e_g sets of orbitals. (Section 27–9)

13. Describe with words and diagrams the Crystal Field Theory as it applies to octahedral and tetrahedral coordination compounds. Explain the reversal in relative energies of t_{2g} and e_g orbitals for the two cases. (Section 27–9; Exercises 32 and 33)

14. Distinguish between and give examples of low spin and high spin complexes. Explain the relationship between electron pairing energy and Δ_{oct} with respect to these kinds of complexes. (Section 27–9; Exercises 34, 37, and 38)

15. Rationalize the relative energies of a set of d orbitals of a metal at the center of a square planar complex. (Section 27–9)

16. Describe what is meant by the terms "strong field ligand" and "weak field ligand." Describe the spectrochemical series and its relationship to the colors of coordination compounds. (Sections 27–9, and 27–10; Exercises 34 through 36)

17. Describe and explain the significance of crystal field stabilization energy (CFSE). (Section 27–11; Exercises 37 and 38)

18. Know how to apply the equilibrium concepts of Chapters 15 through 18 to coordination compounds. (Review Section 18–6.3; Exercises 39 through 41)

Some Important Terms in This Chapter

Write the meanings *in your own words*. Check the Key Terms list and the chapter reading. Then rewrite your definitions, still in your own words, to improve them. Study other new terms and review terms from preceding chapters if necessary.

coordinate covalent bond

coordination compound or complex

ligand

donor atom

coordination number

coordination sphere

structural isomers

stereoisomers

ionization isomers

hydrate isomers

coordination isomers

linkage isomers

geometrical isomers

optical isomers

inner orbital complex

outer orbital complex

t_{2g} orbitals

e_g orbitals

Valence Bond theory

Crystal Field theory

weak field ligand

strong field ligand

spectrochemical series

low spin complex

high spin complex

Preliminary Test

True-False

Mark each statement as true (T) or false (F).

_____ 1. The higher the value of K_d for a complex, the more stable the complex is.

_____ 2. The properties of transition metal ions that enable them to form coordination complexes are their magnetism and their colors.

_____ 3. Whenever a metal is bonded to four donor atoms in a coordination complex, the coordination geometry must be tetrahedral, so sp^3 hybrid orbitals of the metal are used.

_____ 4. Even though the atoms are arranged differently in geometric isomers, the properties of these compounds are alike.

_____ 5. When we say that a substance is exhibiting optical activity, we mean that it is colored.

_____ 6. Ligands must be neutral molecules.

_____ 7. Coordination complexes in which the metal uses d^2sp^3 hybrid orbitals have octahedral coordination geometry.

_____ 8. The disadvantage of the Crystal Field theory is that it can be applied only to complexes when they occur in crystals.

_____ 9. In an isolated metal atom or ion, the five d orbitals with the same principal quantum number all have the same energy.

_____ 10. When a metal atom or ion is bonded to several ligands, the five metal d orbitals with the same principal quantum number all have the same energy.

_____ 11. The ion Fe^{3+} is referred to as a d^5 ion.

_____ 12. Most four-coordinate transition metal complexes have tetrahedral arrangements of the donor atoms around the metal ion.

_____ 13. In the Crystal Field theory description of coordination compounds, ligands that are more electronegative lead to smaller crystal field splitting.

_____ 14. All octahedral complexes of metal ions with d^5 configuration are low spin complexes.

Short Answer

1. A molecule or ion that provides an electron pair for coordinate covalent bond formation is called a Lewis _____; a molecule or atom that accepts the electron pair is called a Lewis _____.

2. The name of the chemist who was responsible for much of the early development of the ideas of coordination chemistry was _____ _____.

3. The molecules or ions that act as Lewis bases in the formation of coordination compounds are called _____.

4. Ligands that can bond through only one donor atom at a time are called _____.

5. Ligands that can bond through two or more donor atoms simultaneously are called _____.

6. A molecule or ion that acts as a ligand in a coordination complex usually has at least one _____.

7. The portion of a compound consisting of the metal ion and its coordinated ligands, but no uncoordinated counter-ions, is called the _____ _____.

8. A ligand that can bond through three donor atoms simultaneously is called _____.

9. When a metal has a coordination number of 2 in a complex, the coordination geometry is _____ and the hybrid orbitals are of the _____ type.

10. When a metal has a coordination number of 4 in a complex, the coordination geometry could be _____ (using ____ hybrid orbitals), or it could be _____ (using _____ hybrid orbitals).

For each of the next fifteen questions, 11 through 25, provide either the formula or the name of the ligand, as required, and classify each ligand as unidentate, bidentate, and so on. When a ligand name is required, be sure that you name it as a ligand, and not as a free molecule or ion. Dot formulas are not required.

Formula	Name	Classification (unidentate, bidentate, etc.)
11. NH_3	_____	_____
12. _____	cyano	_____
13. _____	chloro	_____
14. $H_2N—CH_2—CH_2—NH_2$	_____	_____
15. _____	diethylenetriamine (dien)	_____
16. PH_3	_____	_____
17. _____	carbonyl	_____
18. Br^-	_____	_____
19. SO_4^{2-}	_____	_____
20. _____	oxo	_____
21. _____	hydroxo	_____
22. $O_2C—CO_2^{2-}$	_____	_____
23. OH_2	_____	_____
24. NO_2^- (bonded through the nitrogen)	_____	_____
25. _____	nitrato	_____

26. The two mirror image forms of a molecule are called _____ of one another; one is identified by the term _____, while the other is called _____.

27. The number of geometrical isomers possible for the square planar metal complex with formula MX_2Y_2 is ____. (Note: M is the metal and X and Y are each unidentate ligands.)

28. The number of geometrical isomers possible for the tetrahedral metal complex MX_2Y_2 is ____. (The symbols have the same meaning as in Question 27.)

See instructions at top of p. 405.

Formula	Name	Ox. State of Metal	Coord. No. of Metal
29. $[Cu(en)Br_2]$			
30.	hexamminecobalt(III) ion		
31.	hexacyanocobaltate(III) ion		
32. $[Fe(CO)_5]$			
33. $[CuCl_5]^{3-}$			
34.	cis-diamminedichloroplatinum(II)		
35.	trans-diamminedichloroplatinum(II)		
36. $[Cr(OH_2)_2Br_2(NH_3)_2]^+$			
37.	cis-diaquotetraamminecobalt(III)ion		
38.	trans-diaquotetraamminecobalt(III) ion		
39.	tetraamminedichloroplatinum(IV) chloride		
40.	triamminetrichloroplatinum(IV) chloride		

For each of the preceding twelve questions, 29 through 40, use the preceding table and provide either the formula or the name of the complex, as required. For each complex, give the oxidation state (Ox. State) of the metal and the coordination number (Coord. No.) of the metal. In naming the compounds, do not worry about stereoisomerism, unless sufficient information is explicitly shown.

41. The name of the complex ion $[AlCl_6]^{3-}$ is _____;
    in this complex, the oxidation number of aluminum is ____.
42. The names of the two general theories of bonding in coordination compounds that are discussed in this chapter are the _____ _____ theory and the _____ theory.
43. An octahedral complex in which the d orbitals involved in the formation of hybrid orbitals are in one lower principal quantum shell than the s and p orbitals (e.g., $3d$, $4s$, $4p$) is called a(n) _____ complex; the hybrid orbitals are designated as _____.
44. An octahedral complex in which the d orbitals involved in the formation of hybrid orbitals are in the same principal quantum shell as the s and p orbitals (e.g., $4s$, $4p$, $4d$) is called a(n) _____ complex; the hybrid orbitals are designated as _____.
45. An experiment that is often used to distinguish between inner and outer orbital complexes is to determine the extent to which the complex is _____.

46. According to the Crystal Field theory, the five originally equivalent d orbitals on a metal become nonequivalent under the influence of the array of ligands. If there are six ligands in an octahedral arrangement, these d orbitals then occur in two groups; the two groups are called, collectively, the _____ orbitals (a set of three orbitals) and the _____ orbitals (a set of two orbitals). For this octahedral arrangement of ligands, the _____ set is at lower energy, with the two sets being separated by an amount of energy called _____.
47. According to the Crystal Field theory, the crystal field splitting is larger for ligands that are more able to _____ into vacant metal orbitals; for octahedral complexes, this is expressed quantitatively as a _____ value of Δ_{oct}.
48. If there are four ligands in a tetrahedral arrangement, the metal d orbitals are split into two groups; in the Crystal Field description, the two groups are called, collectively, the _____ orbitals (a set of three orbitals) and the _____ orbitals (a set of two orbitals). For this tetrahedral arrangement of ligands, the _____ set is at lower energy, with the two sets being separated by an amount of energy called _____.
49. Low spin octahedral complexes exist only for metal ions with configurations ____, ____, ____, and ____.
50. The only B group metals commonly involved in tetrahedral complexes

are ——————, ——————, and —————— in their +2 oxidation states; in these complexes, the metal hybridization is ——.

51. The elements whose hydroxides dissolve in excess aqueous ammonia by the formation of soluble ammine complexes are the metals of the ——————, ——————, ——————, and —————— families.

52. According to the Crystal Field description of bonding, the color that an octahedral complex of a particular metal exhibits depends on the value of ——, which in turn depends on the —————————————— of the ligands.

53. The ranking of a set of ligands according to increasing crystal field strength, as determined by the study of the colors of several of their complexes, is called the ——————————————————.

54. For a metal ion in an octahedral field, the energy of each t_{2g} orbital is lowered by an amount equal to ——————, while each e_g orbital is raised by an amount equal to ——————.

55. For a metal in an octahedral field, the change in total energy of the system that has the number N electrons in the t_{2g} orbitals and the number M electrons in the e_g orbitals is given by the expression ————————————; this energy is called the —————————————— ——————————.

Multiple Choice

——— 1. What is the coordination number of cobalt in $[Co(NH_3)_6]^{3+}$?
(a) 2   (b) 3   (c) 4   (d) 6   (e) 9

——— 2. What is the coordination number of cobalt in $[Co(NH_3)_6]Cl_3$?
(a) 2   (b) 3   (c) 4   (d) 6   (e) 9

——— 3. What is the oxidation number of cobalt in $[Co(NH_3)_6]^{3+}$?
(a) 0   (b) +2   (c) +3   (d) +4   (e) +6

——— 4. What is the coordination number of cobalt in $[Co(en)_2Cl_2]^+$?
(a) 2   (b) 3   (c) 4   (d) 6   (e) 9

——— 5. Which of the following types of isomers is not an example of structural isomerism?
(a) ionization isomers   (b) optical isomers
(c) hydrate isomers   (d) coordination isomers
(e) linkage isomers

——— 6. What is the number of geometrical isomers possible for the complex $[Pt(NH_3)_2Cl_4]$?
(a) 1   (b) 2   (c) 3   (d) 4   (e) 6

——— 7. What is the number of geometrical isomers possible for the complex $[Pt(NH_3)_3Cl_3]$?
(a) 1   (b) 2   (c) 3   (d) 4   (e) 6

_____ 8. Which of the following is correctly referred to as a d^8 ion?
(a) Ti^{3+} (b) Ru^{3+} (c) Ni^{2+} (d) Ag^+ (e) Cr^{3+}

Answers to Preliminary Test

Do not just look up answers. Think about the reasons for the answers.

True-False

1. False. Remember that K_d is the equilibrium constant for the *dissociation* of the complex. A higher value for K_d means that the numerator (product concentration) is higher, which would correspond to *less* stable complexes. Section 18–6.3 discusses these dissociation constants in quantitative terms.
2. False. They form complexcs so readily because of the availability of vacant d orbitals. Properties such as magnetism and color are a result of the bonding in the complexes, not a cause of that bonding.
3. False. Many tetracoordinate metal atoms use dsp^2 or sp^2d hybrid orbitals and form square planar complexes. The differences are discussed in detail in the second part of Section 27–8, in terms of the Valence Bond theory.
4. False. A different arrangement of atoms gives different properties. Many examples of this are given in the text chapter, especially regarding the color of the complex.
5. False. Read the second part of Section 27–7.
6. False. Many common ligands are anions, and very few are cations.
7. True
8. False. The term "crystal field" has to do with the symmetry of the arrangements of the ligands and the resulting effects on symmetry of the metal orbitals. Similar symmetry arrangements frequently occur in crystals.
9. True
10. False. In the terminology of the Crystal Field theory, the degeneracy is removed by the arrangement of the ligands around the metal; in the terminology of the Valence Bond theory, some of the d orbitals become involved, along with s and p orbitals, in the formation of hybrid orbitals.
11. True. Fe^0 has the outer electronic configuration $4s^2 3d^6$; on formation of the Fe^{3+} ion, iron has configuration $4s^0 3d^5$.
12. False. See the second part of Section 27–8. Most four-coordinate transition metal complexes are square planar with dsp^2 hybridization. Do you recall which metals commonly form tetrahedral complexes?

13. True. See the discussion of $[Co(NH_3)_6]^{3+}$ versus $[CoF_6]^{3-}$ in the first part of Section 27–9.
14. False. They can be either high spin or low spin, depending on the nature of the ligands. See the first part of Section 27–8.

Short Answer

1. base, acid. Review Sections 11–12 and 27–1.
2. Alfred Werner. In fact, for many years coordination complexes were commonly called Werner complexes. The amminechloroplatinum complexes described in Section 27–1 are now often referred to as Werner complexes.
3. ligands
4. unidentate
5. polydentate
6. unshared pair of electrons
7. coordination sphere
8. tridentate
9. linear, sp
10. tetrahedral, sp^3, square planar, dsp^2 or sp^2d
11. ammine, unidentate
12. CN^- (with the carbon acting as the donor atom), unidentate
13. Cl^-, unidentate
14. ethylenediamine (or en), bidentate
15. $NH_2-CH_2-CH_2-\underset{\underset{H}{|}}{N}-CH_2-CH_2-NH_2$, tridentate

16. phosphino, unidentate
17. CO (with carbon as the donor atom), unidentate
18. bromo, unidentate
19. sulfato, unidentate
20. O^{2-}, unidentate or bidentate
21. OH^-, unidentate
22. oxalato, bidentate
23. aqua, unidentate
24. nitro, unidentate
25. NO_3^- (bonded through an oxygen), unidentate
26. optical isomers (or enantiomers), dextro, levo
27. 2
28. 1. No matter how you arrange the ligands, the two X ligands will be adjacent, as will be the two Y ligands.
29. dibromoethylenediaminecopper(II), $+2$, 4
30. $[Co(NH_3)_6]^{3+}$, $+3$, 6
31. $[Co(CN)_6]^{3-}$, $+3$, 6
32. pentacarbonyliron(0), 0, 5

33. pentachlorocuprate(II) ion, $+2$, 5. Note the use of the "-ate" ending when the total complex ion has a negative charge.

34.

$$\text{H}_3\text{N}\!-\!\!-\!\!-\text{Cl}$$
$$\text{Pt}$$
$$\text{H}_3\text{N}\!-\!\!-\!\!-\text{Cl} \qquad +2, 4$$

35.

$$\text{H}_3\text{N}\!-\!\!-\!\!-\text{Cl}$$
$$\text{Pt}$$
$$\text{Cl}\!-\!\!-\!\!-\text{NH}_3 \qquad +2, 4$$

36. Diamminediaquadibromochromium(III) ion, $+3$, 6. Notice the application of the rule about alphabetizing ligand names. There is no particular convention about the order in which the ligands are shown in the formula.

37.

$$\left[\begin{array}{c} \text{NH}_3 \\ \text{H}_3\text{N} -\!\!|-\!\!-\!\!-\text{OH}_2 \\ \text{Co} \\ \text{H}_3\text{N}-\!\!-\!\!-\!\!\text{OH}_2 \\ \text{NH}_3 \end{array} \right]^{3+} \quad , +3, 6$$

38.

$$\left[\begin{array}{c} \text{OH}_2 \\ \text{H}_3\text{N} -\!\!|-\!\!-\!\!-\text{NH}_3 \\ \text{Co} \\ \text{H}_3\text{N}-\!\!-\!\!-\!\!\text{NH}_3 \\ \text{OH}_2 \end{array} \right]^{3+} \quad , +3, 6$$

39. $[\text{Pt}(\text{NH}_3)_4\text{Cl}_2]\text{Cl}_2$, $+4$, 6
40. $[\text{Pt}(\text{NH}_3)_3\text{Cl}_3]\text{Cl}$, $+4$, 6
41. hexachloroaluminate ion, $+3$. Note that the "-ate" ending is added because the complex ion is negatively charged. We do not specify the oxidation number of aluminum by including (III) in the name, since this is the only oxidation state that aluminum ever has in compounds.
42. Valence Bond, Crystal Field
43. inner orbital, d^2sp^3
44. outer orbital, sp^3d^2
45. paramagnetic
46. t_{2g}, e_g, t_{2g}, Δ_{oct}
47. donate electrons, larger

48. t_{2g}, e_g, e_g, Δ_{tet}
49. d^4, d^5, d^6, d^7
50. zinc, cadmium, mercury, sp^3
51. cobalt, nickel, copper, zinc
52. Δ_{oct}, crystal field strength. This is discussed in some detail in Section 27–10.
53. spectrochemical series
54. $2/5\Delta_{oct}$, $3/5\Delta_{oct}$
55. $N(-2/5\Delta_{oct}) + M(3/5\Delta_{oct})$, crystal field stabilization energy (or CFSE)

Multiple Choice

1. (d)
2. (d). Remember that the coordination sphere is enclosed in the square brackets so that the chloride ions are not bonded to cobalt. Only the nitrogen atoms of the six ammonia molecules (ammine ligands) are bonded to cobalt. This contains the complex ion in Question 1.
3. (c). Each ammine ligand (neutral) has total oxidation number equal to zero. The sum of oxidation numbers in a polyatomic ion must be equal to the charge on the ion, so cobalt must be in an oxidation state of $+3$.
4. (d). Each (en) ligand is bidentate, containing two donor atoms.
5. (b)
6. (b). These are the *cis* and the *trans* isomers.
7. (b)
8. (c). Remember that the two *s* electrons are lost first when transition metal atoms form ions, after which some *d* electrons may be lost also.

28

Nuclear Chemistry

Chapter Summary

We now turn our attention from chemical reactions, in which elements maintain their identity and interact only through electronic changes, to the new topic of nuclear reactions, in which elements are often converted from one to another by alterations in their nuclei. This area of chemistry, called **nuclear chemistry,** is the subject of Chapter 28. As a basis for this study, read the introduction to the chapter, paying close attention to the differences cited between nuclear reactions and ordinary chemical reactions. In this introduction, a preliminary mention is also made of two important types of nuclear reactions, **nuclear fission** and **nuclear fusion,** both of which will be discussed more fully later in the chapter.

Section 28–1 summarizes, in general terms, the main properties of atomic nuclei. Nuclear reactions depend on nuclear instability, which in turn is found to be related to the ratio of number of neutrons to number of protons in the nucleus. This relationship is explained in Section 28–2. As you can see, the most stable **nuclides** are those with an even number of protons and an even number of neutrons; the least common stable nuclides are those with odd numbers of each kind of nuclear particle. (These nuclear particles, the neutrons and protons, are collectively called nucleons.) Nuclides having either a number of protons or a number of neutrons (or a sum of the two) equal to one of the so-called **magic numbers**—2, 8, 20, 28, 50, 82, or 126—are exceptionally stable.

The decay or decomposition of unstable nuclei is accompanied by the emission of **radiation (radioactivity);** other nuclear changes take place with the release of large amounts of energy. Since we have rather little control over the rates of nuclear reactions, we are usually not interested in performing such reactions with the goal of producing particular useful products (except for the research production of new elements, Section 28–11). Rather, the practical objective for carrying out nuclear reactions is often either to make some use of the radiation emitted by nuclear decay or to harness and use the tremendous amounts of energy that are released with many nuclear reactions. The most common types of radiation emitted in nuclear decay processes are discussed in Section 28–3. These various types of radiation may be particles—positive, negative, or neutral—or high-energy electromagnetic radiation, each with its characteristic mass, charge, velocity, and penetrating power as summarized in Table 28–2. Remember, though, that all of these particles are emitted from the **nucleus** of the atom, including the beta particles, which are identical to the extranuclear electrons. The high-energy gamma rays that are often emitted in nuclear decay processes serve to remove excess energy from a nucleus that is in an excited state, in a way quite analogous to the emission of light from an atom whose electrons are in some excited configuration rather than in the ground state configuration.

Of course, each type of decay process causes a characteristic change in the atomic number and mass number of the nucleus. These changes are summarized in the following table.

Process	Change in Atomic Number	Change in Mass Number
beta emission	increase by 1	no change
positron emission	decrease by 1	no change
alpha emission	decrease by 2	decrease by 4
proton emission	decrease by 1	decrease by 1
neutron emission	no change	decrease by 1
electron capture		
(*K* capture)	decrease by 1	no change
gamma emission	no change	no change

Of course, it is not necessary to memorize a table such as this if you just remember the mass number and atomic number for each type of particle which can be emitted (or captured). Just as for atomic nuclei, the symbol that represents each of these types of radiation can include its atomic number as a left subscript and its mass number as a left superscript.

Nuclei that have a ratio of neutrons to protons too high to be stable are said to be above the **band of stability;** these decay so as to decrease the ratio, usually by **beta emission** and less commonly by **neutron emission.** Examples of such nuclei and their characteristic decay processes are discussed in Section 28–4. This section also introduces you to the writing of equations for nuclear reactions, in a way entirely analogous to the writing of equations for ordinary chemical reactions. In such equations, we find it convenient to write the full **nuclide symbol** for all species involved in the reaction. Nuclei below the band of stability, that is, with a too-low ratio of neutrons to protons, decay by processes that increase this ratio — **positron emission, electron capture** (in which an electron from the first, or *K,* shell is captured by the nucleus), or **alpha emission** (especially for heavier nuclei), as discussed in Section 28–5. All nuclei with *atomic number greater than 82* are radioactive and are below and to the right of the band of stability (Section 28–6), so most such nuclides decay by alpha emission. This, of course, includes the heavier representative elements, the most recently produced transition metals, and all of the actinides. Some of these heavy nuclides, especially those beyond uranium ($Z = 92$) also disintegrate by spontaneous nuclear fission into nuclides of intermediate masses, giving neutrons as well.

Many studies and applications of nuclear reactions depend on the detection and measurement of the radiation emitted. Several common methods of **detection of radiation** are described in Section 28–7—photographic methods, fluorescence methods, cloud chambers, and gas ionization counters. Each of these methods depends on the properties and energies of the various types of radiation; you should know the general basis of each method of detection. Photographic detection and use of a cloud chamber are convenient methods for detecting the presence of radiation, requiring little in the way of sophisticated equipment, but they are tedious and inaccurate to use for quantitative measurements of radiation intensity and energy. Use of fluorescence counters such as scintillation counters and use of gas ionization counters both require electronic circuity for effective use, but both techniques can permit quite sensitive studies of energies and intensities of radiation.

Since all radioactive decay processes obey temperature-independent **first-order** kinetics, the rates of all such decay processes can be discussed conveniently in terms of the **half-lives** (Section 28–8) of the decaying nuclei. Review the discussion of the order of reactions, the resulting changes in amount of substance present, and the description of reaction rates in terms of the half-life of a reactant (Section 14–8). Remember that the half-life of a substance in a first-order process is constant, so in that period of time, half of any initial amount of a particular radioactive substance will have decayed. Examples of rate calculations related to radioactive decay processes and the interpretations and applications of these rate calculations are also found in Section 28–8.

While some unstable nuclides can attain stability by a single decay process, many must undergo a series of such decays, known as **disintegration series.** Three well-known natural series, beginning with $^{239}_{92}U$, $^{235}_{92}U$, and $^{232}_{90}Th$, respectively, are discussed in Section 28–9. A careful study of these series will give you further practice in understanding the results of emission of various types of radioactive particles.

The steady, predictable decay rates of unstable nuclei (**radionuclides**) and the resulting steady production of radioactivity make them very useful for many applications. Some of these uses are discussed in Section 28–10. The technique of **radioactive dating** depends on the known rates of decay of various long-lived nuclei. Analysis of the amount of carbon-14 remaining in very old materials of plant or animal origin allows dating of such objects when they are less than about 50,000 years old. Similar dating techniques are based on the ratio of potassium-40 to argon-40 (up to 1 million years old) or on the ratio of uranium-238 to lead-206 (several million years old). The calculations associated with such analyses are, of course, just first-order kinetics calculations. Other uses of radionuclides that are outlined in this section include applications in medicine, chemical research, agriculture, and industry.

Up to this point in the chapter we have been discussing processes associated with nuclei that are naturally unstable. It is also possible to bombard nuclei with particles in such a way that they become unstable by absorption of the bombarding particle, and then decay. This technique, known as **nuclear bombardment,** can be used to artificially transmute one element to another, as described in Section 28 – 11. Such processes have resulted in the production of many nuclides that do not occur naturally, including many new elements — technetium, astatine, francium, and the transuranium elements to name a few. Notice that some of these artificially produced radioactive nuclides also decay in a series of steps.

Most of the nuclear processes studied so far have been ones in which an unstable nucleus emits a particle and is transformed into a nuclide of slightly different mass number or atomic number. Two other kinds of nuclear reactions are discussed in Section 28 – 12: (1) **nuclear fission,** in which the products of the disintegration of the unstable nucleus are two nuclei of intermediate mass and one or more neutrons and (2) **nuclear fusion,** in which two nuclei are combined to make one of higher mass, often with the emission of a neutron. Nuclear fission is comon for isotopes of some elements with atomic numbers above 80, whereas nuclear fusion is favorable for the very light atoms. Both of these processes are accompanied by the release of vast amounts of energy corresponding to the loss of mass that accompanies the reaction.

Sections 28 – 13 and 28 – 14 discuss the two principal applications of nuclear fission reactions, the **atomic bomb** and the **nuclear reactor.** Both of these applications depend on the establishment of a **chain reaction** in which the neutrons from one nuclear disintegration are absorbed by other nuclei; these then disintegrate in their turn, each such disintegration releasing energy and more neutrons to propagate the process. In the atomic bomb, this chain reaction is initiated by bringing together more than the minimum amount of material necessary to sustain the chain reaction, called the **critical mass,** and then allowing the reaction to proceed at an uncontrolled rate. In the nuclear reactor, the rate of fission reaction is controlled by other substances that are present to absorb some of the neutrons. The general design features of the two types of nuclear reactors — **light water reactors** (already feasible to operate) and **breeder reactors** (under development) — are described in Section 28 – 14, along with an indication of some of the problems associated with the application of nuclear energy to power generation. Nuclear fusion reactions produce even greater amounts of energy (the hydrogen bomb, for instance), but these rections are so difficult to contain and control that development of uses of this nearly limitless energy source is in its infancy, for reasons described in Section 28 – 15.

Study Goals

1. Summarize the characteristics that distinguish between nuclear reactions and ordinary chemical reactions. (Chapter introduction and Section 28–1; Exercise 1)
2. Review the meaning and calculation of mass defect and binding energy. (Review Section 4–9; Section 28–2; Exercises 2 and 23)
3. Give symbols, identities, and properties of the common types of radiation: (a) beta particles, (b) alpha particles, (c) positrons, (d) neutrons, (e) protons, and (f) gamma rays. (Section 28–3; Exercise 5)
4. Given a plot of number of neutrons in a nuclide versus number of protons, suggest and give specific examples of the kind of radioactive decay most likely for nuclides that are (a) above, (b) below, and (c) beyond and to the right of the band of stability. (Sections 28–2 through 28–6; Exercises 4 and 9)
5. Describe the following methods for the detection of radiation: (a) photography, (b) fluorescence, (c) cloud chamber, and (d) gas ionization. (Section 28–7; Exercise 10)
6. Calculate rate constants for radioactive decays given half-lives and vice versa. (Section 28–8; Exercise 11)
7. Perform calculations relating the following four variables to calculate the fourth when three are known: (a) an initial amount of radionuclide present, (b) the amount remaining after (c) a specified time, and (d) the rate constant or half-life for the decay. (Section 28–8; Exercises 24 through 28)
8. In disintegration series, be able to relate mother nuclide, daughter nuclide, and the type of emission. (Section 28–9; Exercises 7 and 8)
9. Give several examples of practical uses of radionuclides. (Section 28–10; Exercises 12 through 14)
10. Describe and illustrate the operation of a cyclotron and a linear accelerator. (Section 28–11; Exercise 15)
11. Give specific examples, with balanced equations, of various methods of inducing artificial transmutations of elements. (Section 28–11; Exercise 6)
12. Describe and distinguish between nuclear fission and nuclear fusion. Relate the position of a nuclide on a plot of binding energy per nucleon versus mass number to its tendency to undergo fission or fusion. (Section 28–12; Exercise 16)
13. Describe the principles behind the atomic bomb. Tell how ignition of the detonation process is accomplished and how the reaction is sustained. (Section 28–13; Exercise 17)
14. Describe in detail the operation of a light water nuclear reactor. Understand why nuclear fission explosions are impossible in such a setting. (Section 28–14; Exercises 18 through 21)

15. Describe the vapor diffusion method currently used for separating fissionable uranium-235 from uranium-238 for use in nuclear reactors. Relate this method to Graham's Law of Diffusion (Chapter 11). (Section 28–14; Exercise 20)
16. Describe the principles of operation of a breeder reactor. Give advantages and disadvantages of breeder reactors relative to light water reactors. (Section 28–14)
17. Give the advantages and disadvantages of nuclear fusion reactors as potential future energy sources. (Section 28–15; Exercise 22)

Some Important Terms in This Chapter

Write the meanings *in your own words*. Check the Key Terms list and the chapter reading. Then rewrite your definitions still in your own words, to improve them. Study other new terms and review terms from preceding chapters if necessary.

radioactivity

alpha particle (α)

beta particle (β)

gamma ray (γ)

band of stability

nuclear fusion

nuclear fission

nuclides

positron

half-life

radioactive dating

mother nuclide

daughter nuclide

artificial transmutation

chain reaction

critical mass

nuclear reactor

Preliminary Test

True-False

Mark each statement as true (T) or false (F).

_____   1. In a nuclear reaction, one element can be changed into another.
_____   2. The electrons surrounding the nucleus are usually involved in nuclear reactions.
_____   3. The particles emitted from the nucleus in nuclear reactions are always positively charged.
_____   4. Only very heavy nuclei are naturally radioactive.
_____   5. All nuclei except hydrogen are somewhat unstable because of the very close proximity of the positively charged protons in the nucleus.
_____   6. Nuclei above the band of stability usually decay by nuclear fission.
_____   7. No naturally occurring nuclides with atomic number less than 8 are radioactive.
_____   8. All radioactive decay processes following first-order kinetics.
_____   9. The eventual product of each of the three common natural radioactive series is a stable isotope of lead.
_____ 10. Since lead is the product of the three common natural radioactive series, we can tell that all isotopes of lead are stable.
_____ 11. Any amount of a fissionable material such as U-235 can explode if heated to a high enough temperature.

_____ 12. Light water nuclear reactors use a large amount of water, both for cooling and as a moderator to slow the neutrons produced in the reaction.

_____ 13. Breeder reactors are used to produce new forms of plant and animal life.

Short Answer

1. Nuclides having either 2, 8, 20, 28, 50, 82, or 126 neutrons are said to have a _____ of neutrons and are found to be exceptionally _____.

2. Above atomic number 20, most stable nuclei have _____ protons than neutrons.

3. A nucleus having a proton to neutron ratio either higher or lower than stable nuclei is said to lie outside the _____.

4. Of the common types of radiation, the ones having positive charge are the _____, the _____, and the _____. (For each one, give the name of the particle and an acceptable symbol.)

5. The types of radioactive emission that result in the daughter nucleus having a lower atomic number than the mother nucleus are _____, _____, and _____.

6. The type of radioactive emission that results in a lower mass number of the nucleus but no change in atomic number is _____.

7. The type of nuclear emission that produces no change in either mass number or atomic number of the nucleus is _____ _____.

8. The radioactive particles with the lowest penetrating ability are _____.

9. Nuclei above the band of stability have too _____ a ratio of neutrons to protons; such nuclei usually decay by _____ emission or by _____ emission.

10. The first several steps of the thorium-232 radioactive decay series involve, in order, the loss of an alpha particle, then a beta particle, then another beta particle; the nuclide symbol for the product after these three steps of decay is _____.

11. All nuclides with atomic number greater than _____ are radioactive.

12. When a nuclear reaction occurs, the particles emitted can have different kinetic energies. The kinetic energy of the emitted particle is equal to the energy equivalent of the _____ of products relative to reactants, minus the energy associated with any _____ which are later emitted.

For each of the next seven questions, 13 through 19, tell whether the effect of the change would be to increase (I), decrease (D), or leave unchanged (U) the atomic number and the mass number of the nuclide; tell the magnitude of any increase or decrease.

Change	Effect on Atomic Number	Effect on Mass Number
13. alpha emission	_____	_____
14. beta emission	_____	_____
15. gamma emission	_____	_____
16. positron emission	_____	_____
17. electron capture	_____	_____
18. proton emission	_____	_____
19. neutron emission	_____	_____

20. The half-life of lead-210, one of the nuclides in the U-238 series, is 20.4 years. Suppose we start with 100 μg of lead-210 and allow it to decay. After 20.4 years, the weight of lead-210 present would be _____ μg, after 40.8 years it would be _____ μg, and after 61.2 years it would be _____ μg.

21. The effectiveness of cobalt-60 treatment in arresting certain types of cancer depends on the ability of _____ to destroy tissue.

For each of the next fifteen questions, 22 through 36, fill in the nuclide symbol that correctly completes the equation. Describe each reaction with a phrase, such as beta emission, alpha emission, positron emission, electron capture, neutron emission, gamma emission, nuclear fission, or nuclear fusion. For all reactions *except* those that are nuclear fission or nuclear fusion, tell whether the neutron/proton ratio increases (I), decreases (D), or remains unchanged (U) by the process.

Reaction	Description	Change in Ratio, Neutrons/Protons
22. $_0^1n \rightarrow {_1^1}p +$ _____	_____	_____
23. $_6^{14}C \rightarrow$ _____ $+ {_{-1}^0}\beta$	_____	_____
24. $_7^{17}N \rightarrow$ _____ $+ {_0^1}n$	_____	_____

25. $^{240}_{94}\text{Pu} \rightarrow {}^{236}_{92}\text{U} +$ _____   _____   _____

26. $^{186}_{73}\text{Ta} \rightarrow {}^{186}_{74}\text{W} +$ _____   _____   _____

27. $^{197}_{80}\text{Hg} + {}^{0}_{-1}e \rightarrow$ _____   _____   _____

28. _____ $\rightarrow {}^{39}_{20}\text{Ca} + {}^{0}_{-1}e$ _____   _____

29. _____ $+ {}^{0}_{-1}e \rightarrow {}^{22}_{10}\text{Ne}$ _____   _____

30. $^{236}_{92}\text{U}^* \rightarrow {}^{236}_{92}\text{U} +$ _____   _____   _____

31. $^{223}_{88}\text{Ra} \rightarrow$ _____ $+ {}^{4}_{2}\alpha$ _____   _____

32. $^{1}_{1}p \rightarrow {}^{1}_{0}n +$ _____   _____   _____

33. $^{1}_{1}\text{H} + {}^{1}_{1}\text{H} \rightarrow$ _____ $+ {}^{0}_{-1}e$ _____   _____

34. $^{3}_{2}\text{He} + {}^{3}_{2}\text{He} \rightarrow {}^{4}_{2}\text{He} + 2$ _____   _____   _____

35. $^{235}_{92}\text{U} + {}^{1}_{0}n \rightarrow {}^{93}_{36}\text{Kr} +$ _____ $+ 3{}^{1}_{0}n$ _____   _____

36. _____ $+ {}^{1}_{0}n \rightarrow {}^{99}_{40}\text{Zr} + {}^{139}_{54}\text{Xe} + 2{}^{1}_{0}n$ _____   _____

---

37. For any radioactive decay, the decaying nuclide is called the _____ nuclide and the product is called the _____ .
38. The sequence of radioactive decay processes by which some radionuclides attain stability in several steps is called a _____ .
39. The method of radioactive dating based on the decay of carbon-14 is applicable only to objects up to about _____ years old.
40. The process in which a nuclide is rendered unstable by hitting it with a high-energy particle is called _____ .
41. All nuclides with mass number greater than _____ undergo nuclear fission spontaneously, whereas those between mass numbers _____ and _____ can be induced to do so by bombarding them with particles of relatively low energy.
42. The most stable nuclide is _____ .
43. A material that is capable of undergoing nuclear fission is called _____ .
44. A nuclear reaction in which two smaller nuclei combine to form a larger nucleus, with the release of energy, is called a _____ reaction.
45. Most stable, naturally occurring nuclides have _____ numbers of protons and _____ numbers of neutrons.

Multiple Choice

_____ 1. Which of the following processes produces two nuclei of moderate mass from one heavier nucleus?
(a) alpha emission   (b) nuclear fusion   (c) nuclear fission
(d) fluorescence   (e) ionization

_____ 2. Which of the following is not a commonly used method of radiation detection?
(a) photographic detection
(b) detection by fluorescence
(c) use of a cloud chamber
(d) use of a gas ionization chamber
(e) bombardment with positive ions

_____ 3. The radiocarbon method of dating, based on the decay of carbon-14, would not be applicable to determining the age of which of the following objects?
(a) a piece of charcoal from a fire
(b) a piece of wood
(c) a piece of animal skin
(d) a woven mat made of straw
(e) a flint arrowhead

_____ 4. Measurement based on which of the following radioactive decay processes would be applicable to age determination for objects of greatest age?
(a) decay of carbon-14 (half-life 5,730 years)
(b) decay of potassium-40 (half-life 1.3 billion years)
(c) decay of radium-223 (half-life 11.4 days)
(d) decay of uranium-238 (half-life 4.5 billion years)
(e) decay of uranium-235 (half-life 710 million years)

_____ 5. The source of high-energy positive ions or high-energy negative ions for nuclear bombardment processes is usually which of the following?
(a) a particle accelerator
(b) a nuclear fission reactor
(c) a cloud chamber
(d) an atomic bomb
(e) a nuclear fusion reactor

_____ 6. Which of the following experimental methods has been used for the production of elements that do not occur naturally?
(a) nuclear fusion   (b) nuclear bombardment   (c) gas ionization   (d) natural radioactive decay   (e) labeling experiments

_____ 7. Which of the following is not a problem associated with the operation of a nuclear fission reactor for the production of electricity?
(a) possibility of a meltdown
(b) storage of long-lived radioactive wastes

(c) a nuclear fission explosion

(d) thermal pollution

(e) escape of short-lived radioactive wastes

Answers to Preliminary Test

Be careful—do not just look up the answers without thinking carefully about them. Do not just memorize answers—be sure you could figure them out yourself.

True-False

1. True. The only nuclear reactions for which this is not true are those in which only a neutron is emitted, and these are not common.

2. False. Most nuclear reactions involve only the nucleus. One kind of nuclear reaction, called electron capture (K capture), involves the capture of an electron from the inner electronic shell (the K shell) by the nucleus, but this type of nuclear reaction is relatively uncommon.

3. False. Some are positive, some are negative, and some are neutral. See Section 28–3, and be sure that you are familiar with the general properties of the particles that take part in nuclear decay processes.

4. False. Most very heavy nuclei are radioactive, but so are many light nuclei.

5. False. Many nuclei are nonradioactive, meaning that they are entirely stable and do not decay. It is not entirely understood how the strong coulombic proton-proton repulsive forces in the nucleus are overcome, but it is thought that some of the very short-lived subatomic particles that have more recently been discovered may play a role. See Section 28–1.

6. False. They usually decay by beta emission and less frequently by neutron emission. The only nuclides that spontaneously undergo fission are isotopes of elements with atomic numbers greater than 80, and these are found to the right of the band of stability.

7. False. For instance, the chapter mentions radioactive isotopes of C and N.

8. True

9. True

10. False. Several radioactive isotopes of lead occur in these series. See Table 28–3.

11. False. If too little material is present, the reaction cannot become self-sustaining since too few neutrons are produced. It is necessary to have a critical mass for an explosion. Read the section on the atomic bomb, Section 28–13, and the comments regarding the impossibility of explosion of a nuclear fission reactor, Section 28–14.

12. True. The design and general features of such a light water reactor are described in Section 28–14.
13. False. They are called breeder reactors because they produce more fissionable material than they consume.

Short Answer

1. magic number, stable. The same principle is found to apply to the numbers of protons in the nucleus and to the sum of protons plus neutrons.
2. fewer
3. band of stability
4. positron ($_{+1}^{0}\beta$ or $_{+1}^{0}e$), alpha particle (α, $_2^4\alpha$ or $_2^4$He), proton ($_1^1p$ or $_1^1$H)
5. positron emission, alpha emission, proton emission
6. neutron emission
7. gamma emission
8. alpha particles
9. high, beta, neutron. The first of these, beta emission, is much more common.
10. $_{90}^{228}$Th. You should be able to figure this out without looking at Table 28–3.
11. 82
12. mass loss, gamma rays
13. D (2), D (4)
14. I (1), U
15. U, U
16. D (1), U
17. D (1), U
18. D (1), D (1)
19. U, D (1)

You should be able to answer questions 13 through 19 without looking up the answers, just from knowing the characteristics of the various kinds of radiation.

20. 50, 25, 12.5. During any time period equal to one half-life, the amount of material present decreases to one-half of what it was at the beginning of *that* half-life.
21. gamma rays. This is discussed in Example 28–1, which is also an illustration of calculations associated with radioactive decay.
22. $_{-1}^{0}\beta$, beta emission, D
23. $_7^{14}$N, beta emission, D
24. $_7^{16}$N, neutron emission, D

25. $_2^4\alpha$, alpha emission, I

26. $_{-1}^0\beta$, beta emission, D

27. $_{79}^{197}$Au, electron capture, I

28. $_{19}^{39}$K, beta emission, D

29. $_{11}^{22}$Na, electron capture, I

30. $_0^0\gamma$, gamma emission, U

31. $_{86}^{219}$Rn, alpha emission, I

32. $_{-1}^0\beta$, beta emission, I

33. $_1^2$H, nuclear fusion (also gives off a beta particle, but principally nuclear fusion)

34. $_1^1$H, nuclear fusion (also gives off protons, but principally nuclear fusion)

35. $_{56}^{140}$Ba, nuclear fission

36. $_{94}^{239}$Pu, nuclear fission

37. mother, daughter
38. disintegration series or radioactive series
39. 50,000
40. nuclear bombardment
41. 250, 225, 250
42. $_{26}^{56}$Fe
43. fissionable
44. nuclear fusion
45. even, even

Multiple Choice

1. (c)
2. (e)
3. (e). This method is applicable only to material that originated as a living organism, either plant or animal.
4. (d). It has the longest half-life.
5. (a). This is discussed in the first part of Section 28–11.
6. (b). See Section 28–11 for a discussion of this topic.
7. (c). Read Section 28–14. Reactors use fuels that are neither the correct composition nor the correct physical arrangement to ever achieve the critical mass necessary for an explosion. The other dangers are real.

29

Organic Chemistry I: Hydrocarbons

Chapter Summary

Because of its intermediate electronegativity and its position in Group IVA, carbon can form very stable covalent bonds with as many as four other atoms; its striking ability to exhibit extensive **catenation** (literally, "chain-making") by bonding to other carbon atoms means that it can form a large number and variety of compounds with carbon chains and rings. The study of such compounds involving C—H bonds comprises a major branch of chemistry known as **organic chemistry.** Our study of descriptive chemistry continues in Chapters 29 and 30 with some of the major features of this extensive and varied area of chemistry. While a more detailed, but still introductory, study of organic chemistry is often a course of a year or more at the college level, the present study can be viewed as a preliminary survey of this field. (Remember the warning in Chapter 1 of this Study Guide about not insisting on knowing everything at once about a subject!) Your principal goals in these two chapters should be, in broad terms, (1) to recognize and develop a familiarity with the major classes of compounds of organic chemistry, (2) to recognize and relate to their structures, the principal properties of these major classes of compounds, and (3) to recognize the principal types of reactions in organic chemistry and relate them to the major classes of compounds.

Chapter 29 deals with the types of compounds composed entirely of carbon and hydrogen — the **hydrocarbons;** Chapter 30 will introduce you to the various **functional groups** of atoms, including atoms other than C or H, which characterize other major classes of compounds.

The first major portion of Chapter 29, Sections 29–1 through 29–7, deals with the **saturated hydrocarbons,** or **alkanes,** which contain only single covalent bonds. This means that each carbon is bonded to four other atoms, either carbon or hydrogen, with tetrahedral geometry caused by sp^3 hybridization of the carbon atoms (Section 5–12). Section 29–1 introduces the structures and terminology of **homologous series** of compounds, including both the **normal** or unbranched hydrocarbons and the **branched** hydrocarbons. Do not be misled by the term "straight chain" when applied to organic carbon chains; this is clarified in a marginal note to Section 29–1. You were introduced in Chapter 27 to the idea of **isomers,** compounds having the same number of atoms of all types, but with differing arrangements. Isomerism is very common in organic chemistry. The first type to be encountered, **structural isomerism,** is described in Section 29–1. As you probably expect, we have developed a systematic way of naming organic compounds. The rules for this nomenclature of saturated hydrocarbons are discussed in Section 29–2. Notice the relation between the name of the parent hydrocarbon and the **alkyl group** obtained by removing one H atom. These alkyl groups can be thought of as building blocks that will appear in many classes of organic compounds. Study carefully the examples for naming organic compounds, and you will find that it is not as complex as it seems at first.

Some properties of a compound are markedly dependent on the shape of the molecules that make up the compound. (This is one reason we studied the general topic of molecular shapes in Chapter 5). One of the features that affects the shape of a molecule (or a group that may be a part of a more complex molecule) is the extent of rotation about bonds. Rotation about single bonds (which is relatively easy) gives rise to different **conformations** of the same compound, as discussed in Section 29–3. The carbon-hydrogen bond is so stable that the principal chemical property of the alkanes is their relative chemical inertness (Section 29–4). The two principal types of reactions that these compounds can undergo are **substitution** and **oxidation.**

As examples, reactions involving the substitution of one or more alkane hydrogen atoms by a halogen **(halogenation reactions)** are described in Section 29–5. The principal use of hydrocarbons as fuels involves their oxidation, as described in Section 29–6. The relationship between the structure and chain length of the hydrocarbon and the amount of energy available on complete oxidation (the **heat of combustion**) is also discussed in this section. Petroleum (Section 29–7) consists primarily of hydrocarbons, but of a mixture of many different chain lengths; the refining of petroleum involves the separation of this complex mixture into **fractions** that are suitable for various uses.

Hydrocarbons that contain some carbon-carbon bonds other than single bonds are known as **unsaturated hydrocarbons.** These are three classes of such compounds: (1) those containing double bonds (the **alkenes**), (2) those containing triple bonds (the **alkynes**), and (3) the **aromatic hydrocarbons.**

Sections 29–8 through 29–10 describe the structures and properties of the **alkenes,** or **olefins.** Section 29–8 introduces you to the system by which these compounds containing double bonds are named. Because of the lack of free rotation around a double bond, compounds containing such a bond can exhibit **geometric isomerism.** Notice both the differences in properties of such isomeric pairs and the necessary additional terminology in the nomenclature—the terms *cis* and *trans,* which have the same meaning you learned in Chapter 27. In contrast to the alkanes, which react primarily by substitution reactions, the alkenes are characterized by **addition** reactions, which result in additional substituents being bonded to the carbons originally linked by the double bond. Thus, a double bond is the first example we have seen of a **functional group.** Section 29–9 describes some common addition reactions of the alkenes, including addition of halogens and of hydrogen **(hydrogenation reactions).** Another type of addition reaction involves the linking together of many small unsaturated molecules to form long **polymer** molecules, a process called **polymerization.** Several polymers, both synthetic and natural, are described in this section. Alkenes, like alkanes, can burn (be oxidized), Section 29–10, to CO_2 and H_2O with the liberation of heat, but they have a much greater tendency to undergo incomplete combustion, leaving some carbon as soot. Aqueous solutions of oxidizing agents such as potassium permanganate can oxidize alkenes more or less completely, depending on concentration and temperature. The second class of unsaturated hydrocarbons, the alkynes, which contain carbon-carbon triple bonds, are introduced and named in Section 29–11. As you might expect, the main reactions of the alkynes are similar to those of the alkenes, but they are generally more reactive.

The remainder of the chapter, Sections 29–12 through 29–14, describes the aromatic hydrocarbons. The origin of this term, which you can see is quite a misnomer, is described in the introductory paragraphs to this segment of the chapter. The bonding in all aromatic compounds is characterized by **delocalization** of several pairs of π-bonded electrons around a ring (almost always a six-membered ring) and a consequent lowering of the energy—an effect known as **resonance** (review Sections 5–5 and 6–6). This bonding is described in detail for **benzene,** the simplest aromatic hydrocarbon, in Section 29–12. Other aromatic hydrocarbons, presented in Section 29–13, consist of benzene with one or more hydrogen atoms replaced by alkyl groups (e.g., toluene and the three isomeric xylenes) and the fused-ring aromatics (e.g., naphthalene, anthracene, etc.). The result of the resonance stabilization in aromatic hydrocarbons is that these compounds, though unsaturated, do not generally react by addition reactions as do the alkenes and alkynes, but rather by **substitution reactions,** Section 29–14. The main types of substitution reactions may be **halogenation** or (X, where X is any halogen), **nitration** (NO_2, bonded through the N). Aromatic hydrocarbons can also burn to carbon dioxide and water with the release of large amounts of energy. The aromatic C—H groups are very resistant to more gentle **oxidation,** but the alkyl groups of alkylbenzenes are readily oxidized by chemical oxidizing agents such as permanganate or dichromate ions.

Chapter 30 will extend the discussion of organic chemistry to include several other important functional groups.

Study Goals

This is a quite long and diverse chapter. Be systematic in your study. Study Goal 1 will help you to get a look at the range of the chapter. The other study goals will help you focus in more detail on particular aspects of the material.

1. First, organize your study around the classes of compounds. Know structures, properties, sources or preparations, uses, and reactions that are typical of each class of organic compounds. (You should do this for either the general class or at least two examples of each class.)
   (a) alkanes (Sections 29–1 through 29–7; Exercises 5 through 9 and 15 through 28)
   (b) alkenes (Sections 29–8 through 29–10; Exercises 29 through 47)
   (c) alkynes (Section 29–11; Exercises 48 through 52)
   (d) aromatic hydrocarbons (Sections 29–12 through 29–14; Exercises 53 through 65)
2. Define and give several specific examples of (a) alkanes, (b) alkenes, (c) alkynes, (d) cycloalkanes, (e) cycloalkenes, and (f) aromatic hydrocarbons. (Sections 29–1, 29–5, 29–8, and 29–11 through 29–13; Exercises 5, 7, 21, 22, 29 through 31, 48, 49, and 53 through 55)
3. Describe the bonding and hybridization in, and give three-dimensional drawings of the shapes of, the hydrocarbons in the classes of Study Goal 2. (Same sections as Study Goal 2; Exercises 6, 34, 35, 50, 51, 56, and 57)
4. Apply systematic rules of nomenclature to name saturated hydrocarbons when given their formulas, and vice versa. (Section 29–2; Exercises 10 through 13)
5. Know the trivial names of several of the more common hydrocarbons. (Section 29–2; Exercise 6)
6. Draw and name all structural isomers of the simpler saturated hydrocarbons. (Section 29–1; Exercises 10 through 13)
7. Know how the trends of each of the following properties depend on the chain lengths and on the branching of the alkanes: (a) melting point, (b) boiling point, and (c) heat of combustion (both on a molar and on a mass basis). (Sections 29–1 and 29–6; Exercise 9)
8. Describe why rotation around single bonds is much easier than rotation around double bonds. Describe how this ease of rotation leads to different conformations of a single saturated hydrocarbon. (Sections 29–3 and 29–8; Exercise 14)
9. Write equations to illustrate (a) substitution reactions and (b) addition reactions. Know the kinds of hydrocarbons that undergo such reactions. (Sections 29–5, 29–9, and 29–14; Exercises 16 through 22, 40 through 42, and 61 through 63)
10. Write a series of equations to illustrate a free radical chain reaction. (Section 29–5; Exercises 18 and 20)
11. Write equations to illustrate the oxidation of (a) an alkane, (b) an alkene, (c) an alkyne, and (d) an aromatic hydrocarbon. (Sections 29–6, 29–10, 29–11, and 29–14; Exercises 23, 24, 47, 64, and 65)
12. Identify the ranges of chain lengths associated with at least five fractions of petroleum. (Section 29–7; Exercise 25)

13. Describe what is meant by (a) cracking, (b) engine knocking, (c) leaded gasoline, and (d) octane number. (Section 29–7; Exercises 26 through 28)
14. Describe how the difficulty of rotation around double bonds leads to the existence of geometric isomers. Distinguish between *cis* and *trans* geometrical isomers. (Section 29–8; Exercise 35)
15. Give examples of the following reactions: (a) halogenation, (b) hydrogenation, (c) polymerization, and (d) nitration. (Sections 29–5, 29–9, and 29–14; Exercises 16 through 19, 40 through 42, 44 through 46, and 61 through 63)
16. Describe the bonding in benzene and other aromatic hydrocarbons in terms of electron delocalization and resonance. (Sections 29–12 and 29–13; Exercises 56 and 57)

Some Important Terms in This Chapter

Write the meanings *in your own words.* Check the Key Terms list and the chapter reading. Then rewrite your definitions, still in your own words, to improve them. Study other new terms and review terms from preceding chapters if necessary.

catenation

alkanes

alkenes

alkynes

alkyl group

aromatic hydrocarbons

addition reaction

substitution reaction

hydrogenation

halogenation

structural isomers

saturated hydrocarbons

unsaturated hydrocarbons

Preliminary Test

Be sure to practice *many* of the additional textbook exercises.

True-False

Mark each statement as true (T) or false (F).

_____ 1. The different atomic arrangements obtained by rotation around a carbon-carbon single bond represent different compounds.

_____ 2. The different atomic arrangements obtained by rotation around a carbon-carbon double bond represent different compounds.

_____ 3. The straight-chain hydrocarbons are so called because the carbon atoms lie in a straight line.

_____ 4. In saturated hydrocarbons, each carbon atom is bonded to either two or three hydrogen atoms.

_____ 5. All alkanes up to C_8H_{18} are gases at room temperature and atmospheric pressure.

_____ 6. Generally, the more branched an alkane is (for the same number of carbon atoms), the lower are its melting and boiling points.

_____ 7. The main type of chemical reaction that the alkanes undergo is substitution.

_____ 8. Organic reactions usually form only a single product, so separation is usually not a serious problem.

_____ 9. The reaction in which a nitro group, $-NO_2$, is substituted for a hydrogen atom is called nitration.

_____ 10. Nitration reactions result when a hydrocarbon is mixed with NO_2 gas at high temperature.

_____ 11. Reaction of an organic compound with O_2 is usually an exothermic reaction.

_____ 12. Simple alkanes can exhibit either structural isomerism or geometrical isomerism.

_____ 13. Simple alkenes can exhibit either structural isomerism or geometrical isomerism.

_____ 14. Simple alkynes can exhibit either structural isomerism or geometrical isomerism.

_____ 15. Petroleum consists mainly of hydrocarbons.

_____ 16. Petroleum from all sources is identical, that is, composed of a mixture of the same compounds in the same amounts.

_____ 17. Compounds with carbon-carbon double or triple bonds undergo addition reactions much more readily than they undergo substitution reactions.

____ 18. The alkynes are usually more reactive than the alkenes, with respect to addition reactions.

____ 19. All aromatic hydrocarbons have a pleasant smell.

____ 20. Benzene is an unsaturated hydrocarbon, so it readily undergoes addition reactions like those of the alkenes and the alkynes.

Short Answer

1. The existence of the large number of organic compounds is primarily due to the ability of carbon atoms to _____ other carbon atoms.

2. A compound in which there is one continuous chain of carbon atoms, with no branching, is referred to as a straight-chain or _____ compound.

3. Each member of the series of normal saturated hydrocarbons differs from the next by one _____ (name, formula); such a series of compounds is called a _____ _____.

4. The melting points of the normal alkanes generally _____ with increasing carbon content, and their boiling points generally _____.

5. Atomic arrangements that differ only by rotation around single bonds are called different _____ of the same compound.

6. The hydrogen atoms of alkanes are readily replaced by halogen atoms at high temperatures or in the presence of _____.

7. As the chain length increases for the normal alkanes, the heat of combustion _____ on a molar basis and _____ on a weight basis.

8. The process of "cracking" of petroleum involves _____ _____ _____ to produce more gasoline.

9. Hydrocarbons containing one carbon-carbon double bond per molecule are called _____.

10. The suffix applied to all alkenes, whether open chain or cyclic, is _____.

11. The suffix applied to all alkanes, whether open chain or cyclic, is _____.

12. The suffix applied to all alkynes, whether open chain or cyclic, is _____.

13. The number of isomers of xylene is ____; these are examples of _____ isomers.

14. The number of isomers of trimethylbenzene is ____.

15. The most common kind of reaction of the aromatic ring is _____.

16. The reaction by which a hydrogen atom on the benzene ring is replaced by the group — NO_2 is called _____; the resulting compound is named _____.

17. When a hydrocarbon undergoes complete combustion the two products are _____ and _____.

For each of the following hydrocarbons, either name the hydrocarbon or supply its formula, as required. These formulas should be sufficient to specify the compound uniquely and may be full structural formulas. Write the condensed chemical formula (e.g., C_8H_{18}) for each compound. Classify each compound as an alkane, an alkene, an alkyne, an aromatic hydrocarbon, or derived from one of these by substitution.

Formula	Name	Chemical Formula	Classification of Compound Type
18. $H-\underset{\underset{H}{\mid}}{\overset{\overset{H}{\mid}}{C}}-\underset{\underset{H}{\mid}}{\overset{\overset{H}{\mid}}{C}}-H$	_____	____	_____
19. (benzene ring)	_____	____	_____
20. $CH_3-\underset{\underset{CH_3}{\mid}}{\overset{\overset{CH_3}{\mid}}{C}}-CH_2CH_2CH_3$	_____	____	_____
21. _____	2,4-dimethylhexane	____	_____
22. $H_2C=CHCH_2CH_3$	_____	____	_____
23. _____	cis-2-butene	____	_____
24. _____	trans-2-butene	____	_____
25. (cyclopentane ring with CH₃)	_____	____	_____
26. (cyclohexane ring)	_____	____	_____
27. _____	o-xylene	____	_____
28. _____	p-xylene	____	_____
29. _____	acetylene	____	_____
30. _____	ethyne	____	_____
31. $CH_3C\equiv CCH_3$	_____	____	_____
32. _____	anthracene	____	_____
33. $CH_3CH_2CHCH_2CH_2CH_2CH_3$ with CH_2, CH_2, CH_3 branch	_____	____	_____
34. _____	cyclopentene	____	_____
35. $CH_3CH_2NO_2$	_____	____	_____

36. Br〜 C=C 〜Br / H   H _____   _____   _____

37. Br〜 C=C 〜Br / H   H _____   _____   _____

38. _____   *trans*-2,3-dibromo-2-butene   _____   _____
39. _____   tetrafluoroethene   _____   _____
40. _____   difluorodichloromethane   _____   _____

41. _____   bromobenzene   _____   _____

Multiple Choice

_____ 1. How many structural isomers are possible for the compound with the molecular formula C_3H_7Br? Remember that bromine can form only one covalent bond to another atom.
(a) 1   (b) 2   (c) 3   (d) 4   (e) 5

_____ 2. The molecular weight of *n*-pentane is
(a) 44.
(b) 70.
(c) 42.
(d) the same as the molecular weight of isopentane.
(e) the same as the molecular weight of 2-pentane.

_____ 3. In all saturated hydrocarbons, the carbon atoms have which of the following types of hybrid orbitals?
(a) sp (b) sp^2 (c) sp^3 (d) dsp^3 (e) d^2sp^3

_____ 4. Substances having the same molecular formula but different structural formulas are called
(a) isotopes.   (b) hydrocarbons.   (c) isomers.
(d) fractions.   (e) free radicals.

_____ 5. Which one of the following is an isomer of cyclohexane?
(a) *n*-hexane   (b) benzene   (c) 1-hexene
(d) 2-methylpentane   (e) 2-methylhexane

_____ 6. The possibility of geometric isomerism in some alkenes is due to
(a) the fact that alkenes are saturated hydrocarbons.
(b) the restriction on the orientation of the p orbitals that make up the π bond.
(c) the free rotation about σ bonds.
(d) the acidity of substituted groups.
(e) resonance in these substances.

___ 7. Which one of the following compounds may exist as either of two geometric isomers?
(a) 1,1-dibromoethene
(b) 1,1-dibromoethane
(c) 1,2-dibromoethene
(d) 1,2-dibromoethane
(e) 2-methylpropene

___ 8. Which one of the following compounds is an alkane?

(a) 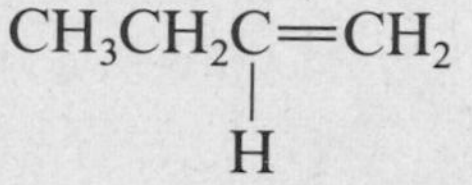 $CH_3CH_2C{=}CH_2$
$\quad\quad\quad |$
$\quad\quad\quad H$

(b) 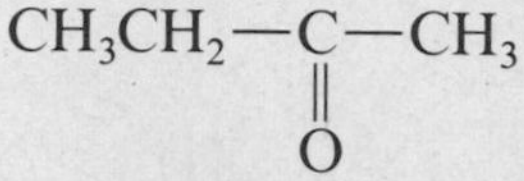 $CH_3CH_2{-}C{-}CH_3$
$\quad\quad\quad\quad\quad \| $
$\quad\quad\quad\quad\quad O$

(c) CH_3OH

(d) 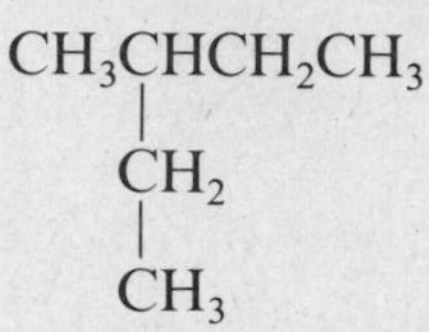 $CH_3CHCH_2CH_3$
$\quad\quad\quad |$
$\quad\quad\quad CH_2$
$\quad\quad\quad |$
$\quad\quad\quad CH_3$

(e) $CH_3CH_2CH_2CH_2Br$

___ 9. The formulas

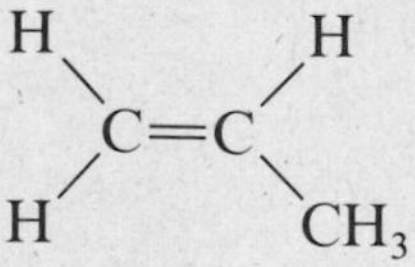

$$\begin{array}{cc} H & H \\ \diagdown & \diagup \\ C{=}C \\ \diagup & \diagdown \\ H & CH_3 \end{array} \quad \text{and} \quad \begin{array}{cc} H_3C & H \\ \diagdown & \diagup \\ C{=}C \\ \diagup & \diagdown \\ H & H \end{array} \quad \text{represent}$$

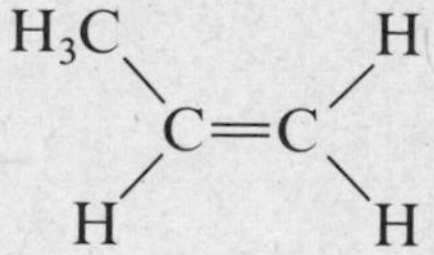

(a) geometrical isomers.
(b) structural isomers.
(c) the same compound.
(d) ethylene.
(e) None of the preceding answers is correct.

___ 10. What is the number of structural isomers of dichlorobenzene?
(a) 1   (b) 2   (c) 3   (d) 4   (e) 5

___ 11. One of the following pairs of compounds is a pair of *structural* isomers. Which pair?

(a) $CH_3CH_2CH_2CH_3$ and
$CH_2{-}CH_2$
$|\quad\quad |$
$CH_2{-}CH_2$

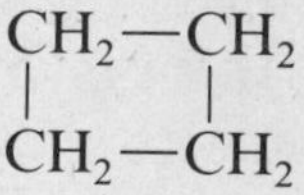

(b) $CH_3CH_2CH_2CH_3$ and $CH_3CH_2CHCH_3$
$\quad\quad\quad\quad\quad\quad\quad\quad\quad |$
$\quad\quad\quad\quad\quad\quad\quad\quad\quad CH_3$

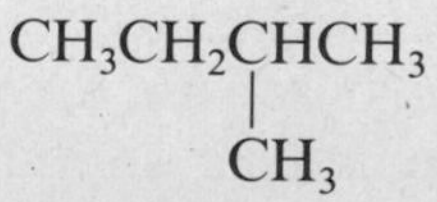

(c)

$$\underset{H}{\overset{H_3C}{\diagdown}} C = C \underset{H}{\overset{CH_3}{\diagup}} \quad \text{and} \quad \underset{H_3C}{\overset{H}{\diagdown}} C = C \underset{H}{\overset{CH_3}{\diagup}}$$

(d) $CH_3CH_2CH_2CH_2CH_3$ and

$$H_3C - \underset{\underset{CH_3}{|}}{\overset{\overset{CH_3}{|}}{C}} - CH_3$$

_____ 12. One of the pairs of compounds in Question 11 is a pair of *geometric* isomers. Which pair?

Answers to Preliminary Test

True-False

1. False. These are just different conformations of the same compound. See Section 29 – 1.
2. True. These are geometric isomers. See Section 29 – 8.
3. False. The carbon chains are not branched. In their most stable conformations, they lie along a zig-zag arrangement.
4. False. In branched hydrocarbons, some carbon atoms may be bonded to only one hydrogen atom, or some even to no hydrogens. Can you write examples of each of these cases of saturated hydrocarbons?
5. False. Only the lightest four normal alkanes are gases at room temperature and atmospheric pressure. The liquefied propane or butane gas that is available in tanks at room temperature is under high pressure.
6. True. This is described in Section 29 – 1 for the three isomeric pentanes and the five isomeric hexanes.
7. True
8. False. Usually a mixture of products is formed, and often these are isomers of one another. A common method of separation is fractional distillation.
9. True
10. False. The source of the $-NO_2$ group is usually nitric acid vapor, HNO_3, at high temperature. Aromatic hydrocarbons may be nitrated by concentrated aqueous solutions of HNO_3.
11. True. Remember that the term exothermic means that the process liberates heat. Another way of making the statement that appears in this question is "Most organic compounds burn." The production of heat energy is often the reason we carry out these reactions.
12. False. They can exhibit only structural isomerism in which the atoms are linked together in a different order.

13. True
14. False. They cannot exhibit geometric isomerism because the environment of the triple bond is linear (*sp* hybridization).
15. True
16. False. Each oil field produces oil with a characteristic composition.
17. True. Addition reactions are the characteristic reactions of the alkenes and the alkynes. See Sections 29–9 and 29–11.
18. True
19. False. Read the introduction to the portion of the chapter on aromatic hydrocarbons. Some have foul odors, others are odorless. The term is used to describe benzene, its derivatives, and other compounds that exhibit similar chemical properties. Can you describe the bonding feature that all aromatic compounds have in common? See Sections 29–12 through 29–14.
20. False. The π electrons of the aromatic hydrocarbons (one of which is benzene) are not available for addition reactions because of delocalization. The main reactions of aromatic hydrocarbons such as benzene are substitution reactions.

Short Answer

1. form covalent bonds to
2. normal
3. methylene group (CH_2), homologous series
4. increase, increase
5. conformations
6. sunlight (or an ultraviolet light source)
7. increases, decreases. See the comparisons in Section 29–6.
8. breaking of hydrocarbons whose chain length is too great
9. alkenes
10. -ene
11. -ane
12. -yne
13. 3, structural. Can you draw and name these three isomers?
14. 3. Can you draw and name them?
15. substitution. Can you describe such a reaction and write an example of it?
16. nitration; nitrobenzene
17. CO_2, H_2O
18. ethane, C_2H_6, alkane
19. benzene, C_6H_6, aromatic hydrocarbon
20. 2,2-dimethylpentane, C_7H_{16}, alkane
21. $CH_3CHCH_2CHCH_2CH_3$, C_8H_{18}, alkane
    $\quad\;\;|\qquad\quad|$
    $\quad CH_3\quad\; CH_3$

22. 1-butene, C_4H_8, alkene

23. 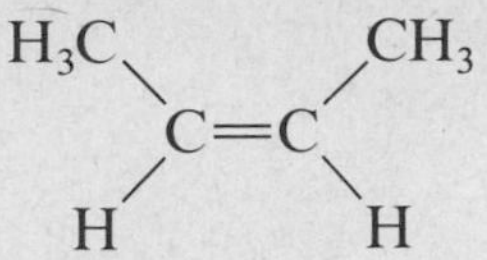 C_4H_8, alkene

24. 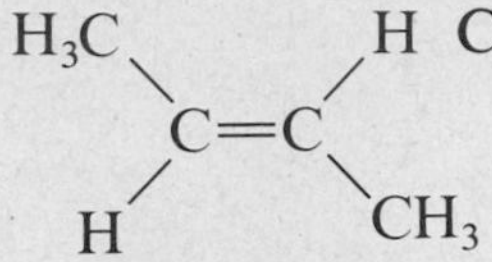 C_4H_8, alkene

25. methylcyclopentane, C_6H_{12}, alkane (cycloalkane)

26. cyclohexane, C_6H_{12}, alkane (cycloalkane)

27. 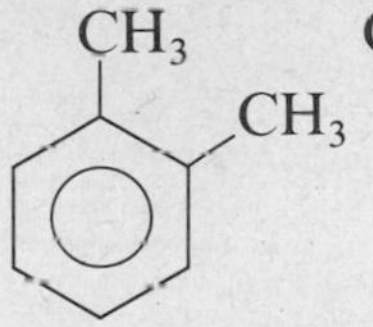 C_8H_{10}, aromatic hydrocarbon

28. 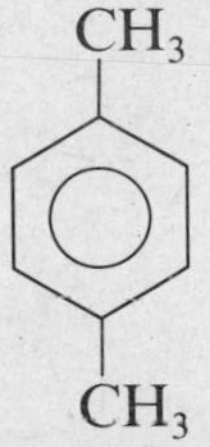 C_8H_{10}, aromatic hydrocarbon

29. $HC \equiv CH$, C_2H_2, alkyne

30. $HC \equiv CH$, C_2H_2, alkyne. This is another name for acetylene. You should be aware of the common, or trivial, names for many of the simple compounds in this and the next chapter.

31. 2-butyne, C_4H_6, alkyne

32. 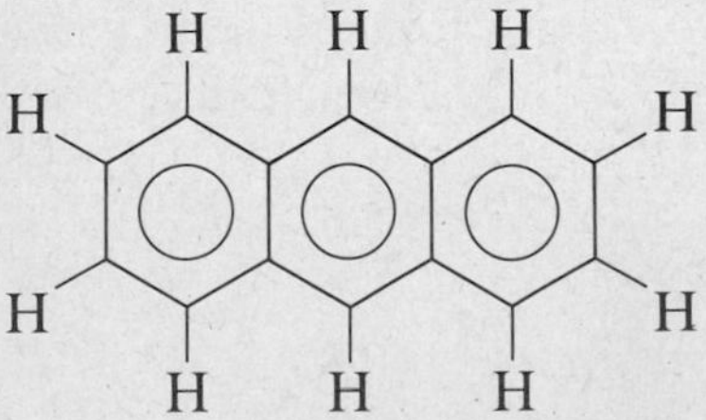 $C_{14}H_{10}$, aromatic hydrocarbon. It would not be necessary to show the hydrogen atoms explicitly, as they are understood to be at each corner of an aromatic hydrocarbon.

33. 4-ethyloctane, $C_{10}H_{22}$, alkane. Remember to name according to the longest chain of carbon atoms, and number so that the substituted group (ethyl, in this case) has the smallest number possible.

34. 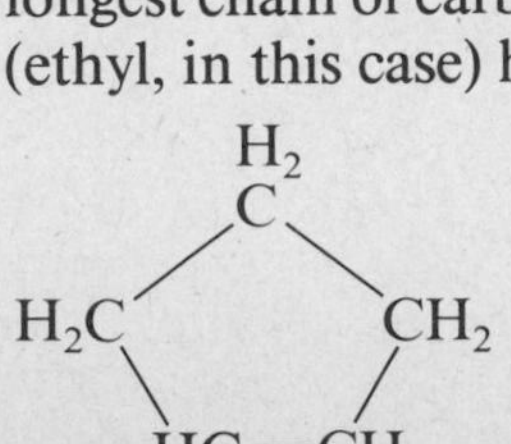 C_5H_8, alkene (cycloalkene)

35. nitroethane, $C_2H_5NO_2$, substituted alkane
36. *cis*-1,2-dibromoethene, $C_2H_2Br_2$, substituted alkene
37. *trans*-1,2-dibromoethene, $C_2H_2Br_2$, substituted alkene
38. H_3C Br $C_4H_6Br_2$, substituted alkene

$$H_3C, Br \diagdown C=C \diagup Br, CH_3$$

39.   F   F C_2F_4, substituted alkene

$$F, F \diagdown C=C \diagup F, F$$

40.   F CF_2Cl_2, substituted alkane. Notice that there is only one

$$Cl-\underset{\underset{F}{|}}{\overset{\overset{F}{|}}{C}}-Cl$$

isomer of this compound because of the tetrahedral shape of the bonding around the carbon. The compound, called Freon-12, is used as a refrigerant.

41. ⬡—Br C_6H_5Br, substituted aromatic hydrocarbon

Multiple Choice

1. (b). Can you convince yourself by drawing them?
2. (d). There is no such compound as "2-pentane."
3. (c). Of course, carbon never forms compounds using the hybrid orbitals indicated in answers (d) or (e) because it does not have any *d* orbitals in its valence shell.
4. (c)
5. (c). You may need to write out structural formulas for each of the answers and figure out the chemical formula (i.e., C_xH_y). Remember that isomers have the same chemical formulas.
6. (b)
7. (c)
8. (d)
9. (c)
10. (c)
11. (d)
12. (c)

30

Organic Chemistry II: Functional Groups

Chapter Summary

Many organic compounds involve some groups of atoms having bonds other than C—C or C—H single bonds. It is found that a given grouping of atoms generally undergoes similar reactions no matter in what compound it occurs. Thus, such a group of atoms is often viewed as a potential reaction site, called a **functional group.** The consistency of behavior of a given functional group enables us to organize large amounts of information about organic chemistry. Chapter 30 deals with the most common functional groups and with their characteristic reactions. It is suggested that you organize your study of each of these classes of compounds to emphasize the functional group common to all of the compounds in that class, the system for naming those compounds, the preparation of such compounds, their typical reactions, and some of their common uses. The representation of unspecified other groups of atoms, usually alkyl (R) or aryl (Ar, not to be confused with argon), is a common, compact notation.

The group of atoms —O—H **(hydroxyl)** attached to a carbon atom is characteristic of the two related classes of compounds known as the **alcohols** and the **phenols;** these related compounds are the subject of the first four sections of this chapter. When the hydroxyl group is bonded to an aliphatic carbon atom, the compound is classed as an alcohol; when the carbon is aromatic, the compound is a phenol. Examples of structures and naming of several compounds of these two classes are presented in Section 30–1. Because of the distribution of electrons resulting from electronegativity differences within the molecule, alcohols are polar molecules, a fact that is responsible for many of the physical properties of these compounds (Section 30–2). Methods for the preparation of alcohols are described in Section 30–3. Note that most industrial procedures for producing alcohols begin with unsaturated hydrocarbons, whereas production from carbon monoxide or sugars can be accomplished with the use of a metal or metal oxide catalyst or with the aid of yeast fermentation. Some typical reactions of alcohols and phenols are briefly presented in Section 30–4. Some of these are analogous to those of water because of the very weak acidity of alcohols. In other typical reactions, the —OH groups of alcohols can be replaced to form **alkyl halides** or **inorganic esters** such as nitrates or sulfates; some of the latter are useful as detergents.

Carboxylic acids (Section 30–5) contain the **carboxyl group,**

$$\overset{\displaystyle O}{\overset{\displaystyle \|}{}}$$

—C—OH, sometimes written —COOH. Most carboxylic acids are weak acids. You have seen acetic acid, which can be represented as CH_3COOH, used many times in weak acid problems or examples. The carboxylic acids can be classed as either **aliphatic** or **aromatic,** depending on the nature of the organic group bonded to the —COOH group. Many carboxylic acids occur in common natural products. The naming and structures of some carboxylic acids are described; be sure that you notice how we name the common groups that are derived from the carboxylic acids (the acyl groups) and how these are related to the parent acid. The strength of a carboxylic acid is related to its structure.

Sections 30–6 through 30–8 describe the preparation and properties of two important types of derivatives of carboxylic acids, known as the **acyl halides** and the **organic esters.** Each of these may be viewed as resulting from the replacement of the —OH group of the carboxylic acid by another group—a halogen atom in the acyl halides and the —OR′ group in the esters. Many commonly recognizable flavors and aromas come from organic esters, and many common fats, oils, and waxes are organic esters. The hydrolysis of esters in the presence of strong soluble bases, the **saponification reaction,** produces useful compounds, including soaps. The **polyester** fibers that are the basis for many synthetic fabrics are composed of long chain molecules connected by many ester linkages, as described in Section 30–8.

The **amines** are basic compounds that may be considered as derivatives of ammonia, NH_3, in which one or more of the hydrogen atoms have been replaced by an alkyl or an aryl group. These compounds, their structures, nomenclature, and reactions are the subject of Sections 30–9 and 30–10. Most reactions of amines are analogous to those of ammonia, with the nitrogen atom acting as a Brønsted-Lowry or Lewis base.

Section 30–11 discusses the **amides,** which contain the $-\overset{\displaystyle O}{\overset{\displaystyle \|}{C}}-\overset{\displaystyle |}{N}-$ group of atoms. These may be thought of as derivatives of primary or secondary amines and organic acids, though they are not usually prepared in that way. Amides find use as medicinal agents such as headache and fever remedies, as insect repellents, and as the starting material for **polyamides,** of which nylon is an example.

Two related groups of compounds, the **aldehydes** and the **ketones,** both contain the $-\overset{\displaystyle O}{\overset{\displaystyle \|}{C}}-$ group, called the **carbonyl** group. Ketones have two alkyl or aryl groups bonded to the carbonyl group, while in aldehydes one of these is replaced by a hydrogen atom. The structure, nomenclature, preparation, and common reaction types of these two classes of compounds are presented in Sections 30–12 through 30–14. Notice that the aldehydes are usually called by their common names, which indicate the number of carbon atoms in the compound. Ketones are named according to the two alkyl or aryl groups bonded to the carbonyl group. Many important natural substances are aldehydes and ketones. Because their aliphatic or aromatic ends make them mix readily with organic compounds, while the polar carbonyl group makes them miscible with water, many ketones find wide use as solvents, of which the most widely used is acetone. Aldehydes and ketones are prepared by the oxidation of primary and secondary alcohols, respectively, usually in the presence of a catalyst such as OH^- or a metal powder. Principal reactions of aldehydes include reduction to alcohols and oxidation to carboxylic acids or their salts.

The final class of compounds, the **ethers,** consists of compounds in which an oxygen atom is bonded to two organic groups, $R—O—R'$, where R and R' may each be either an alkyl or an aryl group. The closing section of this chapter describes these compounds. Except for their ease of combustion, ethers are generally rather unreactive molecules. They are used for a variety of purposes such as anesthetics, artificial flavors, refrigerants, and solvents.

Study Goals

This is another quite long and diverse chapter. Be systematic in your study. Study Goal 1 will help you to get a look at the range of the chapter. The other study goals will help you focus in more detail on particular aspects of the material.

1. First, organize your study around the classes of compounds. Know structures, properties, sources or preparations, uses and reactions that are typical of each class of organic compounds. (You should do this for either the general class or at least two examples of each class.) Know the functional group that is characteristic of each class and give two specific examples of each class.
   (a) alcohols and phenols (Sections 30–1 through 30–4; Exercises 1 through 20)
   (b) carboxylic acids (Section 30–5; Exercises 21 through 25)
   (c) acyl halides (Section 30–6; Exercise 25)
   (d) esters (Sections 30–7 and 30–8; Exercises 26 through 37)
   (e) amines (Sections 30–9 and 30–10; Exercises 38 through 41)
   (f) amides (Section 30–11; Exercises 42 through 46)

(g) aldehydes and ketones (Sections 30 – 12 through 30 – 14; Exercises 47 through 51)

(h) ethers (Section "Ethers"; Exercises 52 through 54)

2. Know how to name members of each of the classes of organic compounds listed in Study Goal 1. (Sections 30 – 1, 30 – 5, 30 – 6, 30 – 7, 30 – 9, 30 – 11, 30 – 12, and "Ethers"; Exercises 4, 7, 21 through 25, 31, 32, 39, 42, 47, and 53)

3. Illustrate with equations the weakly acidic character of alcohols and phenols. (Section 30 – 4; Exercises 16 and 17)

4. Define and distinguish among fats, oils, and glycerides, and write typical formulas for each. (Section 30 – 7; Exercises 29 through 32 and 35)

5. Show esterification and saponification reactions, classify each product and reactant according to functional group, and give the uses of the products. (Sections 30 – 5 and 30 – 7; Exercises 18 through 20, 33, and 35)

6. Write an equation that illustrates the formation of (a) a polyester and (b) a polyamide. (Sections 30 – 8 and 30 – 11; Exercises 36, 37, 44 through 46)

7. Compare the base strengths of (a) ammonia, (b) aliphatic amines, and (c) aromatic amines. Write equations for reactions of each with acids to illustrate their basic character. (Section 30 – 10; Exercises 40 and 41)

8. Distinguish between the terms primary, secondary, and tertiary as they are applied to alcohols and to amines. (Sections 30 – 1 and 30 – 9; Exercises 5, 38, and 39)

9. Compare and contrast the bonding and properties of water $(H-O-H)$, alcohol $(R-O-H)$, and ethers $(R-O-R')$. (Sections 30 – 1 through 30 – 4 and "Ethers"; Exercises 2, 52, and 53)

Some Important Terms in This Chapter

Write the meanings *in your own words*. Check the Key Terms list and the chapter reading. Then rewrite your definitions, still in your own words, to improve them. Study other new terms and review terms from preceding chapters if necessary.

alcohol

phenol

carboxylic acid

ester

ether

amine

amide

acyl halide

aldehyde

ketone

polymer

polymerization reaction

polyamide

polyester

saponification reaction

esterification reaction

Preliminary Test

Be sure to practice *many* of the additional textbook exercises.

True-False

Mark each statement as true (T) or false (F).

_____ 1. Many of the common flavoring agents are simple amines.
_____ 2. Alcohols are polar molecules.
_____ 3. Alkoxides of low molecular weight are strong bases.
_____ 4. Ethers are very reactive compounds.
_____ 5. Some of the reactions of alcohols are similar to those of water.
_____ 6. Many reactions of carboxylic acids involve displacement of the —OH group by another atom or group of atoms.
_____ 7. Most carboxylic acids are weak acids.
_____ 8. All functional groups contain some atom other than carbon or hydrogen.
_____ 9. A single organic compound can have only one functional group.

_____ 10. The common source of the carbon atoms for the industrial preparation of most organic chemicals is carbon dioxide from the air.

Short Answer

1. A compound in which one hydrogen atom of water has been replaced by
an organic group is a(n) _____, while a compound in which both
hydrogen atoms of water have been replaced by organic groups is a(n)
_____.

2. The simplest aliphatic alcohol is _____; the most common one is _____.

3. Alcohols that contain more than one —OH group per molecule are
called _____ alcohols.

4. Aromatic alcohols as a group are referred to as _____; the simplest
member of this group is the compound named _____.

5. Alcohols in which the —OH group is bonded to a carbon atom that is in
turn bonded to one, two, or three other organic groups, respectively, are
called _____ alcohols, _____ alcohols, and _____ alco-
hols.

6. The secondary alcohol with the smallest number of carbon atoms is
_____ (name, formula).

7. The secondary amine with the smallest number of carbon atoms is
_____ (name, formula).

8. Polyhydric alcohol containing two equivalent carbon atoms is
_____ (name, formula);
this substance is frequently used as _____ _____
_____.

9. Dilute solutions of phenols are frequently used as _____.

10. The reaction in which the net result is the addition of water to an alkene is
a common method for the preparation of _____. (The answer is
the name of a class of compounds, not a specific compound.)

11. In a process that is analogous to the reaction of active metals with water
to form hydroxides, active metals react with alcohols to form
_____; in both of these reactions, the gas _____ is
liberated.

12. The reactions of alcohols with organic acids result in the formation of
_____.

13. The hydrolysis of esters in the presence of strong soluble bases, a process
which (with some esters) produces soaps, is called _____.

14. Tollen's test uses the formation of a silver mirror to distinguish between
two closely related classes of compounds; of these two classes, the
_____ undergo the reaction to form the silver mirror, whereas the
_____ do not.

In each of the next twenty questions, 15 through 34, name the compound or give a formula, as required. For each compound, tell the class of which it is an example.

Formula	Name	Class
15. $CH_3CH_2CH_2OH$	_____	_____
16. _____	phenol	_____

17.
$$\begin{array}{c} O \\ \parallel \\ C-OH \end{array}$$
（benzene ring）

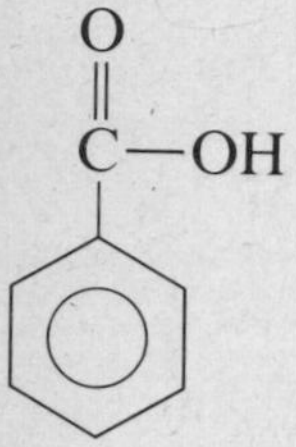

_____ _____

| 18. _____ | pentanoic acid | _____ |
| 19. _____ | 3-chloropentanoic acid | _____ |

20.
$$\begin{array}{c} O \\ \parallel \\ CH_3-C-Cl \end{array}$$

_____ _____

21. _____	methyl n-butyrate	_____
22. _____	glycerine	_____
23. _____	acetone	_____

24.
$$\begin{array}{c} O \\ \parallel \\ CH_3-C-H \end{array}$$

25.
$$CH_3-\underset{\underset{H}{\mid}}{N}-CH_2CH_3$$

_____ _____

26. _____	aniline	_____
27. _____	N-methylacetamide	_____
28. $CH_3CH_2-O-CH_2CH_3$	_____	_____

29. 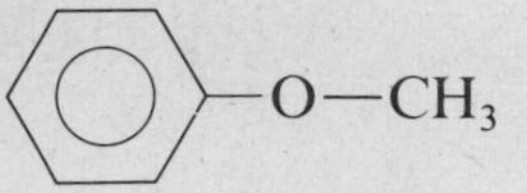 ⟨O⟩—O—CH$_3$ _____   _____

30. $(CH_3)_2NH_2^+$ Cl$^-$ _____   _____

31. _____   oxalic acid   _____

32.
$$CH_3-\overset{\overset{\displaystyle O}{\|}}{C}-O-\overset{\overset{\displaystyle O}{\|}}{C}-CH_3$$
_____   _____

33. 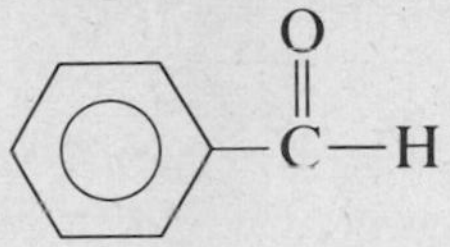
⟨O⟩—$\overset{\overset{\displaystyle O}{\|}}{C}$—H   _____   _____

34. 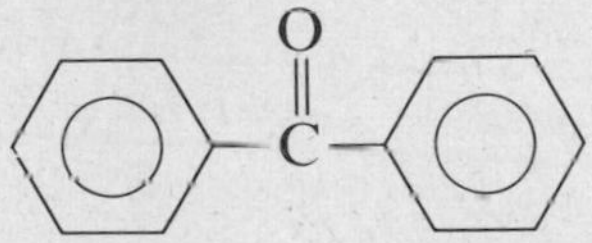
⟨O⟩—$\overset{\overset{\displaystyle O}{\|}}{C}$—⟨O⟩   _____   _____

For each of the following seventeen questions, 35 through 51, classify the reaction according to one (or sometimes more) of the following types: aliphatic substitution, aromatic substitution, addition, halogenation, nitration, sulfonation, esterification, neutralization, displacement, saponification, combustion, dehydrogenation, oxidation, dehydration, polymerization, hydrolysis.

35. $CH_4 + Cl_2 \longrightarrow CH_3Cl + HCl$ _____

36. $CH_3CH{=}CH_2 + Cl_2 \longrightarrow CH_3\underset{\underset{\displaystyle Cl}{|}}{CH}{-}\underset{\underset{\displaystyle Cl}{|}}{CH_2}$ _____

37. $CH_3CH{=}CH_2 + H_2 \longrightarrow CH_3CH_2CH_3$ _____

38. $CH_2{=}CH_2 + HOCl \longrightarrow \underset{\underset{\displaystyle OH}{|}}{CH_2}{-}\underset{\underset{\displaystyle Cl}{|}}{CH_2}$ _____

39.
$$\underset{\underset{\displaystyle CH_2OH}{|}}{\overset{\overset{\displaystyle CH_2OH}{|}}{CHOH}} + 3HNO_3 \longrightarrow \underset{\underset{\displaystyle CH_2-ONO_2}{|}}{\overset{\overset{\displaystyle CH_2-ONO_2}{|}}{CH-ONO_2}}$$ _____

40.
$$CH_3-\overset{\overset{\displaystyle O}{\|}}{C}-OH + PCl_5 \longrightarrow CH_3-\overset{\overset{\displaystyle O}{\|}}{C}-Cl + HCl + POCl_3$$ _____

_____

41. $CH_2{=}CH{-}\underset{\underset{Cl}{|}}{C}{=}CH_2 \longrightarrow [{-}CH_2{-}CH{=}\underset{\underset{Cl}{|}}{C}{-}CH_2{-}]_n$

_____
_____

42.

$CH_3{-}\overset{\overset{O}{\|}}{C}{-}OCH_2CH_3 + NaOH \longrightarrow CH_3{-}\overset{\overset{O}{\|}}{C}{-}O^-, Na^+ + CH_3CH_2OH$

_____

43. $3C_2H_4 + 2KMnO_4 + 8H_2O \longrightarrow 3\underset{\underset{OH}{|}}{CH_2}{-}\underset{\underset{OH}{|}}{CH_2} + 2MnO_2 + 2KOH$ _____

44. $CH_3CH_2OH + O_2 \xrightarrow{Cu} 2CH_3\underset{\underset{O}{\|}}{CH} + 2H_2O$ _____

45. $CH_3C{\equiv}CH + 3Br_2 \longrightarrow CH_3CBr_2CHBr_2$ _____

46.

$CH_3{-}\underset{\underset{H}{|}}{\overset{\overset{OH}{|}}{C}}{-}CH_3 \xrightarrow[heat]{Cu} CH_3{-}\overset{\overset{O}{\|}}{C}{-}CH_3$ _____

47.

$2CH_3CH_3CH_2\overset{\overset{O}{\|}}{C}{-}H + O_2 \longrightarrow 2CH_3CH_2CH_2\overset{\overset{O}{\|}}{C}{-}OH$ _____

48. 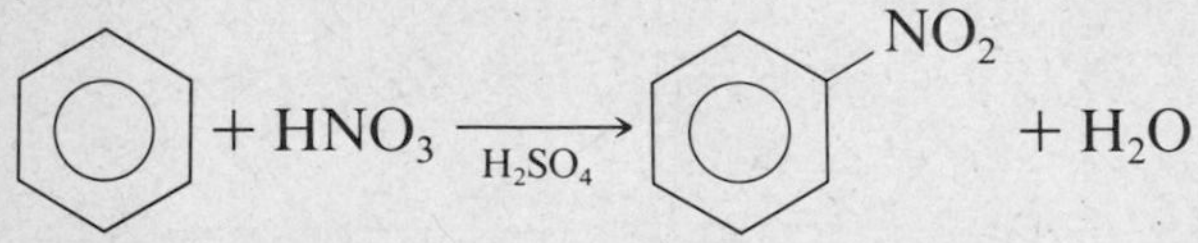 ⬡ $+ HNO_3 \xrightarrow{H_2SO_4}$ ⬡^{NO_2} $+ H_2O$ _____

49. 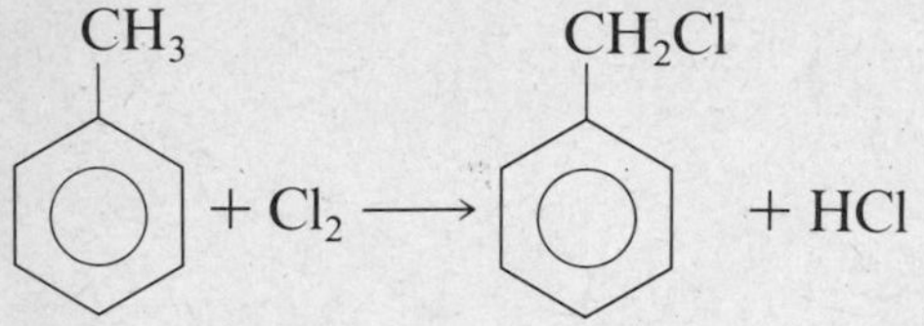 ⬡^{CH_3} $+ Cl_2 \longrightarrow$ ⬡^{CH_2Cl} $+ HCl$ _____

50. 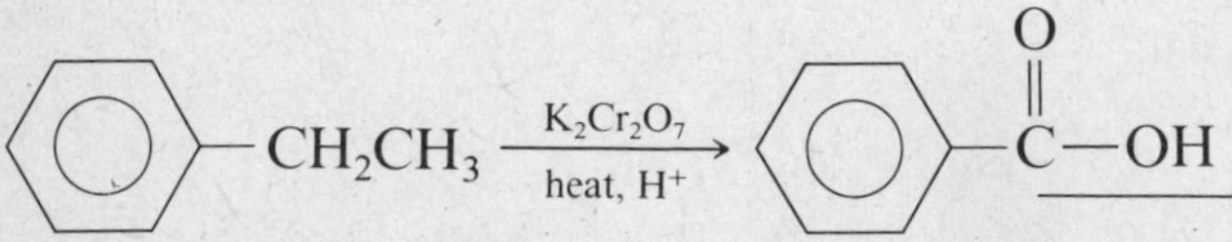 ⬡${-}CH_2CH_3 \xrightarrow[heat, H^+]{K_2Cr_2O_7}$ ⬡${-}\overset{\overset{O}{\|}}{C}{-}OH$ _____

51. $2C_8H_{18} + 25O_2 \rightarrow 16CO_2 + 18H_2O$ _____

Multiple Choice

____ 1. The molecule $CH_3{-}\underset{\underset{H}{|}}{\overset{\overset{OH}{|}}{C}}{-}\underset{\underset{NH_2}{|}}{\overset{\overset{H}{|}}{C}}{-}\underset{\underset{H}{|}}{\overset{\overset{H}{|}}{C}}{-}\overset{\overset{O}{\|}}{C}{-}H$ contains the functional groups that are characteristic of

(a) aldehydes, amides, and ethers.
(b) amines, ketones, and esters.
(c) aldehydes, halides, and alcohols.
(d) alcohols, aldehydes, and amines.
(e) acids, alcohols, and halides.

_____ 2. The group of atoms characteristic of aldehydes is

(a) —C—C—C   (b) —C—O—C—   (c) —C—O—
              ‖   ‖
              O   O

(d) —C—H   (e) —C≡C—
    ‖
    O

_____ 3. The group of atoms characteristic of esters is

(a) —C—NH₂   (b) —C—O—C—   (c) —C—H
                                            ‖
                                            O

(d) —C—O—   (e) —C—C—C—
    ‖   ‖
    O   O

_____ 4. The compound

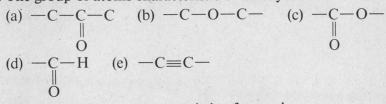

is

(a) an alkane.   (b) a carboxylic acid.   (c) an alkyne.
(d) an alcohol.   (e) an amine.

_____ 5. The reaction in which water is eliminated between a molecule of an
alcohol and a molecule of an organic acid is called
(a) elimination.   (b) esterification.   (c) substitution.
(d) oxidation.   (e) neutralization.

_____ 6. Which of the following is a secondary alcohol?

(a) CH_3OH (b) CH_3CH_2OH (c)

```
                                    OH
                                    |
                              CH_3—C—CH_3
                                    |
                                    H
```

(d)

```
        OH
        |
  CH_3—C—OH
        |
        CH_3
```

(e)

```
        OH
        |
  CH_3—C—CH_3
        |
        CH_3
```

_____ 7. The structures of malonic acid and fumaric acid are, respectively,

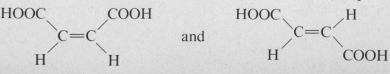

Which of the following terms describes the relationship between these two acid?
(a) a conjugate acid-base pair   (b) structural isomers
(c) geometrical isomers   (d) polymers   (e) dicarboxylic acids

Answers to Preliminary Test

True-False

1. False. Amines generally have quite unpleasant odors. Many common flavoring agents are organic esters.
2. True
3. True. They hydrolyze (react with water) to form the parent alcohol and a strong soluble base. This reaction is described in Section 30–4.
4. False. They burn very readily but otherwise are not particularly reactive.
5. True
6. True. Examples of classes of compounds so formed are esters, amides, acyl halides, and acid anhydrides.
7. True. See, for instance, the K_a values for some common carboxylic acids, which are listed in Section 30–5.
8. False. Any potential reactive site on a molecule is termed a functional group; this can even include double or triple bonds.
9. False. Many organic compounds have several functional groups; you have seen many examples of this in Chapter 30.
10. False. Most organic chemicals are produced from petroleum; this is another, though less highly publicized, difficulty with our decreasing supply of petroleum.

Short Answer

1. alcohol or phenol, ether
2. methyl alcohol, ethyl alcohol
3. polyhydric
4. phenols, phenol
5. primary, secondary, tertiary
6. 2-propanol (or isopropyl alcohol), CH_3CHCH_3
   |
   OH
7. dimethylamine, $CH_3 - N - CH_3$
   |
   H
8. ethylene glycol, $HOCH_2 - CH_2OH$; permanent antifreeze
9. disinfectants

10. alcohols
11. alkoxides, hydrogen (H_2). See Section 30–4.
12. esters
13. saponification
14. aldehydes, ketones
15. 1-propanol or *n*-propyl alcohol, alcohol
16. OH, phenol. (Note that this is the name of the class and of the compound itself.)

17. benzoic acid, carboxylic acid
18. $CH_3CH_2CH_2CH_2\overset{\displaystyle O}{\overset{\displaystyle \|}{C}}$—OH, carboxylic acid

19. $CH_3CH_2\underset{\underset{Cl}{|}}{CH}CH_2\overset{\displaystyle O}{\overset{\displaystyle \|}{C}}$—OH, carboxylic acid. Note that this is not an acyl chloride. Do you know the difference?

20. acetyl chloride, acyl halide (or acid halide)
21.
$$CH_3CH_2CH_2\overset{\displaystyle O}{\overset{\displaystyle \|}{C}}—OCH_3, \text{ester}$$
22. $\underset{\underset{H_2C}{}}{HO}\;\underset{\underset{CH}{}}{OH}\;\underset{\underset{CH_2}{}}{OH}$, alcohol (a polyhydric alcohol)

23.
$$CH_3—\overset{\displaystyle O}{\overset{\displaystyle \|}{C}}—CH_3, \text{ketone}$$
24. acetaldehyde (or ethanal), aldehyde
25. methylethylamine, amine
26. NH_2 amine

27.
$$CH_3—\overset{\displaystyle O}{\overset{\displaystyle \|}{C}}—N\overset{\displaystyle H}{\underset{\displaystyle CH_3}{\Big\langle}}, \text{ amide}$$

28. diethylether, ether
29. methylphenylether, ether
30. dimethylammonium chloride, an amine salt
31.
$$HO—\overset{\displaystyle O}{\overset{\displaystyle \|}{C}}—\overset{\displaystyle O}{\overset{\displaystyle \|}{C}}—OH, \text{ carboxylic acid (actually a dicarboxylic acid)}$$
32. acetic anhydride, acid anhydride
33. benzaldehyde, aldehyde
34. diphenylketone, ketone

35. aliphatic substitution, halogenation
36. addition, halogenation
37. addition, hydrogenation
38. addition
39. esterification (inorganic)
40. displacement
41. polymerization
42. saponification, hydrolysis of an ester
43. oxidation, addition
44. oxidation, dehydrogenation
45. addition (actually, two steps of addition, as is common for alkynes), halogenation
46. oxidation, dehydrogenation
47. oxidation
48. aromatic substitution, nitration
49. aliphatic substitution, halogenation
50. oxidation
51. oxidation (combustion, complete combustion)

Multiple Choice

1. (d)
2. (d)
3. (d)
4. (d)
5. (b)
6. (c). This is 2-propanol, or isopropyl alcohol. It is the substance familiarly known as "rubbing alcohol."
7. (c). Each one *is* a dicarboxylic acid, but this does not describe the *relationship* between the two compounds.